The Heart of a Mother

Edited by:

Anna Marie Jaworski

Baby Hearts Press
Panama City Beach, Florida

The Heart of a Mother

Edited By: Anna Marie Jaworski

Published by:

Baby Hearts Press

6618 Sunrise Drive
Panama City Beach, Florida 32407 U.S.A.

© 1999 by Anna Marie Jaworski
First Printing 1999

Library of Congress Cataloging-in-Publication Data
Jaworski, Anna Marie
        The Heart of a Mother / by Anna Marie Jaworski,
                p.   cm.
        ISBN 0-9652508-1-4
        1. Congenital heart disease in children   I. Title
        2. Heart—Diseases
        3. Children—Diseases

        99-90528
          CIP

Table of Contents

Foreword by Edward L. Bove, M.D.   *i*
Preface by Anna Jaworski   *iii*
Introduction by Judy Norwood   *v*

Discovery

Chapter One: Discovering Heart Defects In Utero

A Brother for Markie *by Christine Prior*   *3*
Learning to Love and Trust God *by Kerrie Van Eck*   *7*
Getting a Better Look *by Edie Spears*   *13*
God Doesn't Make Mistakes *by Caroline Ahrens*   *20*

Chapter Two: HLHS Care Options

Cardiac Transplantation

Happy Lifeday, Little Angel *by Amanda Eason*   *26*
The Right Heart for Travis *by Dawn Martin*   *30*

Compassionate Care

Letting Go *by Kari Barr*   *35*
A Letter to Ethan *by Kelley Madden*   *39*

The Norwood Procedure

Giving Tyler a Chance *by Rene Winters*   *42*
A Born Fighter *by Cindy Tishka*   *46*
Pioneer Woman *by Jill Sorensen*   *49*

Chapter Three: Special Problems, Special Solutions

Feeding Problems *by Jennifer Nachbur*   *54*
Developmental Delays—Physical *by Caroline Ahrens*   *56*
Developmental Delays—Speech and Language *by Anna Jaworski*   *62*

Support

Chapter Four: The Life Givers

My Special Son *by Karen Brandle*   *71*
Hope in Tomorrow *by Bonnie Munden*   *76*
My Son, Heart and Soul *by Jeanne Imperati*   *82*

Chapter Five: More than a Mom

Taking Care of Things *by Anita Moreno Marcelo*   *90*
Never More Than You Can Handle *by Brenda Vignaroli*   *93*
A Stepmother's Story *by Karen Pritchett*   *98*

Chapter Six: Military Moms

In the Navy *by Gabriele Stiltner*   *102*
The Army Way of Life *by Lou Ann Wright*   *106*
Overseas with the Air Force *by Shiloh Hanshew*   *112*

Chapter Seven: Grandmothers' Stories

Part of the Team *by Carol Self*   *120*
Allowing Jane to Focus on Marcus *by Clarice Warrick*   *123*
Supporting a Mother's Love *by Linda McAdam*   *126*
Being Strong for Teresa *by Joanne Clarkson*   *129*
A Tribute to My Mother *by Anna Jaworski*   *133*

Chapter Eight: Mothers Around the World

A Little Bit of Heaven—Canada *by Carolyn Thompson*   *138*
A Miracle—Germany *by Beate Lemmer*   *142*
Chrysanthemums for Paesan—Singapore *by Helen Ng*   *147*
Running the Race—Australia *by Lyn Chappell*   *152*
A Light in My Life—New Zealand *by Jasmina Henderson-Rauter*   *157*
A Saint for Sebastian—United Kingdom *by Susanne Mühlhaus*   *164*

Chapter Nine: Mothers in the Hospital

Our Love for Alex *by Julie Schlapfer*   *172*
Supporting Sadie *by Holly Scheyer*   *174*
Finding the Good *by Patty Roswick*   *179*
A Mommy's Feelings *by Tracy Adams*   *180*

Chapter Ten: Teaching Others, Learning Ourselves

Internet Innovator: *Mona Barmash*   *184*
Resourceful Librarian: *Alysanne Crymes*   *186*
Joining the AHA: *Michelle Rintamaki*   *186*
Saving Our Children Through Educating Ourselves *by Lenore Cameron*   *188*

Chapter Eleven: Mothers As Advocates

How To Be An Advocate *by Tricia Christensen*   *194*
Working with the Media: *Jane Hunt*   *200*
Seeing Myself as an Advocate: *Anna Jaworski*   *202*
Helping a Friend: *Sheri Berger*   *203*

Chapter Eleven: Mothers As Advocates(cont.)

HLHS Resource: *Laura Ulaszek*   *204*
CHD Leader: *Sally Pearson*   *205*
Support/Advocacy Groups   *207*

Chapter Twelve: Shooting Stars

My Candle in the Wind *by Deb Gilmore*   *214*
387 Pictures *by Aleta Riesberg*   *217*
An Angel's Cause *by Deirdre Bronchick*   *226*
My Shooting Star *by Jan Heckman*   *232*
Face of a Child *by Dolly Lee*   *234*

Hope

Chapter Thirteen: Life After Surgery

A Birthday Reminiscence *by Deanna Brennan*   *237*
Having a Healthy Baby *by Deb Chapman*   *240*
An Anniversary *by Anna Jaworski*   *247*

Chapter Fourteen: Mothers With Congenital Heart Defects

Mind Over Matter *by Michelle Veschi*   *251*
Leading the Troops *by Carolyn Wise*   *253*
A Baby for Allison *by Allison Matthews*   *257*
A Healthy Baby *by Becky Blauvelt*   *260*

Chapter Fifteen: Rites of Passage

Summer Camp *by Beth Hutchinson*   *268*
Moving Day *by Arlyn Kerr*   *273*
Karen's New Car *by Mary Kay Klein*   *279*
Victoria's Ski Trip *by Rita Scoggins*   *282*
Camp Del Corazon *by Jill Sorensen*   *284*
When Milestones Become Miracles *by Cheryl Goldstein*   *286*

Appendix A: Native Language Essays
        Lebens und Leidensweq eines herzkranken Kindes *(Beate Lemmer)*   *293*
        Tjasijeva Zgodba *(Jasmina Henderson-Rauter)*   *297*

Appendix B: Summer Camps (in the United States)   *305*

Appendix C: Cardiac Anatomy
        Basic Heart Anatomy   *307*
        Pediatric Heart Anatomy   *308*

Glossary of Terms   *309*

Warning–Disclaimer

This book is not intended to be medical advice. Medical information described in this book is solely for illustrative purposes. This book is not intended to be a text for medical treatment of children with congenital heart defects. Parents should consult with medical personnel whenever they feel compelled, regardless of what is written in this book.

The area of congenital heart defects is constantly changing. This book has reported some mothers' past experiences. For a more in-depth analysis of treatment of congenital heart defects, the reader is encouraged to visit the library or conduct an online search in relevant medical journals. None of these mothers is a doctor or has a medical degree.

Every effort has been made to insure this book is as accurate as possible; however, there **may be mistakes**, both typographical and in content. Consequently, this book should not be used to define medical treatment for any child. Many of these stories are written from mothers' memories of what has happened with their children. Because these women are not doctors, and may have been in shock when given certain medical information, there may be some inaccuracies. These mothers have taken great pains to write with as much accuracy as possible.

The purpose of this book is to inspire others. The authors and Baby Hearts Press shall have neither liability nor responsibility to any person or entity with respect to any loss or damage caused, or alleged to be caused, directly or indirectly by the information contained in this book.

If you do not wish to be bound by the above, you may return this book to the publisher for a full refund.

Acknowledgements

The Heart of a Mother has taken over two years to compile, edit and publish. It has been a labor of love by all. Perhaps the greatest joy in creating this book has been the opportunity to work with extraordinary people who gave this book more than their time— they shared a part of their heart. I would like to thank the following people for their dedication and contributions, without which this book would not have come to be:

Frank, Joey and Alex, who gave me constant encouragement, love and nourishment for my body and soul.

Michelle Jestice, for copyediting this entire manuscript several times and for meticulous attention to detail. Michelle, thank you for meeting with me so often and helping to keep me on track.

All the mothers who submitted contributions for the book; although I was unable to use all of the contributions, I was deeply touched by the kindness shown by all as they shared such heartfelt stories. Special thanks to the mothers whose essays and poems I did include: Christine Prior, Kerrie Van Eck, Edie Spears, Amanda Eason, Dawn Martin, Kari Barr, Kelley Madden, Rene Winters, Cindy Tishka, Jill Sorensen, Jennifer Nachbur, Caroline Ahrens, Karen Brandle, Bonnie Munden, Jeanne Imperati, Anita Moreno Marcelo, Brenda Vignaroli, Karen Pritchett, Gabriele Stiltner, Lou Ann Wright, Shiloh Hanshew, Carol Self, Clarice Warrick, Linda McAdam, Joanne Clarkson, Carolyn Thompson, Beate Lemmer, Helen Ng, Lyn Chappell, Jasmina Henderson-Rauter, Susanne Mühlhaus, Julie Schlapfer, Holly Scheyer, Patty Roswick, Tracy Adams, Mona Barmash, Alysanne Crymes, Michelle Rintamaki, Lenore Cameron, Tricia Christensen, Jane Hunt, Sheri Berger, Laura Ulaszek, Sally Pearson, Deb Gilmore, Aleta Riesberg, Deirdre Bronchick, Jan Heckman, Deanna Brennan, Deb Chapman, Michelle Veschi, Carolyn Wise, Allison Matthews, Becky Blauvelt, Beth Hutchinson, Arlyn Kerr, Mary Kay Klein, Rita Scoggins, Cheryl Goldstein and Dolly Lee.

Edward L. Bove, M.D., for reading a draft of the book and writing a warm and heartfelt Foreword.

Judy Norwood, a special friend and contributor, who passed away before this book was printed. Thank you for writing such a wonderful essay—which I decided to use as the Introduction to the book.

Janet Fendt, for letting me know of Beate Lemmer and for providing a translation of her essay. Thanks, too, to Susan Kaser, who also provided a translation of Beate's essay.

Karen Klein and Anthony Cordova (ACHA), Sheri Berger (The Congenital Heart Disease Resource Page), Mona Barmash (C.H.I.N.), Sarah Moran (Center for Families, Boston Children's Hospital) and Connie Ginsberg (Family Connection of SC, Inc.), for information which helped me compile the support group section and summer camp sections of the book. Thanks, too, to all of the members of support groups throughout the world who kindly send me their newsletters or provide information on the Internet.

Frank Jaworski and Jeanne Imperati, for help with the Glossary.

All of the women and mothers who read essays or the manuscript draft and provided helpful feedback, especially Sue Meadows, Betsy Adler, Desiree Vaught, Renee Balter, Kerri Evans, Lisa Scott, Debra Johnson, Erin Ross, Karen Ely, Maureen Adams, Lisha Seibert, Marie Obremski, Joni Loyd, Gabrielle Harlow, Ellie Heinly, Gertrude Johnson, and Laurie Hobbs.

Mona Barmash, Jeanne Imperati, Jane Hunt, and Julia Fincher for constant encouragement and support.

Beth Hutchinson and all of the people who participated in the Pampered Chef *Recipes from the Heart* cookbook fundraiser: Patricia Holzer, James McAdam, Myrna Lee, Sherryann Morrison, Elaine Wheat, Dr. Bobby Greenberg, Jim Baughman, Meg Banes, Kelley Madden, Dana Morgan, Steve McCain, Nanci Duke, Natalie Lalonde, Susie Arnold, Jane Hunt, Lou Anne Wright, Jess DuPont, Margaret Mikulastik, Debbie Combs, Kelly Miller, Mike Mullholland, Shiloh Hanshew, Lisa Knight (Camp Del Corazon), Anita Marcelo, Woodinville License Agency, Debbie Baize, Sue Loerwald, Debbie Grmela, Linda Maxwell, Lanelle Petty, JoAnn Sugg, Jennifer Nachbur Farrell, Kimberly Calhoun, Kerrie Van Eck, Caroline Ahrens, Cristie Pittman, Lynnell Holden, Bill Childers, Kathy Talton, Judy Culbertson, Kaitlin Hutchinson, Teresa Sorlie, Julia Fincher, Nancy Duerr, Michelle Jones, Linda Springham, Gertrude Johnson, Anita Ramos, Bobbye Woody, Ellie Heinly, Debbie Chapman, Christine Prior, Deirdre Bronchick (Paige Bronchick Foundation), Tamar Kieval Brill, Katherine Bein, Sue Meadows, Evelyn Dyer, Jennifer Raesch, and Sheri Berger.

Jane Hunt and the HLHS and PDHeart listservs for spreading the word about the book and encouraging mothers to participate.

Steve McCain for constant support and help when I was frustrated. Daniel Hand for help with PageMaker, the program I used to typeset the book. Frank Jaworski for final proofing and suggestions.

Allan and Tina Campbell (Affordable Printing) and James Sovel (Mailboxes, Etc.) for help in the copying, production and distribution phases of the book. Allan Campbell for helping to create the cover.

Myra Ehrke and the Panama City Writers' Guild for allowing me to read from the book and for their encouragement with this project.

Because of the enormity of this project, I may have inadvertantly left out the names of some people who helped me along the way. If so, I am sorry—please know that I really do appreciate all of you.

I am truly grateful for the many hearts, hands and angels who helped make this book possible. I love you all!

Foreword

by Edward L. Bove, M.D.

There is, quite possibly, no more devastating an event for parents to endure than to be given the news that their child has a potentially life threatening condition. Congenital heart disease affects nearly 1% of all newborns and is the single most common significant congenital defect. Although the treatment of these heart defects has come a long way since its early days in the 1950's, for many of these innocent children and their parents it remains a condition which will have a dramatic impact on the quality or even the length of their lives. This book underscores what all of us who treat these children should always remember, that it is a condition which affects the lives of an entire family.

The Heart of a Mother is, at first glance, a collection of narratives written by mothers with children who have congenital heart defects or, in some cases, have a heart defect themselves. However, this book, edited by Anna Jaworski, is more than a compilation of individual stories, it is really a story about courage. For it is that central theme that runs throughout this collection of personal tales.

As a surgeon specializing in the treatment of congenital heart disease, I have long ago appreciated that special bond that exists between a mother and her child, a bond made that much stronger when a child is affected by a heart condition. Mothers (and fathers, too!) are by necessity the advocates for their children. It is the parent who must make the emotional and sometimes life-threatening decisions regarding the treatment of their child. They are the ones who must assimilate as much knowledge as possible, often in a short period of time, and all while emotionally stressed. Who and what to believe can be difficult and confusing.

A number of the stories in this book are written by mothers of children with hypoplastic left heart syndrome. Until recently, the diagnosis of this particular form of heart disease was a death sentence for there was no available treatment. Over the last fifteen years, however, the outlook for these children has dramatically improved. There is little doubt that my own personal interest in this condition has taught me more about the unique courage of these parents than any other problem that I treat. Many years ago, when successful surgery was more the exception than the rule, I seriously considered no longer offering reconstructive surgery for these newborns because it was so disheartening to meet with failure after failure. It was one particular mother, however, whose encouraging words written to me after her child's death stimulated me to continue. Although her son lived for only two years, her powerful words of gratitude for the time they had together taught me a great deal about the meaning of quality of life, hope, and courage.

As you read the stories in this book, it is hard not to be moved by the emotion that leaps out from each page. Joy, sadness, fear, hope, uncertainty are all expressed over and over again, and often in the same story. If there is only one thing that is obvious to the reader, however, it is the realization that it is the parents and their children who are the heroes in the fight against congenital heart disease.

Edward L. Bove, M.D.

Preface

by: Anna Marie Jaworski

How many people are affected by birth defects? The number one birth defect, affecting one in a hundred births, is simply labeled "heart defects" but is a range of birth defects as benign as a small hole which will close on its own, to a defect so severe that a child dies within hours of birth—sometimes regardless of medical intervention. How many people are affected? Of course the afflicted person is, but this book shows how the whole family is affected. When a person is born with a congenital heart defect, the entire family's life changes forever.

The purpose of this book is to inspire and educate others about life with congenital heart defects. Some heart defects were considered a death sentence just a couple of decades ago. Now there is treatment. Now there is hope.

What kind of life can a child with a severe, congenital heart defect hope to lead? Can that child experience normal childhood events? Will the child be able to run a race? play in a band? celebrate religious ceremonies? go to college? have a baby?

At two months of age my son, Alexander, was diagnosed with a severe, congenital heart defect known as hypoplastic left heart syndrome (HLHS). He is four years old now and has survived two open-heart surgeries. When he was first diagnosed I asked myself the questions above. I wanted reassurance. I wanted to know my son would grow up. I wanted him to have a normal life. I wanted him to live.

Like many other parents of children with congenital birth defects, I was worried about my son's quality of life. What kind of life would he lead? Would he hate his father and me for putting him through a number of open-heart surgeries? Would he be angry if he could not participate in activities which his older brother never thought about twice? Would he be in and out of hospitals for most of his life? I wanted to know. I wanted some kind of preparation.

Over the course of several years I had come to know many parents of children with congenital heart defects (CHDs) and considered some of them friends even though we had never met face-to-face. I "met" some people through the Internet when they found out they were pregnant with their HLHS baby and corresponded by email with them through their pregnancy and their child's open-heart surgeries. We became very close because of our special bond. We prayed, cried and rejoiced in each child's triumph and as each of our babies beat the odds. And, yes, sometimes we grieved for and with each other when one of our angels didn't make it. I discovered that it did not matter which country we lived in, how old we were, how much money we had in the bank—all of us had the same concerns, the same dreams and the same hopes and fears.

We all wanted the same thing—reassurance that our children could lead a normal life. Parents asked me questions about what kind of future their child might have. In March of 1997, I realized I knew many wonderful stories about inspirational children and mothers. When people called or wrote to me about their situation, I could share stories about Alexander or other children and parents I had come to know. I felt rich with information and empowered by the beautiful stories I knew were told from the heart. I was finally beginning to have some answers to some of those questions.

I couldn't be selfish and keep all of those stories to myself! I decided to gather those stories into a book, a special book, to inspire and educate others about CHDs. This book, written by mothers, would be a tribute to our children, husbands, parents, doctors, nurses and everyone else involved in caring for our children. Originally the book was to have about fifteen contributors. After the idea for this book spread, however, over eighty mothers offered to share their special stories. Inside this remarkable book you will find a sampling of those stories. You will meet women and children who have faced the greatest challenges a

Introduction:
A Great-Grandmother with a Congenital Heart Defect

By: Judy Norwood

If you are reading this book, you are probably the parent of a child with a congenital heart defect (CHD). Or, maybe you are a young person born with a CHD. I would like to tell you a little bit about myself. I was born in 1938 with the CHD called Tetralogy of Fallot (TOF). And as you can see by the date, I am sixty years old. Experience is my credential for writing this introduction.

I know the questions that are in the hearts and minds of parents, young women, and yes, young men, when a congenital heart defect (CHD) is present in their lives. Parents ask themselves so many questions. How long will our baby live? What kind of quality of life will the baby have? Will she be able to have children? Will he be able to father a child? Should we trust our child's life to the hands of a surgeon? What will happen to him/her if something happens to us? Mom will worry that she did something to cause the CHD or that it could have been avoided had they done things differently. Dad will worry that somehow he is responsible for his child's CHD as well. There is guilt, frustration and yes, there is anger.

There are many questions in the mind of a young woman with a CHD. How could any man ever want me? And if there is such a man, how could I take care of a husband? Will I be able to be intimate with my husband? Will I be able to have a baby? Will I be able to experience the delight of holding my baby close in my arms and watch as a little smile curls upon his tiny lips? Will I be able to caress her soft hair? Will I be able to see my baby grow and mature? Will I be able to take care of my baby as she grows and matures? Will I be able to take care of my two-year-old toddler as he runs circles around me? And how can I keep up with him/her as the teen years approach? Will I be there for the teen years?

Even though the young man will not have to face the physical stress of childbirth, there are other stresses that are typical to men. Young men will have many questions, too. Will a young woman ever want me? Will I be able to be a lover to my wife? Will I be able to protect her? Will I be able to father a child? Will I be able to roughhouse and play football or baseball with my son? Will I be able to swing my little girl high into the air, see her hair sparkling in the sun and hear her laughter?

And of course there is the big question of all involved: Will the progeny of a person with a CHD inherit that CHD? And there are questions in the minds of those of us as we have matured, and yes, aged. How much longer do I have? Will I be a burden to my loved ones? Will I end up in a nursing home? Will I become a vegetable on a life-support system? The questions swirl around and around, sometimes becoming difficult to bear.

In the 1940s most children born with TOF died before or during their teens. It was also believed that children born with TOF were unable to learn. The school nurse told my mother that she might be able to teach me to cook and sew, but, thankfully, my mother was not satisfied with that. She taught me how to read and write. When the school nurse found out that I was able to learn, she went to the school board, and they set up a tutor for me. After my first surgery in 1949 (a Pott's shunt), I was able to go to public school for the first time. And because of my mother's diligence, I was able to enter the fifth grade with the other children my age. I graduated from high school in 1957.

When I had my first surgery a great and wonderful change came into my life. I bounded around in a way that I was never able to do before. I learned to swim, ride horseback, ski, and skate. I was just like any other normal teenager. But one of the first questions that I asked my doctor when I came to be old enough to be thinking about it was, "Will I be able to have a baby?" The answer was, "You can have six babies if you so wish." Well, I did not want that many, but, oh how happy I was to hear that!

Yes, there was a man who loved me and wanted me. His name was Richard. January 2, 1959, I gave birth to our baby girl, Peggy. I had a very difficult time because the hours of labor and the delivery took their toll on me, but when I saw my beautiful baby girl for the first time, I was so happy! The pain of childbearing was forgotten. There she was, all red and wrinkly and screaming her head off. She had good lungs! "But, how is her heart?" I asked the doctor. Her heart was fine. She was perfectly healthy, all five pounds, twelve ounces of her.

The first surgery in 1949 gave me sixteen wonderfully healthy years, but I began having trouble in the early sixties. By that time, they were doing open-heart surgery. In 1965 I had my first open-heart surgery. This surgery gave me fifteen more wonderfully healthy years. In 1977 Peggy was married and ready to start a family of her own. One year later, I became a grandmother. Peggy had given birth to my granddaughter, Rebecca. How wonderful it was to hold my granddaughter in my arms. This person, who had very little hope of living to adulthood, was actually holding her first grandchild. What a wonderful feeling.

I found myself back in the hospital having my second open-heart surgery in 1980. At the same time, Peggy was pregnant with my oldest grandson, Isaac. It was a while before I first saw him, but I was there when he took his first steps. I was so proud of him. In 1984 my second grandson, Daniel, was born. Fortunately, I had gone to be with Peggy before Daniel was born and was there to see him when he came home from the hospital.

In 1988 I had my third open-heart surgery. At this time, Peggy was pregnant with my granddaughter, Elisabeth. She was born a few days after I was discharged from the hospital. They came to see me soon after I was home, and I found myself holding another beautiful little grandchild in my arms.

Now, thirty-nine years later, my daughter's family has grown. Since Peggy remarried David, I became a step-grandmother to Connie. Now I have three granddaughters, two grandsons, and one great-granddaughter. Rebecca and her husband, Vic, are now the proud parents of Asia Renee. Yes, I have a great-granddaughter. What a blessing to sit there and hold this beautiful little girl in my arms. The first time I saw her, I could not hold back the tears. And Rebecca is pregnant again. An ultrasound tells us that there is a great-grandson coming in March of 1999. I am so proud of each one of them. All I can think is, *look at what I would have missed if Mom and Dad had not trusted me to the hands of a surgeon.*

I have seen cardiology grow to the high-tech, computerized, sophisticated profession we know today. Whereas in the 1940s, there was little hope for people like me; today there is much hope for a person born with a CHD to live a full and purposeful life.

Editor's Note: Sadly, Judy Norwood passed away on December 23, 1998 after another open-heart surgery. She died due to a blood clot to her lungs while recuperating in a rehabilitation center. She will be missed by her family and those of us in the CHD community who had the honor of getting to know her.

Dedication

*To my mother, Carol Ann Daigneault,
and to all mothers everywhere who strive
to protect and love their children.*

iscovery

Most parents have an innocent perception of parenthood. If asked what their role as parent is, most would say to provide for, love and protect their children. While those things may be true, there are some things a parent cannot protect their children from.

This chapter deals with discovering the unthinkable—that our precious babies have a severe, congenital birth defect. A birth defect that could very well claim that baby's life. This birth defect is summed up in the label "congenital heart defect (CHD)" but includes a variety of defects from "innocent murmurs" to life-threatening heart deformities.

While most of the essays for these first three chapters are written by mothers of children with hypoplastic left heart syndrome (HLHS), the feelings these mothers describe are common to mothers of children with other congenital heart defects as well. It is the discovery of the birth defect and the shattered dreams that all of us share and know.

This chapter could be a dismal testament to a crisis, but it is not. Instead, this is a chapter about strength and hope, in spite of the inevitable sadness accompanying the horrible truths all of us have had to face. While we have all come to discover the world of congenital heart defects, we have also discovered an inner strength many of us did not know we possessed. Perhaps the greatest discovery, though, is the power of a mother's love.

You cannot alter the course that life takes.
You can only alter what you expect from it.
Forget things as they once were; accept them as they are.

Discovering Congenital Heart Defects In Utero

What is the number one birth defect in the United States? Few people know the answer is heart defects. Heart defects actually occur in one of every hundred live births. We have no way of knowing how many times heart defects cause miscarriages. We do know that the number one cause of cardiac death among newborns is a complex heart defect known as hypoplastic left heart syndrome (HLHS).

Ironically enough, every mother in this chapter discovered in utero that her baby would be born with HLHS. Many doctors encourage mothers to abort babies with this heart defect. Some doctors do not recommend aborting but advocate an option for care known as the compassionate route or compassionate care which entails allowing "nature to take its course" an almost certain death within the first days of life.

How does a woman react when she is told that her baby is going to be born with a life-threatening heart defect? How does her husband, her family react? What gives these women hope? What did they do to survive the interminable weeks or months before birth? How did they arrive at their choice for treatment? What gives them strength?

A Brother for Markie

By: Christine Prior

We were not trying to get pregnant with a second child, but when I took the home pregnancy test, I was very excited to find out that it was positive. I remember calling Mark at work and saying "Guess what?

I'm pregnant!" He was very happy. We told our five-year-old son, Markie, that I was going to have another baby. He was not too happy at first, but he got used to the idea and wanted a sister. It was important to Mark and me to have Markie very involved in the pregnancy.

My pregnancy was going along fine; the only problem I had was some spotting in the beginning. The OB said that the baby's heartbeat was good and that the baby was growing just like he should be. Markie went along for my OB visits. He heard the baby's heartbeat and felt the baby kicking. I would ask Markie what kind of names he liked for the baby, and, of course, he would always give me some outrageous name, but he thought it was funny!

We went for a routine ultrasound at thirty-three weeks and were excited to find out we were having another boy! The ultrasound tech seemed to focus on the heart and took several measurements and pictures of it, but we just thought this was normal. After she finished, the tech took the pictures and said she would be back after showing them to the doctor. Since the doctor was in the hospital delivering another baby, though, she let us go home.

I was getting ready to go to work later that night when the phone rang. It was my OB, Dr. Elisabeth Righter, M.D. She said that they found a heart defect with the baby but could not tell me exactly what was wrong because she did not know. She could tell me that the baby had a very small left ventricle. She wanted me to call the next day and schedule a fetal echocardiogram at Rainbow's Babies and Children's Hospital, in Cleveland.

As I hung up the phone, I remember that I did not even say goodbye. I was crying and my head swirled with questions. Why did this happen to our baby? It was not fair; we were supposed to have a healthy baby! We saw our baby today on the ultrasound, and he looked totally normal. I called Mark at work, crying. I told him the news I had just heard, and he hurried home. We proceeded to call our parents who tried to reassure us that the baby would be fine and that modern technology today could fix a lot of things.

When I found out that our baby had a problem called hypoplastic left heart syndrome, I still did not feel as if I had enough information on the subject. My father told me to get on the Internet and use a search engine (I used Yahoo), and I typed in the words hypoplastic left heart syndrome. A bunch of sites came up. The first thing I read was the definition of HLHS and brief descriptions of the three-step surgery.

I had no idea how to use the Internet, but I learned that night. After I would read one parent's story, there would be other addresses to click on at the bottom of the page to take you to another story or address. Somehow I traveled to something called "Sheri's Page" and that is where I read about a book for parents dealing with HLHS by Anna Jaworski. I was very excited that I could get a book on this, so I emailed Anna and asked her how I could get it. I also read stories of other parents who had gone through this and remember crying and being very upset. All I could think was, "Why did this have to happen to our baby?"

I printed three copies of all the information I found that night, one for myself, one for my mother and one for my mother-in-law. I wanted to get as much information as possible so I could educate myself on this. The first night I was on the Internet for three hours.

I went back to the Internet every night for a week trying to find more information. After my second echo, the doctor used new terms, and I would go to my search engine and type in those keywords to see what it would bring up. After I had exhausted my search of HLHS, I typed in key words like "CHD" or "Congenital Heart Defect," "Heart Disease," "Dr. Bove," "University of Michigan."

I emailed Anna Jaworski, too. I remember telling her I was very scared of what the future held for my little guy. I also wrote a few other parents from stories I had read to find out more information about their trials. I remember emailing the father of John Horsager to find out what exactly happened to John, how he made it through the first two surgeries and then lost his courageous battle. I wrote to other families who had children with HLHS and inquired about their experiences and what I could expect.

From what I read on the Internet and heard from our pediatric cardiologist (PC), I knew that the best place for our baby to be was inside of me. I knew that I was not due for another three weeks and just kept hoping and praying that he would stay inside for as long as he needed so he would be strong. I was very scared about his birth because I knew that he could die, and I was very upset most of the time. I cried a lot.

At my last ultrasound at thirty-three weeks, we found out the baby was a boy, and we named him Tyler Andrew. We did not name him after anyone or anything special, we just liked the name. From that time on, I always referred to the baby inside of me as "Tyler" not "the baby."

Day to day I cried a lot; I knew that there was nothing I could do but wait. I prayed everyday, many times a day, always asking that my baby would be okay. I think that I talked to everyone I could, my mother, cousin, friends and family about this.

The doctors gave us the worst case scenario, and I kept hoping that Tyler would even be 10% better than they thought. I wanted someone to tell me that my baby was going to be healthy instead of "just have to wait and see." I went to church every week and would pray so hard that I would actually break into tears after communion. I thought a lot about how I could possibly handle Tyler dying. I did not know how I could cope if he died. I knew I had to be strong for Markie's sake. I did not know how I would explain anything to Markie since I did not understand it completely myself!

I went through many stages; at first I was very sad, then I was very angry at the baby and at God. I used to think, "Why is God doing this to us? I took such good care of myself with this pregnancy!" I do not think I can explain why I was mad at the baby, but I was. I got very depressed. I had a very hard time dealing with the fact that I felt Tyler kicking and moving inside of me, yet he was considered sick. How could he be so sick if he felt so healthy? I tried bartering with God. I would say, "I will do anything if You just let my baby be okay. I will go to church every week if You let my baby live."

I had enormous support from my family and friends. Finding all of the stories on the Internet especially helped me. I found wonderful friends all over the world, and their support was tremendous. My mother was always there, listening to me and giving me advice.

I was very lucky that when Tyler was born my mother took advantage of The Family Leave Act and took time off when we were in Michigan to watch Markie for us so that his life would not be interrupted.

Tyler is now one year old and he is doing wonderfully. He is not developmentally delayed in any way. He walked at ten months. He says "da, da" (no ma, ma yet), "stop," "hot," and "arf." He dances and gets into everything! He loves to play with Markie and our dog, Cruiser!

Tyler is scheduled for his completion Fontan in Michigan the first week of June. And I pray everyday that Tyler will do as wonderfully as he did for his first two surgeries. I also say a little prayer every evening before bed to thank God for letting me have one more day with Tyler and to keep him "healthy" for many more days to come.

Christine and Tyler

Editor's Note: Tyler is now two years. old. He had his completion Fontan done at the University of Michigan in July of 1998, and is scheduled for the Amplatzer closing fenestration in April of 1999.

Learning to Love and Trust God

By: Kerrie Van Eck

In early June 1996, I realized that I was pregnant with my third child. This was a complete surprise to me, and I knew that God must have a special plan for this child—little did I know.

I did not know exactly how my husband, Bob, would react to my wonderful news, so I waited a couple of weeks, until Father's Day to tell him. On the way home from church that day, I said, " Honey, God wants you to become a father again." He was very surprised, but after the initial shock, he was very happy. We then told each of our families. Our biggest concern at that time was whether or not our house was big enough for our growing family.

On September 9, 1996, Bob, my mom and I anxiously watched the first ultrasound of our baby boy. I was twenty weeks pregnant. It was very exciting to see this unborn baby. Just after the ultrasound, Bob had to return to work, and I talked to the doctor about the ultrasound. He told me that the ultrasound technician could not get a clear picture of the baby's heart and wanted me to go to the hospital for another scan. They had an opening that same morning, so my mom and I went to the hospital. I could not contact Bob at this time. The technician and the doctor were very serious, but the baby was moving a lot, and they could not get a clear picture, so they asked if we could come back later that afternoon for yet another ultrasound with yet another doctor.

I finally reached Bob on the phone just before this third ultrasound, but he was in a meeting and could not get to the hospital in time. My mom and I went back to the hospital and were soon in a room with four doctors as well as the technician. There was a lot of discussion amongst the doctors. Finally all the doctors left except one, and he just told us that there was a very serious problem, but he needed to consult with my obstetrician, and he would contact me the next day. Mom and I were both shaken. When Bob heard this news, he was upset and angry that we did not know anything more.

I remember our pastor calling that evening to see how we were doing. He told me that I would grow closer to God through this situation, and I told him that I had already. I had been praying for our baby all day.

Also, that day I started making a baby afghan for my little child within. It sounds crazy, but I needed to do something specifically for him. It was the only thing that I could think of at the time.

The next day, I called my doctor, and he told me that he wanted us to meet with a pediatric cardiologist and a maternal-fetal specialist and have another test called a fetal echocardiogram. The appointment was two and a half weeks away. He could not give me any information about the baby's heart because he really did not know what the problem was.

The next two and a half weeks were the hardest of our married life. I kept thinking that things like this did not happen to "normal" people like us. They did not even happen to people we knew. We did not know what to expect, only that something was not right with our baby. We thought that maybe the baby might have to have some kind of surgery, and then he would be okay. What we found out was devastating.

On September 26, we met with the maternal-fetal physician, Dr. Cook, and the pediatric cardiologist, Dr. Donald Malcomb. After a fetal echocardiogram we were told that our baby boy had hypoplastic left heart syndrome. We had never heard of this before. It was explained that the left ventricle was too small and would not support the blood flow to the body. The aorta was small, and the mitral valve was not working properly. Dr. Malcomb told us that we had three options: 1) to do nothing— our baby would probably live a few days or maybe a week, 2) to have a heart transplant, or 3) a series of three surgeries to reconstruct the heart, which were still fairly new surgeries. He said that we did not have to make a decision right away because ironically, until the baby was born, he was fine.

We were in shock and did not even know what kind of questions to ask. Here we were expecting a perfect child, only to discover that he was fatally ill. We asked if there was any type of surgery that could be done in utero. There was not. We asked some questions about heart transplants. We were told about Dr. Edward Bove in Ann Arbor, Michigan, about two hours away who has very good results with the three-stage reconstruction. At that time we were also offered an amniocentesis to see if there was a chromosomal defect. We had not had that test with our other pregnancies and did not think that we could handle it right then, so we declined.

We also met with a social worker who tried to comfort us and help direct us to more information. She gave us Dr. Bove's phone number and also told us that she could get us in touch with other couples who had faced this terrible decision.

We went home. I was numb, yet I could not stop crying. Bob went back to work and called his parents. My dad was with our other boys, Noah and Nicholas, so my mom, who had been with us at the hospital, explained it all to him on their way home from our house. When I asked her later how he took it, she said that he cried. I remember feeling awful that our families had to go through this, too. I felt helpless.

I turned to God a lot in those very difficult weeks. He was, and still is, my source of strength, and I do not know how I would have managed without the peace and comfort that came only from Him. I had been praying for God's will and also that God would be glorified through this.

We decided that we should have the amniocentesis and had it done the next week. We almost backed out at the last minute because of the risks involving a miscarriage. It took about two more weeks for the results which yielded no chromosomal disorders. The genetics counselor was primarily concerned about Down syndrome.

We tried to find more information about HLHS, transplants and staged reconstruction. At first the heart transplant seemed like a good option to us. It would involve only one surgery easier than the reconstruction. It would also mean a new heart. We met with our pediatric cardiologist again but this time with a list of questions. He was very helpful. He told us that a lot of babies die waiting for a transplant because there just are not many infant donor hearts. He also told us the risks of the anti-rejection medications and that the transplant centers require patients to live close by for weekly visits. He told us that the best transplant center in the country would be Loma Linda, California. The second best was Chicago, three hours away from us. We learned that the success rate was about 70- 75%.

We also talked about the staged reconstruction surgeries and about Dr. Bove at the University of Michigan Hospitals. Dr. Malcomb told us that the success rate was slightly higher than the transplant, about 75-80%, although there were three surgeries involved. The first one would be about four days after birth, the second four to six months, the third eighteen to twenty-four months. Some of these statistics Dr. Malcomb had explained the day he told us that the baby had HLHS, but my mind could not comprehend everything at that time.

We were told that if we chose the staged reconstruction, then we could deliver our baby in Grand Rapids and be transported to Ann Arbor a few days later, or we could deliver in Ann Arbor. We were told that because of my previous Caesarean section, we had a choice of having Caesarean delivery or a vaginal birth, which meant more decisions.

During this time I was going back and forth to my obstetrician, Dr. Stephen Hickner, and the maternal-fetal specialist. Although my pregnancy was not high risk, the baby would be high risk immediately following the birth. I ended up seeing all three of the doctors in the practice, and each time I had to explain everything that we knew, where we were in the decision-making process and all about my past pregnancies.

At my obstetrician's office the normal policy is to see each of the four doctors in the practice at least once so that you would know them in case they were on call the day you went into labor. At this point I was considering a Caesarean section to avoid all of the doctors and hospital teams in the delivery room with us. If I had a Caesarean section, Dr. Hickner would be available, and we could avoid seeing the other doctors. Also, if we decided to have the birth in Ann Arbor, then there was no point in seeing all of the different doctors. I was getting tired of explaining the whole situation each time I had an appointment, which was every week for awhile.

During this time we received floods of cards, notes and phone calls expressing support for us, which gave us an overwhelming sense of love and peace. Most people tried to understand what we were going through, but they could not. It was really nice to talk with some couples who had gone through having a child with HLHS. They were the only ones that could truly understand what we were feeling.

In early November we went to Ann Arbor to meet with Dr. Bove. We had a list of questions for him about the staged reconstruction surgeries. He was very kind and caring and answered all of our questions so that we could understand him. He told me that I would probably be able to breastfeed after the surgery. He also explained that he was concerned about the atrial septal defect that our baby might have. This would mean an immediate heart catherization, putting a balloon in to open up the ductus arteriosus. We asked him if he felt that we should deliver the baby in Ann Arbor, and Dr. Bove thought that it would alleviate some of the transport risk; in addition, if the baby needed the heart cath, the doctors would be completely ready for it. We also asked him a little about transplants, and he preferred to do the staged reconstruction first, leaving the transplant as a last resort.

We took tours of the hospitals and the Ronald McDonald House while we visited Ann Arbor. We met with a social worker, Barb Shaltis, who told us that they see a lot of HLHS babies each year and that Dr. Bove has great success with the surgeries. We also stayed overnight in the Med Inn that is connected to the medical complex.

I guess it was while we were speaking with Dr. Bove that Bob and I realized that our decision was being made. We decided to have the staged reconstruction. We went back and forth as to where to have the delivery but finally decided to have it in Ann Arbor. We did not want to be separated from our baby. Our family and friends would have to drive two hours to visit us, but we decided it would be best for the baby. We also decided that the heart transplant would be our backup option should the staged reconstruction not be successful.

We met with an obstetrician, Dr. Margaret Punch, at the University of Michigan Hospital who would be handling my case. She had many patients deliver HLHS babies. The medical complex was prepared for this situation. We set the induction date for January 23, 1997. We needed to check in one day prior. The baby's surgery would be around three to five days after birth, and the average recovery time for this surgery was ten to fourteen days. We were planning on being away from home for two to three weeks.

In late November we started making plans for the delivery and the baby's surgery. My parents told us from the beginning that if we needed to be in Ann Arbor they would be willing to take care of Noah and Nicholas for us for as long as we needed. It was such a relief to know they would be cared for.

I started making lists of things to bring for the delivery, our stay in Ann Arbor and our other children. I rented a breastpump to take with us. I made a phone list and an email list for contacting our family and friends from Ann Arbor. Our church was very gracious and loaned us a notebook computer so we could email from Ann Arbor. We saved a lot of money not having to make phone calls. Everyone we knew was long distance from Ann Arbor.

My parents decided to bring Noah and Nicholas to Ann Arbor on the day of the delivery and were planning on staying until after the surgery. It was about this time that we named our baby. We had a lot of people praying for him, and some expressed that they would like to pray for him by name if we had selected one. We finally decided on Jonah. Jonah, in the Bible, was a man who learned to love and trust God—that was what we hoped for our baby.

On January 22, 1997, we dropped Noah and Nicholas off at Grandpa and Grandma Smith's house along with a carload of their belongings. We then left for Ann Arbor and checked in at the Med Inn. We started learning our way around a little and met with Barb Shaltis. Neither Bob nor I slept very well that night. We knew we were about to have a baby but also that once he was born he would be in trouble. This was very scary. He was so safe inside me that I wanted to keep him there as long as I could, and yet I was getting tired of being pregnant.

On January 23, labor was induced around 1:00 p.m. and continued all day without a baby. My parents had brought the boys down, and they were so excited. They kept asking when they could see Jonah. We stopped the Pitocin and were going to try again in the morning. This was frustrating because I had been induced with my first child, and labor went very smoothly and quickly.

They still wanted to monitor me off and on during the night, so it was another sleepless night. January 24 was another long day. Labor had started getting stronger, but the baby's head had not dropped, so the OB was reluctant to break my water for fear of cord prolapse. Finally around 10:00 p.m., she decided to break my water but prepared me for a Caesarean section just in case the cord came down. Everything was fine, and about an hour and a half later, Jonah was born on January 25 at 12:50 a.m. Bob and my mother witnessed the event. Jonah weighed seven pounds, thirteen ounces and was twenty-two inches long. His APGAR scores were eight and eight, marked down only for color.

I asked the doctors if I would be able to hold Jonah after his birth, and they said no because there would be a team of doctors waiting for him and time was critical. When Jonah was born, I reached for him and something wonderful happened: Dr. Punch picked him up and laid him on my lap for just about ten seconds—that was the most wonderful thing she could have done. I told him that I loved him and that there were a lot of people praying for him. I told him I was sorry that he had to be taken away, but the doctors would do everything they could to help him. Then he was gone. A doctor was waiting during the delivery with a blanket, and he whisked him out of the room. They told me that he was just across the hall. I was so happy. I got to hold him! I did not think that I would get to hold him until sometime after his surgery. This was so wonderful. It was so much easier to let him go.

Exhausted after three sleepless nights in a row, we went back to my room around 2:00 a.m. and fell asleep waiting for the cardiologist to meet with us. At about 4:00 a.m. he finally came and said that Jonah was doing very well. They put lines in his belly button and an IV in his arm. They were giving him prostaglandin to keep the PDA open, and he was stable. The atrial septal defect was not causing any problems, and they did not anticipate any. A nurse wheeled me down to see Jonah. He was beautiful. Even though Jonah was in the Neonatal Intensive Care Unit with all the medicine lines, he looked great. He was bigger than most of the other babies in the NICU. All of the nurses and doctors kept saying that they had been waiting for two days for this baby to be born.

The next few days were a blur. I had a severe spinal headache and almost fainted when I was on my feet. I finally received a blood patch and that relieved the headache, but two days later it came back. Another blood patch worked again.

Jonah was moved to the Moderate Care Unit in the Mott Children's Hospital, in another part of the hospital complex. We were able to hold him, and I was also able to initiate breastfeeding. At first Jonah did very well, but he was so sleepy all the time that he was mostly tube fed using what little milk I could produce plus formula.

The night before surgery, Bob and I prayed over Jonah. We prayed for God's will for him and for the doctors as they held his little heart in their hands. We prayed that God would be blessed and glorified in this situation, no matter what the outcome. Also that night we toured the PICU and saw babies just coming out of heart surgery so that we would not be quite so shocked seeing Jonah after surgery.

Jonah had surgery when he was four days old. We walked down with him as far as they would let us, kissed him and said, "Goodbye," maybe for the last time. It was so hard to let go this time.

In the waiting room we tried to keep the children entertained and to keep our minds off what they were doing to Jonah. Finally the doctors came and told us that they were done, that he was okay, but he had some bleeding. We were able to see him for about two minutes, then they made us leave so they could make decisions about treatment. Two hours later Dr. Bove came out and said that Jonah looked great. I asked about the bleeding, and he said, "It just stopped!" What an overwhelming sense of relief and joy! We praised God. He had chosen to save our baby!

As I look back, I realize that I was afraid of losing Jonah, so I had tried not to get too attached. It was not until after we came home from the hospital that I realized we had a special bond, maybe even more special than with my other boys. I was still afraid of losing him, but I just kept holding him and telling him how special he was. I prayed for him all the time. I prayed that God would use him for His glory.

Editor's Note: Jonah has now had all three surgeries and is doing well. He is now two years old and weighs twenty-eight pounds. Jonah also had the Amplatzer, a new device, to close his fenestration. The device is used during a catheterization to close the fenestration.

Jonah Van Eck

Getting a Better Look

By: Edie Spears

On November 5, 1996, at almost thirty-five weeks into my pregnancy, I went in for a routine ultrasound to check the size of the baby boy I was carrying. This was the third ultrasound due to bleeding throughout the pregnancy, and since my previous two had been perfectly normal, I was not expecting any surprises. I was prepared to hear the baby was large and that I would need an early induction to deliver safely. I was excited that I would possibly get better pictures of the baby than from the prior ultrasound.

During the ultrasound I watched closely as the spine, brain, heart and other major organs were scanned. I have always found ultrasounds fascinating and was amazed at this tiny little boy growing inside me! The friendly technician identified everything as we went. I am a talker, so I chatted the whole time. As I saw my baby's heart beating, I commented how hard it must be for him when he did an ultrasound and

13

the mother could see it was not beating. I asked him how he handled it when that happened or when it was obvious something major was missing. The tech commented that it was very difficult and that it was always a relief when this did not happen. I laughed and said he must be happy then because the heart was obviously beating and definitely was not missing, and all the major parts seemed to be intact. He smiled, and for the life of me I cannot remember his response.

After about forty-five minutes and many position shifts and manipulations of my belly, the technician told me he was not seeing the heart as well as he would like, and he called in a more experienced tech to take a look. He said not to worry that he just wanted a better look. I accepted this and kept talking. After another forty-five minutes with both techs still trying to get a better look by shifting and manipulating my belly, I was growing concerned but not too worried. Thirty minutes later the techs asked me to return the following day, giving the baby time to shift. They reassured me that this was routine and did not mean anything was wrong.

I left feeling a vague sense of unease but did not believe anything major could be wrong. Afterall I had three perfectly healthy children already. That night I told Arthur, my partner, that a return appointment did not seem routine and I felt something was wrong with the baby. Arthur thought I was worrying unnecessarily. I spent a sleepless night with the day's events going round and round in my head, anxious for the next day.

At my appointment after another forty-five minutes with both techs, they said to keep my regular OB appointment and thanked me for my patience. I left feeling concerned, but only mildly, because the techs' attitudes were so casual.

At the doctor's that afternoon, I asked right away if something was wrong with the baby. My OB, Peggy Cox, said the techs indicated the possibility of hypoplastic left heart syndrome. She set up an appointment with a pediatric cardiologist to do an echocardiogram on the baby's heart to be sure.

I went a little numb and tears welled up in my eyes. Peggy immediately said not to be upset yet because it might be a mistake. She told me not to worry until I was sure. I asked her to tell me how serious the condition was, but she brushed it aside and told me to wait for the echo. As soon as I got home I called my pediatrician, Dr. Sarah Wright, and told her what I knew. I asked her to tell me how serious this really was. She very quietly told me how sorry she was and proceeded to say that I needed to prepare myself and my family for a very sick baby who would need open-heart surgery or a transplant and could very possibly die. I went into even greater shock, hollowly thanked her and told her I would let her know when I got a definite diagnosis.

I was not supposed to see the PC, Dr. Mary Rice, for almost a week, and I was not sure I could survive the wait. When the receptionist called and changed the appointment for two days later, I was so relieved!

That night I called several people and asked them to pray for my baby—to ask God for a miracle. I hoped we would do the echo and be told that everything was fine and that it had all been a big mistake! All of my loved ones and I prayed during those two days, and I think we really believed it would all be fine.

Dr. Rice told us the echo confirmed that our baby boy had HLHS, and then she gave us some information, briefly explained the defect and outlined our choices: three stages of surgeries, transplant, or do nothing and let the baby die while being made as comfortable as possible.

I sat there feeling stunned with a weird ringing in my ears and the oddest sick feeling. I could not stop shaking, but I did not cry. I wanted to cry and kept feeling like I should; I just could not. I was too frozen to cry. I asked dozens of questions until I realized I was asking them because it seemed like I should, not because I needed more information.

Dr. Rice left Arthur and me alone to talk while she contacted our pediatrician. We sat there in shock not talking, not touching, just sitting. Finally I asked Arthur if he had any questions; he had been very quiet. Arthur felt I had pretty much asked them all.

I assumed we would not take the third option. When I told Arthur, he agreed. Doing nothing was simply not an option. I am so thankful that we both felt this way because it would have torn me apart if Arthur had wanted to let the baby die. I found myself needing Arthur and his support over the next several weeks.

We did not know how to make this life and death choice for our unborn baby. When Dr. Rice came back we asked her if she could refer us to other parents confronted with this choice. We felt that talking to other parents who had made this decision would be even more helpful than talking to a doctor; however, Dr. Rice felt that it would not be appropriate to give other parents' names until after we had made our decision. She said the baby was large, and we only had a week to decide if I wanted to avoid a C-section. We would need a couple of weeks to arrange insurance, doctors and hospitals.

Dr. Rice shook our hands, gave us our fliers and sent us home to decide our baby's fate. On the hour long drive home Arthur and I said maybe twenty words to each other. It was simply too much to cope with. We needed time to absorb this terrible news.

When we got home there was a message from Dr. Wright on the machine saying we could call her that night with questions even though she was not on call. When I called her, she was great, explaining as much as she could about the pros and cons of our two options. When I asked her what she would do, she answered honestly and explained why it would be her choice. Then she told us how to go about gathering information to help us come to a decision. Her last comment was to write everything down as we thought of it, so we did not waste time trying to remember what we wanted to know when we had the resource available. It was very good advice. Our pediatrician has proven to be a very dedicated, conscientious, caring source of support. We would be lost without her.

Our children were at my parents', and I called my mom and told her that there were problems with the baby. I asked her if the kids could spend the weekend while we tried to come to grips with the situation. I needed all my energy to focus on keeping myself together. We gathered as much information as possible and tried to think of intelligent questions so that we could make this overwhelming decision in only seven days. At this point, I was still shaking.

Arthur suggested making a list of questions, resources and lists of whom we needed to talk, doctors, hospitals, insurance companies, etc. For a while it gave us something to focus on other than our emotions. I kept asking myself why I was not crying, but I was too numb to cry. We decided to escape the "issue" for awhile, and Arthur suggested getting something to eat. Of course, we were not hungry, and all we could think of was our baby. We could not sleep that night. The weekend prevented us from researching information about this surreal situation, yet we were unable to escape from it either. I can't describe how awful that weekend was for us.

Late Sunday, in the middle of the night, the week's events hit me like a ton of bricks, and I fell apart. I had literally shaken all weekend long, but now I cried and cried so hard it physically hurt. I felt as if I would never be able to stop crying. I had never before cried like that in my life. The pain I felt was so overwhelming and consuming I felt like I could not survive. I wanted to curl up in a ball and just cease to be; it was so intense. Arthur just held me until I was so exhausted I cried myself to sleep. Arthur was strong and comforting.

When Monday came I was relieved to begin asking questions, calling hospitals and doctors across the country, and getting answers. After several days of research, Arthur and I decided that the three-stage surgery beginning with the Norwood was the best choice we could make for our baby.

I believe talking to other parents with HLHS children would have helped greatly and hope in the future doctors encourage, rather than discourage, contact with other parents.

First, we called Dr. Rice and told her our decision, and she told us all the things we needed to set in motion. Then we had to break the news to our children and families. We also fought with our insurance company to allow our child's out-of-state birth so we could be close to the Seattle Children's hospital where his first surgery would take place. It took a week each of haggling constantly with our respective insurance companies to get approval. I also needed to choose a hospital for delivery of the baby. Dr. Rice lined up our surgeon, Dr. Lupinetti, and PC, Dr. Herndon.

Finally, we arranged for Arthur's parents to stay with our daughters, Kaitlin and Jaimie, for the first few days. If the baby survived surgery, he could be hospitalized for ten days to two months or maybe even longer; he only had a 50/50 chance of survival. Our nineteen-year-old daughter, Lori, came with her husband and son. If the baby did not make it, we all would spend some time no matter how short. The girls spent the last several months anticipating their baby brother's birth, and we felt that they needed to see and touch him so that there would be some sense of reality for them. We were trying very hard to prepare our children and ourselves for the possible death of our baby.

On November 25, 1996 in the thirty-eighth week of my pregnancy, we made the four hour drive to Seattle to meet Dr. Luthy, the perinatologist who would deliver my son. That afternoon, Dr. Luthy decided that my blood pressure was so high he wanted to induce labor that evening. I was not prepared for this, and I became upset. My son was safe inside me, and I was not ready to let go of him and put his life at risk.

Dr. Luthy gave me until 8:00 p.m. to adjust to the idea before he induced labor. At 3:11 p.m. on Tuesday, November 26th, I gave birth to a beautiful seven pound, ten ounce boy. He was so beautiful and yet so sick that I just fell apart. They whisked him away after letting me hold him for less than two minutes.

My daughter, Jaimie, came in to see me just after they took my son away. When she saw me crying, she asked if I was in pain. I told her no; my tears were for the baby who looked so beautifully healthy and normal. Seeing my beautiful baby for the first time should have been one of my most joyful moments, but instead, I was slapped with the reality that I could lose him. The pain I felt was indescribable. Then the doctor started talking about murmurs and blueness. I realized no matter how hard I tried, I had not really believed the baby could die. It was so hard to let him go and trust in other people to keep him safe.

After about an hour the nurse wheeled me into the ICU so that I could hold my son one more time before he was ambulanced to Children's Hospital. He was already beginning to look sick; his color was poor, and he was beginning to swell. Touching or moving him made him cry, and there were IVs and monitors hooked up to him. I held my son for the ten or fifteen minutes that it took them to get everything ready for the transfer, kissed him good-bye, and they took him away.

Arthur opted to follow the ambulance and see our son settled in. The doctor traveling with our son said that as soon as they had him stabilized in the PICU, the nurse would call me and let me know. This was at about 5:45 p.m., and by 9:00 p.m. no one had called yet. I was in a panic!

I frantically kept calling the nurse and asking if she could find out what was going on. Finally just after 9:00 p.m., Arthur called and told me that when he arrived at Children's, almost an hour after the ambulance (due to rush hour traffic), he was ushered into a parent conference room and told that our baby had stopped breathing on the ambulance ride. The baby was resuscitated and intubated, and the doctors were trying to stabilize him so Arthur could see him. We waited separately, each of us wondering if this was it.

Finally at 10:00 p.m., the PICU nurse caring for our son called and told me that our baby had had a rough time but he was finally stable, and I could call as often as I needed to check on him. If there were any major changes, she assured me she would call. Arthur called and said how horrible it had been sitting in that room by himself, not knowing if he would be told our son had died. Arthur decided to stay awhile longer before coming back to spend the night with me. I said that was fine but to come back because I did not think either one of us needed to be alone, and it was going to be a long, long night. That night we named the baby Michael Samuel.

I believe that finding out our son had a heart defect before he was born saved his life. He was so sick he had to be put on a respirator when less than four hours old. His heart was so unstable that the stimulation of being touched sent his vitals dropping dramatically, so the nurses instituted a no touching rule for the rest of the family and an extremely limited one for Arthur and me.

The next day I was released from Swedish Hospital and went straight to Children's to be with my son. I was shocked to see Michael hooked up to so many tubes, wires and monitors. He was very puffy and bluish, no longer looking like the "perfect" baby. It was scary to see the difference a half of a day made. The surgeon, Dr. Lupinetti, came into the ICU and told us he had decided to operate on Friday, the day after Thanksgiving.

On Thanksgiving night, even though touching was not a good thing for Michael, I requested that his father and I be allowed to hold him because I was very afraid that it might be our last chance to hold him while he was alive. It was a selfish thing, and Michael's vitals dropped severely, but I do not regret it. If he had not made it through surgery, I think not having held him would have been unbearable.

That night everything finally hit Arthur. He was tense and difficult to be around. He decided to shower that night rather than in the morning because we needed to be at the hospital at 6:00 a.m. When he came out of the bathroom his eyes were red and swollen, and I knew he was having a hard time coping with this, too. I do not think either one of us slept that night. We just cuddled and cried.

On November 29, 1996 Michael had his Norwood procedure. Four hours into the surgery a woman came over to us and asked us to go to the parent conference room. She told us that Michael had not made it off the bypass machine and that there would be a few more attempts, but if they were not successful then our son would die. For forty-five awful minutes we waited for news and prayed. She came back smiling and said it was okay. Michael was being taken to recovery.

I thanked God and have been doing so regularly ever since. After that, when we would pass that room, Arthur would comment on how much he hated that room. Every time I saw another family in that room, a part of me was so relieved it was not us.

Michael had many ups and downs in the next few weeks. His chest could not be closed for several days after the surgery due to swelling of his heart; he was on a respirator for three-and-a-half weeks due to pulmonary edema and a temporarily paralyzed diaphragm; and he needed a duodenal feeding tube for over a month due to a temporarily paralyzed vocal cord. Michael was such a fast breather that he was at risk of being acidotic, and for awhile it seemed for each step forward, Michael took two steps back. But all in all he did very well and came home just short of four weeks after birth. It was an amazingly difficult time, but he is so very worth it!

Michael is almost eight months old now and has had the second surgery and many ups and downs in his health. Overall he is a very normal, healthy, happy, beautiful boy, and one would never know he had such a special heart without seeing his scars.

Michael Odom

I am so thankful we knew in advance and could go where he had a much better chance of survival. If we would have given birth in our home town of Salem, Oregon Michael might have died.

A few weeks after Michael and I came home, we went to see the ultrasound techs that had seen Michael's heart defect. I thanked them for being part of the process that saved Michael's life. To this day I believe that their insistence to get a better look did just that!

Editor's Note: Edie was very happy for every moment she had with Michael and does not regret any choices she made regarding his care. Michael passed away on 7/21/98 due to complications following the completion Fontan; he was twenty months old. Naturally he is terribly missed by his whole family.

God Doesn't Make Mistakes

By: Caroline Ahrens

Pregnancy is like a long walk up a flight of forty to forty-two steps. Each step is a new week of exciting changes and totally alien feelings taking place in our bodies. Even a rush to the bathroom in the morning is a time-honored ritual of mothers who have come before us. A whole new purpose to our lives becomes clearer. The focus of our relationship with our mate changes to that of expectant parents. Wow, we are going to HAVE A BABY. The steps to the top will fly by and be nothing but a blurred memory once we hold our beautiful baby. A problem with the pregnancy is usually just a bad dream for most women, a feeling best dismissed as indigestion. For me, the nightmare became real.

"Something just doesn't look right," the obstetrician said. "I could be wrong but you should get checked out at the hospital." These words would forever alter the lives of my husband, Dennis, and me and our yet-to-be-born child. At my thirty-four week checkup, my obstetrician planned a sonogram to check the status of the baby. I was so excited not only did I have my husband there, but I also invited my sister. The date was March 16, 1995, her birthday. We were only six weeks from the big event, and the goal was in sight; the steps were flying by. I had so many things yet to do, the nursery, baby showers, our childbirth class, all the minute details that I had put off, knowing that there would be the last month and these projects would keep my mind and fingers occupied.

There was more than a foot of new snow on the ground the morning of my appointment; everyone was running late including the doctor. We sat and waited for the doctor, joking with the nurse about the size of my belly and playing guessing games about our baby. Was it a girl or boy? We wanted to be surprised. How much would it weigh? We listened to the heartbeat; it registered in the 130 range and was a beautiful sound. Everything was right with the world.

Starting with the head position the doctor worked his way around my belly checking all the vital organs on the baby. He became very quiet and kept moving back to one certain area. His sonogram equipment did not have a good resolution on the screen, so without guidance we had no clue to what he was looking at or why. He did not say much for the next twenty or so minutes; it seemed much longer. I kept asking questions, trying to break the silence. I think he wanted my sister to leave before he said anything to us about a problem. What he finally said was that he was going to refer us to Alaska Regional Hospital for a high-resolution sonogram. He went on to explain that the heart did not look right. He did not elaborate but said if the problem was very serious the baby may have to be born at a hospital with a surgery center. That was it. He left us saying that there was a 50% chance that it was nothing.

The sonogram appointment the next day, a Friday, went fine. The technician did a very thorough job. The resolution was great, and I got some great pictures of our baby's profile. The only problem was the doctor we had hoped to see was not in. The technician, who was looking right at the heart, would not say if she saw anything wrong, so we spent the weekend believing that everything was fine and our OB was just trying to rack up more medical charges to our insurance. If it were so serious they would have said something; would they not? The technician scheduled an appointment for us on Monday morning.

Our odyssey into the world of Congenital Heart Defects began on that fateful Monday in March. It seemed that no one wanted to tell us what the sonogram showed. The doctor that viewed the sonogram at the hospital would only say that it was a serious problem with the baby's heart and that the structure did not look right. He referred us to Dr. David Brauner, one of the two pediatric cardiologists in Alaska.

Unfortunately we could not get in for two days since Dr. Brauner was at a conference out of state. With what information we could pry from the doctor at the sonogram, my husband quickly learned to find his way around the University of Alaska Nursing School Library. We were guessing at the defect and trying to educate ourselves simultaneously. It seemed very strange that no one wanted to discuss it with us, leaving us hanging until our appointment with the pediatric cardiologist.

I was a wreck, very emotional with lots of tears. My husband was quickly cast into the role of "rock to cling to." I tried to go back to my part-time job to keep busy until our next appointment, but it was a lost cause. I was crying too much, which would lead to bouts of throwing up. I kept trying to think about my baby and stay sane for its sake. I ended up staying at home in bed with a box of Kleenex, weeping over every diaper commercial on television.

The confirmation of hypoplastic left heart syndrome (HLHS) came at the pediatric cardiologist's office. It is hard to see the heart of a baby in utero in the last trimester, so they ended up sending me for coffee to wake up the baby and get it moving around for a better look. Before we left the exam room, we asked about the worst case scenario, and the technician said HLHS. Upon our return the "worst case" was confirmed. My mind was in overdrive; the thoughts were chaotic at best. "This couldn't be happening to us, we have a perfect life and deserve a perfect baby. We have waited so long for this baby to love. What on earth could I have ever done to cause this?" My outward reaction was tears and silence; I was too dazed to manage anything else. Dennis stepped in to handle the details of setting up another appointment to discuss our options. I just headed for the elevators as quickly as my lumbering body could go without running. I had to get out of there and be alone with my husband; I needed to cry and scream. We went home to grieve for our lost dreams.

At the library Dennis found a handful of medical articles regarding HLHS. We read them that night and our hopes sank deeper. The articles were written for doctors in a language foreign to us. I kept returning to my eighth-grade health class and simple heart anatomy. Four chambers to the heart, the aorta takes the blood away; the veins bring it back. At one point in my life that was all I needed to know. Most of the information available to us was four to five years old and dealt with lots of statistics high in mortality rates. In my eyes these articles did not deal with children, but with numbers. In my heart I kept the hope alive that the doctors were all wrong and our baby would be born healthy. Or that a miracle would happen, and she would grow another heart chamber. How could this strong kicking active baby be so seriously ill? Denial is a powerful thing.

Within ten days from our initial sonogram, we were on a flight headed for Portland, Oregon and Legacy Emanuel Hospital. We spent the time in between trying to learn as much as we could, notifying family and friends and organizing our lives for the future whatever that may be. This included trying to go a whole day without crying. After our arrival we began another round of sonograms or echocardiograms. Our pediatric cardiologist, Dr. David McIrvin, and nurse advocate, Carolyn Ramwell, gave us the options for our baby: the three surgery palliative repair beginning with the Norwood at three days old, complete heart transplant or compassionate care. Remembering that a baby's heart size is comparable to the size of his fist, I could not fathom how surgery could be preformed on an organ that small.

I think we always knew that we were going to give our baby every possible chance at life, but we were still overwhelmed by the massive amount of medical information given to us. The first thing we read that gave us hope for the future was "A Guide to Hypoplastic Left Heart Syndrome" by Terrance M. Wright. It was written for physicians and parents using language and detailed illustrations that we could understand. We passed copies on to family and friends to help them understand the seriousness of the situation. The next and most important step was to contact other parents of HLHS children. We had seen the medical side and had to hear the real-life side.

Dennis had returned to Alaska to work until our due date, while I stayed with my brother in the Portland area. I was put in contact with a family close by that had a two-year-old boy with HLHS. Talking to his mom was the best thing I could have done. It was such a relief to learn of the relative normalcy of her son's life and that life was not one constant trip to the doctor. She also told me that God did not make mistakes, and there was a reason I was being given this very special child. I had been wondering what I had done to deserve this or cause this. My rational mind became very irrational when I was alone late at night lying in bed. Her statement helped to change my view of the situation somewhat. I was still very upset over everything, but I was coming closer to dealing with it in a calmer state of mind. I would still get choked up over seeing babies at the mall, where I would go to pass the time, and get very angry upon hearing news reports of child abuse and neglect.

At home Dennis was put in touch with the family of another HLHS child. It turned out to be Dr. Norwood's oldest surviving HLHS patient. She is a very special child that went through a great deal to be alive. His conversation with her father changed his thinking greatly, offering a more positive outlook on the future. The night that Dennis talked to this father, the daughter had just run a mile in school.

From our only other perspective of reading articles with extremely high mortality rates for HLHS children, this was truly miraculous. The idea of an active fourteen year old with the same condition as our unborn baby made us happier than we had been in weeks.

I am glad that the defect was detected when it was. If we had found out earlier, there would have been a lot more sitting around worrying over the whys and hows. I would have been looking at the rest of my pregnancy as bad time waiting to get worse. My obstetrician did not give us any hope for the survival of our child. I do not think he had ever dealt with a patient whose baby had such a serious defect, and he did a poor job of it.

If the defect would have been found after her birth, the complications could have been disastrous, considering the three-hour-plus life-flight charter that would have been necessary to get our baby to a surgery center. And since I delivered by Caesarean, I would not have been there for her surgery.

Hannah was born April 24, 1995; she has been through all three of the repair surgeries and is doing very well. She is a happy child who

brings joy to all who meet her. Her smile is like sunshine. Of course she is also a two year old now and can scream very loudly when she doesn't get her way. The fact that she is with us is a miracle, and we remind ourselves of that daily.

Hannah and Caroline

May I never miss a rainbow or a sunset because I am looking down.

HLHS Care Options

Many of the mothers who have contributed essays for this book have children with hypoplastic left heart syndrome (HLHS). The most commonly occurring congenital heart defects are ASDs and VSDs (also known as "holes in the heart") followed by transposition of the great arteries (which is where the pulmonary artery and the aorta are switched). The fourth most common congenital heart defect is hypoplastic left heart syndrome, a catch-all phrase for a complex combination of heart defects often including a hypoplastic left ventricle, problems with the aortic or mitral valve, problems with the aorta as well as other problems. It is *the* most common cause of cardiac death among newborns. Left untreated, HLHS is uniformly fatal.

Oddly enough, aside from terminating the pregnancy, mothers of children with other heart defects are seldom given any options for care. Usually doctors simply tell the parents how they will treat the heart defect. In an HLHS case, doctors require the parents to make the treatment decision. If a woman finds out in utero that her child will be born with HLHS, she may terminate her pregnancy and may be encouraged to do so. The other three options include: 1) the Norwood procedure—a 3-staged surgical procedure to reconstruct the heart, 2) a heart transplant or 3) compassionate care, which is where the parents let nature take its course. After the baby is born, the doctor may decide that transplant is the only option due to the seriousness of the heart defects. In some cases a child may not be viable for any kind of surgery and the parents are left with only one option—compassionate care.

Without the advantage of medical training or expertise, this decision is extremely difficult and stressful. Many parents do not want to be responsible for making a selection, especially if the result is less than desirable. This chapter contains essays from many mothers who chose different options for different reasons. Each story shares a heartfelt account of the extremely difficult decision parents of HLHS children face.

Cardiac Transplantation

Happy Lifeday, Little Angel!

By: Amanda Eason

Our first child, a son we named Jacob, was born on Thursday, December 12, 1996, after an uneventful pregnancy. The delivery turned into an emergency C-section because Jacob's heart rate was having difficulty recovering from contractions. This should have been a clue to someone that something was going on, but he received two nines on his APGARs. He weighed eight pounds, five ounces and we were thrilled to have such a healthy, happy bundle of joy. Healthy, we thought, until our world came crashing down the following day, Friday the 13th.

My husband, Mike, had gone home for the evening to get some rest, so when Jacob's pediatrician came to my room on the 13th, I was alone. The doctor told me he heard a murmur but not to worry; many babies have murmurs, and it would probably go away on its own. To be safe, however, he ordered an echocardiogram and chest X-ray. He said he would talk to me when he received the results. Regardless of his reassurance, I knew immediately something was terribly wrong. Shortly thereafter, still before Mike had arrived, a lady came to my room. She said she was a cardiologist. She told me Jacob had a condition known as hypoplastic left heart syndrome. I think she tried explaining the condition to me, I can't remember; all I can remember from that conversation is her telling me that Jacob's condition was fatal.

Fatal? My precious, newborn son had a fatal heart condition. Dear God, why?!? My husband arrived to find me sobbing. He asked what was wrong, and I told him the news. He was devastated but optimistic. Our parents and friends began arriving, not having a clue as to what was going on. Mike took them in the hallway to tell them the news. I can still remember the heart-wrenching sound of my precious father bursting into tears. Once we had collected ourselves to some degree, Mike and I told the nurse we wanted to see our son. At first they did not think I should, since I had just had surgery twelve hours prior, but after some forceful demands, they found a wheelchair for me, and we were off to the NICU.

There he was; my beautiful baby lying helpless in a little warming bed. Next to all of the premature babies, he looked so healthy, as if nothing were wrong, except for the one IV line coming from him. We later learned the IV carried prostaglandin E1 to his body. The prostaglandin, also known as PGE, was the medicine keeping him alive, because it kept open the patent ductus arteriosus in his heart (also known as the PDA). We were able to touch Jacob a little before another cardiologist, Dr. Bryant, came to us and requested to have a conference immediately.

We followed Dr. Bryant to a room. He was with the lady cardiologist whom I had met earlier. Dr. Bryant proceeded to tell us the severity of Jacob's condition. He said they would need to perform a balloon catherization on Jacob to open up some holes in his heart to maintain his stability, a procedure we agreed to immediately.

Dr. Bryant then told us that we had three options: a transplant, a three-staged surgical procedure starting with the Norwood, or do nothing. Immediately we said doing nothing was not an option. Dr. Bryant explained, to a limited degree, what we could expect if we decided to go with a transplant or with the surgical procedures. Both he and the lady cardiologist left the room so Mike and I could discuss our options. We did not like the statistics we were hearing from Dr. Bryant about the surgery; we also did not like the idea of putting Jacob through so many open-heart surgeries at such an early age. Within five minutes Mike and I had decided on a heart transplant.

We told our family our choices and our decision. They all stood behind us one hundred percent. My father immediately jumped on his computer, researching everything he could about HLHS, about heart transplants, and about the Norwood Procedure. Through the information he received, we learned that so many people opt for the surgical correction that Mike and I began questioning the decision we made for our baby. We talked it over and decided we would just pray about it, and God would lead us in the direction we needed to take. As always, God came through for us.

On the fifth day of Jacob's life, the cardiologist from the hospital that would perform the heart transplant called. He asked that we transport Jacob to their facility so that he could be monitored there, since they had more experience in dealing with this condition. We agreed and Jacob was off in his little "space shuttle" within a few hours. The hospital, Shands, in Gainesville, Florida, is only an hour drive from the hospital where Jacob was born, so they transported him with me by his side in an ambulance. As soon as we arrived in Gainesville we were told about the Ronald McDonald House (RMH), where we stayed for the rest of our journey.

Soon after arriving in Gainesville, cardiologist Dr. Jay Fricker, a group of doctors, nurses and Mike and I were gathered for a conference. Dr. Fricker again explained Jacob's condition, and again we were told compassionate care was a viable option. At that point Mike and I requested we never be given that option again; it was no option for us. Dr. Fricker went on to explain that Jacob would continue to be given the PGE as well as Lasix. The Lasix would help keep fluid out of his lungs which was a concern. Jacob would also be under a hood which we called the "cake box" to assure minimal stress on the lungs. Dr. Fricker mentioned that another baby with the same blood type as Jacob had been waiting for a heart for nine weeks. Although we were concerned by this news, it did not dampen our spirits.

We knew waiting on Jacob's heart would be a long, difficult road, and it was. It was fraught with too many emotions to go into. The days seemed to drag and visiting the NICU during every visiting time became a routine of life. We were fortunate enough to be able to stay at the RMH. Mike had accumulated leave time from work, and I was still on maternity leave. Our friends and family generously donated enough money to pay our expenses while in Gainesville. Mike and I were still receiving our weekly paychecks, so the home bills were paid. Our families came down virtually every day, even though they had spent all day at work themselves.

On the sixth week of our wait we were told there was a donor heart coming. Although a relatively short wait, it seemed like an eternity, and Jacob's condition started to deteriorate. We were told about the heart at approximately 2:00 p.m. The heart was a good distance away, and surgery was scheduled for 8:00 p.m. The events of the day moved quickly yet seemed to drag at the same time. They had to draw blood and do some X- rays in preparation for the surgery. Later on that evening we were told the surgery would be postponed until 11:00 p.m. because they had to ready the surgical team to retrieve the heart (there is one team that takes the heart from the donor and another waiting at the hospital to place the heart in the recipient, Jacob). We were anxious but still excited. The fact that everything was still moving along was a relief to us.

At 10:45 p.m. Jacob was taken to surgery. At this point they put Jacob to sleep and opened him up, prepping him for surgery. Mike and I said our good-byes at the doors to the operating room. Although we knew the dangers of the surgery, I do not believe either one of us were thinking of them at that point. At 11:55 p.m. the plane with the donor heart arrived, and the heart transplant began! By 3:00 a.m. we were told the heart was in place but having trouble sustaining Jacob's lung pressures, so he was being put back on the heart-lung machine. We were upset and scared. After coming so far we could not lose our little angel now. We all began praying a lot! At 3:50 a.m., we were told Jacob was off of the heart-lung machine, and the heart was working with a lot of support, but it was working. Happy lifeday little angel! We were finally able to see Jacob at 4:30 a.m.

Jacob was hooked up to every imaginable machine with tubes coming from all parts of his body, but he was alive, much more so than when he had left us just six short hours before. Jacob had few complications in the immediate days following his heart transplant. The main concern was seizures (from swelling) which were controlled and subsided within a few days. Jacob spent just under two weeks in the cardiac intensive care unit. He did very well and was then moved to an isolation room on the regular pediatric floor. At this point we moved out of the RMH and into Jacob's room. Mike went back to work, although he planned to visit everyday.

I was very excited about moving to the floor with Jacob. Little did I know how nerve-racking it would be. I felt like a caged bird. Worse, I was scared because I was learning how to give Jacob all of his medicines, ten at the time, *and* I was also learning for the first time how to take care of a baby. It was a lot to absorb on my own, so Mike did not return to work after all.

We were planning to go home after one week of being on the floor. The day before he was to be released, Jacob had a rejection episode. This was very frightening for us. Dr. Fricker explained Jacob would be on an IV steroid for four days which should clear it up. Assuming everything else looked good, we were told that we would be able to go home as soon as that was done. Jacob started the medicine right away, and immediately there was a drastic change in his behavior. The medicine made him irritable and hungry all of the time, which was very difficult.

On the second day of the medicine, I noticed blueness and swelling in the leg where Jacob had a central line after the transplant. Doctors from all over the hospital came to look at it to figure out what it was. Their first guess was thrombophlebitis (an infection in the vein of the leg). A serious infection like that could easily kill him. They also did an echo of his veins and arteries in the leg to look for a blood clot; however, they did not see one. Dr. Fricker decided to take him off of the steroid after three days to see if the swelling would subside, which it did. To this day, we do not know why his leg swelled like that. A couple of days later we were on our way home. Jacob was two-and-a-half months old.

Being at home was odd. I had not been home the entire time Jacob was in the hospital. At first I felt like I was babysitting someone else's baby, but we adjusted quickly. Initially we took Jacob to the cardiologist once a week. Gradually our appointments became monthly.

Jacob is down to eight medications, and he takes them like a champ. The doctors hope to wean him off of most of them, so he should be down to two or three before too long. Our cardiologist is adamant that we treat Jacob like a normal baby. Although we need to be careful about whom he is around and what he gets his hands into, we do take him out and about on occasion. Jacob is not developmentally delayed by any means, and he has had no problems with weight gain. He will be seven months old very soon and weighs sixteen pounds, fourteen ounces. He is a handful, but he is such a wonderfully sweet, precious little boy. We are happy for the course of treatment we sought for Jacob. We feel that God has blessed us, and we are thankful.

Current photo of the Eason Family (Jacob—2 years old)

The Right Heart for Travis

By: Dawn Martin

Travis Wayne Martin was born October 21, 1992 weighing eight pounds, five ounces with 8 and 9 APGAR scores. Having a history of spina bifida in the family, I was relieved to see this healthy little boy enter my world. Our first two months were heavenly. Being a mother was everything I had dreamed. We moved closer to family and set up our two month checkup. My biggest concern—the soreness in his legs after immunizations.

At the checkup I was surprised to see that his weight was only nine pounds, twelve ounces. He had been ten pounds at two weeks. Then I watched as the doctor listened to his heart; he was listening too long. When he finally faced my husband and me, he explained that Travis had a murmur. I feverishly explained that I too had a murmur as an infant. He quickly informed us that Travis' was not an innocent murmur.

The doctor was calm as he referred Travis to a cardiologist. My thoughts were that we were still dealing with something simple. Look at my baby; he is healthy! When the doctor returned with an appointment just a few hours away the reality that something was wrong started to hit me. We were meeting with the head of pediatric cardiology at a local children's hospital. Still, as I watched my beautiful little boy nursing and saw his smile, I could not believe that it was anything serious.

At the hospital Travis had his first echo, an ultrasound of the heart. As the technician and the cardiologist made comments to themselves, I became lightheaded, knowing that if everything was fine they would not have that many comments to make. Travis was oblivious to all that was happening, happily chugging away on a bottle—a distraction from what these strangers were doing to him. We were then taken to another room to wait. I sat holding my sweet baby. I told him that everything would be all right and that I loved him. A few minutes passed and suddenly the room was filled with doctors and nurses. Because we had been squeezed in, the head cardiologists gave us a brief explanation of what they had found.

Our son was in congestive heart failure, due to a congenital heart defect, an unbalanced atrioventricular septal defect with a small left ventricle (it would be months before we learned the term hypoplastic left heart). My immediate thought as they shared this news was to run from the room with my baby in my arms; they were not taking my baby away. Instead, I sat and rocked him with tears streaming and asked the doctor what we would do to fix this defect. He looked at me and replied, "It's not fixable." At that moment my world crumbled. My baby who had been "perfectly healthy" just hours before was now dying in my arms, and there was nothing they could do.

The next few days were a whirlwind. The first big hurdle was a heart catheterization so the doctors could be certain about Travis' heart defects. Travis came through this fine. He was started on digoxin to help his heart function more efficiently and Lasix to pull fluid off his body. Unfortunately, the digoxin reached a toxic level in Travis' body causing severe vomiting. I could not understand why my little boy, who seemed fine before, was now in the hospital acting and looking sick. It was difficult for me to trust the doctors. I was often defensive and angry when dealing with them. In my mind they were hurting my baby.

The results of the catheterization showed no surprises; we still had no hope. Christmas was in two days, and we just wanted our baby home, still not fully understanding what we were facing. After the

31

catheterization I had a dream of jars with photographs on them and pictures of people needing transplants. I sat up and told my husband, "They are going to want to do a transplant." Finally, on Christmas day we were discharged with a follow-up appointment in four days. At this appointment we would be scheduling a surgery called a pulmonary artery banding which would relieve the pressure in Travis' pulmonary artery. The doctors had finally shared with us that transplant may be an option. We went home praying to stay for a while.

On December 29, after just three days at home, Travis had his next appointment. Because he still had not gained any weight, he was readmitted. At this point Travis started nasogastric tube feedings (food is put directly into the stomach through a tube in the nose). His surgery was scheduled for six days later. At this point I was panicked that we were reaching the end, so I called our pastor who baptized Travis in the hospital chapel.

While waiting for the surgery date to come, there was more talk of transplant. We would soon meet with the doctors and social workers to determine if Travis was a good candidate for transplant. The surgery was a stopgap measure to buy him time to grow and get stronger before a transplant was inevitable.

A fever caused a cancellation of the original surgery date, so it was postponed two days. Almost immediately after the surgery, we were told that it did not work. The only hope was that somehow he would grow into the PA band. This put more pressure on everyone to make a decision about transplantation. My husband and I were concerned about quality of life. If we took this heroic measure to save his life, would it be a life worth living? At this point we met our first transplant child and mom, finally giving me some hope. To see this seven-year-old boy running down the halls of the hospital and listen to his mother talk about him going to school made all the difference for me. At this point I knew that Travis must have a transplant.

The funny thing about a transplant is that the timing has to be just right. We were told that Travis was not yet sick enough to be listed. We spent the next month in the hospital trying different medicines to see if we could postpone the need. As each new medicine failed to provide any relief for his failing heart, I became more despondent. Things that should have helped were not. Would they list him quickly enough? Would they be able to save my baby?

On February 3, 1993, Travis was listed for a heart. This day was almost a relief. Finally we knew what to expect. Now it was time to pray the hardest prayer of my life, that some family would bestow the gift of life to my son. I hurt already for the family that would have to make such a decision. Could I make the same decision if it were mine to make? Finally, I began to pray for God's will. I was praying for a miracle.

On February 8th, one of Travis' doctors informed me that a heart may be available. It was a shock that it might happen so quickly; we had been told that six to seven weeks was an average wait (even though they said there was really no way to determine averages). Within a few hours we found out that we would have to wait a little longer—the heart was not suitable for Travis. I was disappointed but not crushed. I had been warned that this might happen. We would just wait for the right heart for Travis.

Over the next month and a half, Travis' weak body faced many challenges. He seemed to run a fever continuously and was admitted to the Pediatric Intensive Care Unit (PICU) more than once. We spent five days at home from January to March. The hospital became our home. On one occasion in the Pediatric Intermediate Intensive Care, we almost lost Travis.

With a rising fever and more difficulty with his breathing, he was transferred back to PICU, but during the move his kidneys failed, and his blood pressure bottomed out. It took nearly two hours for the doctors to stabilize him, and then we just had to wait. We were told the next eight to twelve hours were critical. Our biggest fear—that we would lose Travis before a heart became available—was quickly becoming a reality. I refused to give up hope. Travis was a fighter; he had proven that already!

Travis recovered and by March 25th was back in the intermediate intensive care, and we were looking forward to having him back in a private room. Just a few days before, one of Travis' doctors informed us that he was in "perfect" condition to receive a transplant. On March 27, 1993, my husband and I were on a date. Grandpa had taken to spending Saturday nights with his favorite guy, so Mom and Dad could have a little time to hang on to each other. We were at the circus, when a quiet, suspenseful moment came. We both heard the pager go off, the pager that told us a heart was available.

I have never run so fast in my life! We made it to the hospital in record time. I scooped my baby into my arms, somehow knowing that he would now be all right. His surgery lasted about eight hours. It seemed like an eternity. Early that Sunday morning, we got a glimpse of our pink, bloated, beautiful baby boy. He had an incredible recovery. He was off the respirator in just over twenty-four hours following the transplant. Within forty-eight hours he moved from cardiac recovery to pediatric intensive care, and nine days later he was in his own room. The biggest hurdles we faced were feeding issues and weaning Travis from his pain medications. Because Travis had been tube fed for so long, he had forgotten how to suck. With effort and patience he relearned what a joy it was to drink. On April 15th we got to take our baby home for good!

Learning to give Travis his medicines and record all of the

information the doctors wanted was frightening and stressful. Doctors visits were frequent, two to three times a week at first, gradually slowing to once a week, then every two weeks over the next six months. Now, almost six years later, Travis visits his cardiologist once every six months. He has blood work every two months—a great excuse to visit McDonald's for breakfast and hit the playground! He is on two medications, cyclosporine and immuran, which he takes with his fluoride and Flintstone vitamin just like his brother.

Travis takes Tae Kwon Do (a martial art). He competed in the National Tae Kwon Do tournament this summer. He also began playing T-ball at the age of four and will soon be starting his third season. Last season he hit at least one home run a game! Travis is now in kindergarten and loves learning to read and playing with his friends. It is hard to believe that we really had to fight so hard to save him, as he streaks through the house and demonstrates new kicks.

The first few years post-transplant were more tenuous with frequent doctors' appointments and caution concerning his immunosuppressed state. At this point I can say he is just as normal, on a day-to-day basis, as the next kid. We know that his future is uncertain (transplantation of infants is only about thirteen years old), but at this point I can smile and look ahead when he tells me of the ten children he is going to have someday. I will be the luckiest and busiest Grandma around!

Grant, Dawn and Travis

Compassionate Care

Letting Go

By: Kari Barr

"What is it?" I asked.

"It's a boy!" exclaimed my husband, Brad.

His name was Matthew Charles Barr, named after Matt King, our best friend who died in 1996. He was born July 1, 1997 and weighed six pounds, five ounces. We knew it was a boy, just like we knew our daughter, almost six years earlier, was a girl. We did not even have a girl's name picked out. The ultrasound did not reveal the baby's gender because the baby would not turn over to show us. When I was about five months pregnant, I tested high for spina bifida. The baby revealed his spine, and the doctor said it was just fine. He tried to get the baby to turn over to check out his organs, but the baby would not cooperate.

About an hour after Matthew was born, a nurse noticed Matthew's respiration was high. They took him to the nursery. They brought him back to me about 11:00 p.m. to nurse him, but he would not wake up. I was getting magnesium because I had pre-eclampsia, so I could not keep him in the room with me. They brought him back again in the night, but Matthew still was not interested in eating.

About 10:30 the next morning, a nurse noticed Matthew looked bluish. She took him back to the nursery. About 1:30 p.m., while my parents were visiting, a neonatologist said Matthew was in the "transitional nursery" because he might have aspirated some fluid. After Brad returned to the hospital after work, I was told Matthew was in the Special Care nursery (ICU). The doctors still thought he had lung problems. We were not too worried; the doctors did not seem to be. My best friend had a baby with lung problems, and her baby turned out fine. I just thought Matthew's condition was similar.

About midnight two days later, the neonatologist came in and told us Matthew was not responding to any lung medication, so they were going to test his heart. He took us to see Matthew explaining various heart problems and told us the worst case was HLHS, but he did not really think that was the problem. We went back to my room, but by now we were getting nervous. Never before had we experienced any serious health problems with our family. We called our Episcopal priest. He asked if we wanted him to come to the hospital, and we declined but requested he pray for Matthew. About thirty minutes later, he showed up anyway.

The neonatologist told us that Matthew's tests indicated heart problems. They were going to transport him to St. Francis Children's Hospital. We were at Hillcrest which did not have the capability to take care of Matthew's problem. Brad was to follow the ambulance and await diagnosis, since I had not yet been released from the hospital. St. Francis was only about twenty minutes away.

The nurses brought Matthew in my room on his way to the ambulance. They opened the circular doorway in his enclosed crib and let us touch him. Brad and our priest, Father Don, followed them to the other hospital. I could not sleep, so I took a shower. My OB called me because the hospital nurse had notified her about Matthew's condition. She told me that I could go ahead and leave the hospital whenever I needed to. About 2:30 a.m. Brad and Father Don returned from St. Francis.

Brad said he talked on the phone to the cardiologist who diagnosed Matthew with HLHS. At 9:30 a.m the Hillcrest neonatologist explained the very serious and fatal nature of HLHS. He said there were a series of surgeries to treat HLHS; however, they were relatively new procedures and very hard on the baby. He told us the cardiologist would explain further at our meeting.

I was numb—in shock. I couldn't cry. I couldn't scream. I just laid in the hospital bed and kept thinking that it was all a bad dream and I would wake up from it and my baby would be fine. "How can anything be wrong with Matthew?" I asked. "He looks so perfect. He's beautiful!"

Amidst the turmoil I felt that night, I also felt an inner strength that I had never experienced before. I believe in God. But I had never really "felt" Him before. He was with me and my family that night and for the next week. I felt His presence.

At 9:30 my parents, Brad's parents, Brad and I met with Dr. Jackson, the cardiologist. He explained what a normal heart does and compared that with an HLHS heart. He gave us the three options and explained the Norwood surgery in great detail. He told us Matthew had the worst of the worst case of HLHS. Matthew's heart had no mitral valve, and the left side of his heart was virtually not there. Taking us into his office, he showed us the ultrasound of Matthew's heart and told us the surgeries had varied percentages of success. He thought Matthew had approximately a 10% chance of surviving the surgeries but could not tell us what the quality of life would be for our son. Dr. Jackson told us to think about what he said, and he would come back later to answer any questions.

Our family and friends filled the hallways. The parents and grandparents were the only ones allowed in the ICU, and only two people could go in at a time. Brad and I asked Father Don if he would baptize Matthew. That morning, with the nurses' permission, about twenty people gathered around Matthew's crib in the ICU. Everyone cried— even Father Don.

That afternoon, Dr. Jackson came back. We gathered in a family waiting room. He and two other nurses answered our questions. I could think of none. My parents, in-laws and Brad asked all the questions. I laid on the couch and listened, praying for an answer. After about an hour and a half, Dr. Jackson told us to go home and get some rest. Matthew was stable at the time, and we could go home and come back the next day. We had had very little sleep in the last fifty hours. We could not make any decisions yet. Brad and I drove home alone, while Lindsey, our five-year-old daughter, went home with her aunt.

When we got home, we tried to go to sleep. I was exhausted but felt so alone and scared. I finally broke down and cried. I asked Brad, "How can this be happening to us? How can we make a decision like this?" We finally went to sleep. I slept until about midnight. Brad had gotten up earlier. I went into the living room and sat down beside him. We held each other for a while. We talked about what we were going to do. I told Brad I felt God was telling me what decision to make; he told me he felt it too. We talked about that decision.

The next morning was the 4th of July. We went to the hospital and Dr. Jackson was there. He asked us if we had made any decisions yet. We told him we had and that we could not put Matthew through any surgeries. We were going to let him go. We asked him if he would keep Matthew on the prostaglandin until the next day so we could "celebrate" Independence Day with our daughter.

Later that morning, when our family got to the hospital, we gathered them together and told them what we had decided. Everyone cried. Both sets of our parents said they supported us completely. Father Don agreed with us but said he was still praying for a miracle.

Saturday morning, July 5th when we arrived at the hospital, they removed the prostaglandin medication and took out the respirator. They let us use a family waiting room to allow family and friends to hold Matthew. Later that afternoon the neonatologist suggested taking Matthew home. We quickly told her no. Brad and I were scared to take him home.

Saturday evening, Brad and I finally had Matthew to ourselves. The hospital said we could stay the night in the room if we wanted. Brad laid down and took a nap about 7:00. I had Matthew all to myself for two hours. I sat in the rocking chair and rocked him the entire time. I fed him, sang to him, kissed him and stroked his beautiful red hair. About 11:00 p.m. my parents called saying Lindsey was crying for us. We left the hospital about 1:00 and went home to our daughter.

Monday morning a nurse, the wife of a co-worker of mine, suggested taking Matthew home for the day with a hospital pass. She said we could do that, and later have Matthew released from the hospital if we felt we could. We decided to try. We were going to have Matthew home! The nurse wrapped him up tightly and put him in his car seat. On the way home, I sat in the back with him, unable to take my eyes off him. The only part showing was his head. I rubbed his beautiful face all the way home.

When we got home, I showed him around. I took him in his bedroom, and he looked around. We put him in his bassinet for only a moment and took turns holding him the rest of the time. Family and friends filled our house. We had to have Matthew back by midnight, so we took him back but decided to bring him home for good. The next morning we had him released from the hospital. Matthew's nurse made an appointment at Moto Photo to have our family portrait taken on the way home. Moto Photo told us we could have all the pictures we wanted at no cost!

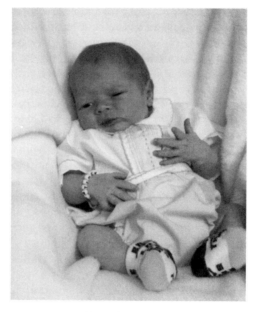

Matthew Barr

We had Matthew at home for only one night. He died at 9:05 a.m. Wednesday, July 9th. Matthew, propped up on pillows beside us on the couch, opened his eyes and looked at us. My mother said, "He's not breathing like he was!" She picked him up, and we stood up from the couch. Matthew let out a sigh. That was his last breath. He looked so peaceful. We called hospice and Father Don. Brad, my mother and I took turns holding Matthew and kissing him. We kept him at our house for a couple of hours, and then the hospice nurse took him to the funeral home.

Matthew touched so many peoples' lives in his short week on earth. I believe he was a gift from God to everyone that knew him. He changed the lives of my entire family, especially mine. Whenever I see a beautiful sunrise or sunset, I think of my beautiful baby in Heaven. I cherish my life more and thank God for my beautiful children. My son will be in my heart forever. Wherever I go, whatever I do, he will always be with me.

Brad and I have attended support group meetings for infant loss and have had a couple of counseling sessions with a professional counselor. I think it is very important to get outside help with such a loss. Even though at the time we were so sure of our decision, I struggle with making peace with myself. I miss Matthew so much that it feels as if my heart has been torn apart and will never heal. But not knowing what the future held for Matthew, and the odds being against him, we could not have put him through the surgeries.

I now gather any information I find on HLHS and give it to our local hospital. I want the hospital to have information on hand to give to parents of babies with HLHS in the future so that their decision can be made easier. When parents are faced with the life and death of their child, they are in shock. They are faced with the making the biggest, hardest decision of their lives. I want to be able to make that easier for others by providing them with as much information as possible.

A Letter to Ethan

By: Kelley Madden

Kelley, Tom and Ethan

Dear Ethan,

I am writing this letter for you now, when you are three years old, to tell you about a baby boy who would have been your brother. Your dad and I were very excited about the prospect of having another kid like you in our family, but then we learned that there was something wrong with this baby. Babies sometimes have things wrong with them that doctors can fix, but this was a very serious problem.

This baby had a heart that did not develop right; he had a birth defect called hypoplastic left heart syndrome. Babies who are born with this defect die unless they have surgery soon after they are born.

Your dad and I were told that this was high-risk surgery, which meant that the baby might not survive.

We would need to travel to another city to have the surgery because only certain hospitals could treat infants with such serious problems. If the baby survived the surgery, more surgeries might follow. If the surgeries were successful, the baby had a chance of living a fairly normal life, with some limitations. He would go to school and play in ways very much like you. He would see the doctor more than you do. He also might spend some time in the hospital for operations or complications from his heart defect.

There was also a chance that he could die of heart failure even if he survived the surgeries. The doctors told us we could terminate the pregnancy or carry the baby to term—in which case the baby would face many surgeries or die with compassionate care. For us, there was no obvious choice because no outcome was clearly better than another.

I do not know how much you understood what was going on. You were almost three years old when I was pregnant. We had not told you yet that a new baby was on the way because you were so young. When your dad or I felt sad, the other one would play with you; based on your behavior, I do not think you sensed too much of the anxiety we were feeling. We spent much more time than usual on the phone talking to doctors, friends, and family. I know you noticed that, but we always tried to have one of us there to give you the attention you needed.

We took a trip to Michigan to talk to our family there and just to get away. We also visited Pastor and Mrs. Anderson while you stayed at your friend Andrew's house that evening. These visits were very important to your dad and me. We found out how supportive your grandmas, grandpas, aunts and uncles are, how supportive our church is of parents in situations like this, and how caring our friends are. I do not know that we could have made it without being honest and open with the very important people in our lives, so I feel we should be honest and open with you.

Your dad and I at first did not know how we were going to make such a decision. We talked about many different things. Should we make use of the surgery option and give this baby a chance? Is every life worth saving? We talked about nothing less than life and death, suffering, the nature of baptism, and God's will. We talked about the severity of the defect, about the nature of the surgery. The doctors could not restore the heart; they would try to make it work with the parts that were functional. And we discussed the quality of life for the baby. We also talked about the impact on you and on our life as a family if we had this baby. We knew our lives would be turned upside-down. We would become intensely focused on the new baby, and this would have been very hard on you. I think that we could have done it with help from friends and family if the baby would have had an acceptable quality of life, but that was the question no one could answer without a crystal ball.

Doctors had developed the technology to give this baby a chance at life but at what price? It was a decision that only your dad and I could make. Together we decided that the price to be paid was ultimately too high for the baby, for you, and for our family as a whole. In the end, we decided that terminating the pregnancy was the most acceptable option for us. There are many people who say that terminating a pregnancy is a bad thing to do under any circumstance. You need to understand that there are situations we face in life where there is no right or wrong solution, and for us, this was one of those times.

We had a private memorial service with Pastor Anderson to help us acknowledge and give thanks for the short existence of this baby. We mourn the loss of this baby, but we are comforted knowing that he is in the loving hands of God.

Have we had second thoughts? Right now, no. I feel we made the right choice, and we feel at peace with the decision. That might change, but I suspect we would have had second thoughts no matter what decision was made. From the start, we asked God to help make the right decision for our family. I think He was with us all the way, and I will always be grateful for that.

One of the things we have learned from this experience is the importance of having non-judgmental, supportive people to talk to when making a life-altering decision. My wish for you is that you will find the courage to come to us with whatever difficulties arise in your life. We hope that we can be there for you when you really need us, just as our family was there for us during this critical time. We also learned that even when facing such a difficult situation, we were provided with the strength and courage to not only make a decision but also to grow in love and faith from the experience. Although this baby lived a tragically short life, I believe his life had a profound purpose; he will never be forgotten.

Parents have many decisions to make everyday, and we do the best we can in making those decisions. There may be times when you will not agree with us and even be angry with us, especially for decisions concerning you. At those times, please remember this letter. Having this baby, even for the short time we did, reminded us in a profound way how important you are to us. Always remember that we love you and will protect you and take care of you the best we can.

Love,

Mom

The Heart of a Mother

The Norwood Procedure

Giving Tyler a Chance

By: Rene Winters

Our son, Tyler Blaze Winters, was born on September 2, 1994 at University Hospital of California in Sacramento. He was born at thirty-five weeks and weighed five pounds and one-fourth of an ounce. We were told that he would have to stay at the hospital for one or two weeks since he was born early. I was released the next day and went home to South Lake Tahoe, about ninety miles from Sacramento. We planned to return to the hospital the following day with our older son, Joey.

As we were preparing to leave our house on September 4th, we received a phone call from the hospital asking us if they could run some tests on Tyler because he was looking a little dusky. In the meantime Tyler was on oxygen. We gave permission for the testing and at the nurse's request waited for the results before leaving the house.

About an hour later, the nurse called and told us to hurry to the hospital because our son had a heart problem, and they needed our input for treatment. I asked what was wrong, but they wanted to wait to explain everything once we arrived. Things did not look very good.

My husband drove my mother, our son Joey, and me to the hospital. All we could do was wonder what in the world was wrong with him. We were thinking that he had a hole in his heart.

At the hospital we were taken into a room where we waited for a doctor and Tyler's diagnosis. He came in and explained Tyler's heart defect in words we did not understand. He drew a picture of a heart, and then showed us what Tyler's heart did not have.

The doctor proceeded to tell us that we had three choices: 1) take Tyler home with us, and he would only live "a little while longer"; 2) get Tyler a heart transplant, which he said were very rare for newborns since not many parents donated their baby's organs, and the baby would probably die before then anyway; or 3) endure a three-step procedure that would take around three years to complete. We were stunned to hear the doctor speak to us so callously about our baby boy. He told us that Tyler did not have a good chance of making it through the three-step surgery because he was six weeks early and did not weigh very much. He then told us that a heart transplant was not a good choice either for reasons he had already explained. The doctor was so emotionless and cold-hearted towards the situation. He recommended that we "just take him home, since there wasn't much chance of him surviving any kind of surgery anyway."

We had lost our second son, Ryan Chase, to SIDS (Sudden Infant

Death Syndrome) on January 19, 1994. He was only two and a half months old. My husband, Joe, and I were still very much in pain over the way he had died. When a baby dies of SIDS there is no explanation as to why they die; they just do. We had a very hard time trying to understand why God would take our newborn baby boy from us for no reason. We still do not fully understand why or how, but we are trying.

I started screaming at everyone saying, "I've already lost one baby this year; I'm not losing my other one no matter what!" I could not believe that we could actually lose Tyler, too. My husband told me not to worry because we were going to do everything possible to help him.

I told the doctor that with Ryan we did not have a choice, but with Tyler we did, and we were going to give him that chance no matter what the doctors or anyone else said. The doctor did not seem too happy about our decision, but we did not care.

Six-year-old Joey said to me, "Don't worry, Mom. God took Great-Grandma to Heaven to take care of Ryan for us, and He's going to let us keep Tyler. All we have to do is pray to Him." Joe, my mom and I all looked at each other stunned that Joey would know about that. My Grandma had passed away on December 30, 1993, only twenty days before Ryan had died.

I looked at Joey and said, "You're right! We're not going to give up. We're going to pray to God to let us keep Tyler since it's all up to Him, and He's our only hope of Tyler making it." I looked the doctor in the eye and told him that we had to give our son a chance and that we were going with the three-step procedure. He told us that our decision went against his suggestion.

Tyler was to be transported to University Hospital of California, San Francisco. We signed some papers to grant permission for the transport and asked to stay with Tyler until the ambulance arrived. My mother waited outside with Joey while Joe and I went in. When we first saw our baby boy lying there, looking so tiny with tubes and IVs everywhere, we both started to cry. He was bruised everywhere from the nurses trying to find his veins. I sat down next to him and held his fingers while I talked to him. I told him that he could not leave me; he had to stay strong to make it through this surgery.

He opened his bright blue eyes as I talked to him and just looked at me. Joe and I looked at each other and knew that we had to be strong so that Tyler would make it. We knew the doctors were not giving him a very good chance to survive. We were told there was a 90% chance he would *not* make it through surgery. We just continued to pray and to let Tyler know that we were there for him.

Joey wanted to see Tyler, but the doctor felt that the tubes and IVs attached to Tyler would frighten Joey. After Joey cried in protest, we asked again and a nurse took a picture of Tyler first to see his reaction. They also wanted to make sure that Joey did not have a fever or a runny nose. Finally, Joey was allowed to see his brother and he said to him, "We need you ' cuz we already lost Ryan and Mommy and Daddy would be really sad and so would I because I don't have any other baby brothers since Ryan's gone." Then Joey looked at me and told me that everything would be okay now.

Tyler was transported at around 3:00 a.m. to UCSF. Joe and I decided that since my parents only lived about thirty-five miles from San Francisco, they would go home to be close to Tyler while Joe and I closed up our business in Lake Tahoe. We needed to pack everything up, put it in storage and move to the Bay Area.

Tyler went into surgery on September 13, 1994 at 6:30 a.m. The doctor who performed the Norwood Procedure was Dr. Gary Haas. Tyler was on by-pass for two hours twenty minutes. His surgery had taken seven and a half hours. At around 1:00 p.m., a nurse came out and informed us that we were not to leave the waiting room because the doctor was coming to talk to us. She refused to answer any of our questions but told us the doctor would be out soon.

When Dr. Haas walked in the waiting room, he looked at us and said, "Well, he's a lot stronger than we thought. Everything went fine. There were no complications. The next seventy-two hours are the most crucial, so if he remains this way, he will be fine." Tyler was only given a 10% chance of surviving, and he made it! We knew he was going to fight this and win. Now he needed to get well so he could come home.

When he was released on October 7, 1994, Tyler was on several drugs including Aldactone, Lasix, digoxin, captopril and baby aspirin. The next six months were very scary and hectic. Tyler was not supposed to cry at all, as any stress could harm him; however, everything was going along fine, and Tyler gained weight and grew very healthy.

The doctors planned to do a catheterization on him at three and a half months of age. On December 13, 1994 his cardiologist, Dr. Casey Culbertson, performed the cath at Oakland Children's Hospital. Everything went fine, and Tyler was home two days later. Tyler was on the road to his second surgery, the bi-directional Glenn shunt. This procedure was done at around six months of age on February 10, 1995. Dr. Haas also performed this surgery which made us very happy. This surgery also lasted seven and a half hours.

Those were the longest hours of my life. It was so scary waiting to hear how Tyler did during the surgery. Our eyes were constantly focused on the doorway, waiting for the news. The doctor came out and told us things had gone extremely well, and Tyler was doing just fine.

I was allowed to go into the Recovery Room to be with him as he slowly came to. He looked so pale. He was all swollen and puffy, and I started to cry. I did not want my baby to go through all this pain. I would have taken his place in an instant if I could. He had been through two major surgeries! He recovered very quickly and was discharged after about two and a half weeks.

Finally, I was ready to try to get into a somewhat normal routine. Tyler was delayed in gross motor skills such as rolling over and sitting up. We started teaching him to do things so he could catch up with babies his age. He was rolling over at seven months, sitting up by himself at about eight and a half months and crawling at around ten to eleven months. He was picking up on things quickly. He had a two-year-old cousin and a seven-year-old brother to help him. By thirteen months Tyler was learning to walk by himself. At Christmas 1995 he was saying about ten words. He was not that far behind other babies his age. He just got a later start.

A speech therapist visited with us once a week to help him develop speech skills. He caught on very quickly. My whole family would work with him on a daily basis. He had a large extended family helping him learn.

On November 6, 1995 Tyler went in for a catheterization. By this time his cardiology visits occurred only once every six months. Tyler was gaining weight and appeared very healthy. His SATs were 82-84, which seemed to satisfy the cardiologist.

I am forever catching him climbing on the counter tops and microwave stand. When he is really active and running around a lot, I make him come in and sit down because I am afraid he is overdoing it. He knows that he has a "sick heart" and his doctor is going to make it better for him.

Tyler Winters

Tyler's August, checkup went well, and he will have a catheterization on November 4, 1997 to prepare him for the third stage of surgery, the Fontan procedure, scheduled for March 1998.

The doctors want him gain a few more pounds prior to surgery, and we are preparing him mentally, too. He is older now, and will not understand that he cannot go home. He is an independent little boy who knows what he wants and will get it no matter if he has to pull a chair over and get it himself!

Tyler is now thirty-seven months old and weighs twenty-nine pounds. He is thirty-four and a half inches tall. Whenever anyone hears about his heart condition, they say, "You could never tell by looking at him that he has only half a heart."

A Born Fighter

By: Cindy Tishka

Anne Marie came into this world on October 6, 1996 at 4:31 p.m., our beautiful baby girl. After several miscarriages and a rocky pregnancy of pre-term labor starting at nineteen weeks, we were both excited and relieved. Within the hour she was met and held by her three older siblings, who were fighting over who would get to hold her first and who had held her the longest. A nurse's aide took our first family portrait.

That evening we talked to her, held her, and I got a chance to nurse her. It all felt so right. We could not have been any happier at that moment. Little did we know how quickly that would change.

At 10:30 p.m. my nurse came in and asked me if I wanted to keep the baby or send her to the nursery for the night. I wanted to keep her with me, but being a nurse myself, I know that the first twelve to twenty-four hours after birth babies can be "spitty" or "gaggy," and I was afraid I would not hear her if I fell asleep. So I sent her back where I knew she would be watched. I told the nurse to bring Anne Marie in for feedings. My night nurse came in around midnight and told me that she had noticed the baby was breathing a little fast, so she took her to special care. A neonatologist was there checking another baby, and he looked at Anne Marie. He said she seemed fine but that they should monitor her for a couple of hours. She took me to the nursery to see Anne Marie.

She was sleeping and was on a heart and respiratory monitor. I remember looking at her SATs which were in the upper 80s. The nurse told me she would bring Anne Marie to me for her next feeding. As I walked back to my room, I prayed for God to watch over her. At that point I did not believe anything was wrong, but I could not sleep. I just laid there waiting for them to come back.

At 3:30 a.m. the doctor and the nurse from the nursery came in to tell me that Anne Marie had another episode of rapid breathing. They did a chest X-ray and said she had aspiration pneumonia. They would start her on antibiotics, and she would be in the hospital for seven days. They asked a lot of questions about the pregnancy, labor and delivery. They thought I had had an infection and passed it on to her. I told them I had not, and there was nothing remarkable about the labor or delivery.

Once again I went over to special care. They had her on an open unit and were getting ready to put in an umbilical line for giving antibiotics. I gave consent and stayed a few minutes until they made me leave.

I went back to my room but once again could not sleep. I was so scared. It was not supposed to be this way. I wanted my baby with me, not in the special care unit. I wanted to call my husband but was afraid of upsetting the whole house.

My nurse came in around 6:30. She told me I could go back to the nursery after the day shift came on, and the nurses finished giving report. She then mentioned that the doctor had heard a heart murmur, and Anne Marie would probably have an echocardiogram. No one had ever mentioned a murmur before. I really did not give it a second thought. My son and my husband both had murmurs, but they were insignificant. My husband was stopping by on his way to work, so I stayed in my room to wait for him. I did not want him to be worried if I was not there. He came in a little after 8:00. As soon as I saw him, I burst into tears and told him there was something wrong with our baby.

We walked down to the nursery, but we could not see her. A cardiologist was doing the echocardiogram, and we had to wait. Now I was scared. I knew there was something wrong. I started to think that something worse than aspiration pneumonia might be wrong with Anne Marie. Now there was a cardiologist involved. A different neonatologist came out and told us there was something seriously wrong with our baby's heart and the doctor would be out in awhile to talk to us.

At this point I lost it completely. I could not believe it. After all we had been through, my baby could be taken from me. I was in shock, numb. This was not happening.

After what seemed like an eternity, the doctor came out. We went into a room, and he told us our baby had a very serious heart defect called hypoplastic left heart syndrome. He went into great detail explaining the defect. To be honest, I only half listened. All I wanted to know was if my sweet baby girl was going to be all right. He told us we had three options. He named transplant first. He told us the pros and cons with the biggest con being we would have to wait for a match for an unknown amount of time. In the meantime her condition could deteriorate. Of course Anne Marie would be at the hospital while she was waiting for her heart. He told us that the infant mortality rate had improved due to medical technology however, there was a risk of rejection, and she would be on a lot of medication which he felt would diminish her quality of life. Also, he could not guarantee how long a heart would last. She might need another transplant at a later time. On the up side, with a transplant we would have a whole working heart.

The second option was a series of three surgeries. The Norwood procedure would be done later that week if we chose that option. The Glenn would be done around six months of age, and the Fontan would be done at eighteen to twenty months of age. He explained each of the surgeries and what they accomplished. The surgeries do not cure the problem but help to manage it. He told us the risks involved with the surgery and that not all children survive it. He told us that the children who have had the surgery are thriving. The third option was compassionate care, which he felt ethically should not be an option because HLHS children can be saved and are living quality lives.

I will never forget what he told us then. He said Anne Marie was stable, and she was a fighter! She was downright mad that everyone was poking and prodding her. He said, "Anne Marie doesn't know she has a heart defect, and we're not going to tell her!" We have found out during the past year that he often uses levity to lighten a serious or difficult situation to help keep things in perspective. He said she was in the next room fighting and then waited for our answer.

For us, compassionate care was not even a choice. Letting her go without giving her a chance was something we could not do. When it was all said and done, no matter what the outcome, we would know in our hearts that we gave her every chance to survive. She was a living, breathing human being. We did not have the power to take her life away without a fight. She was our child. If Anne Marie, less than twenty-four hours old, was in there fighting, we could find the courage to fight, too.

At this point my husband and I did not even discuss it. I felt like we needed to make this decision right away. I looked at him and asked him what he thought we should do. We have been together so long it is as if we are one mind; we decided to do the surgery.

The doctor said Anne Marie would be transferred to Christ Hospital because the surgeon there was one of the best. The baby would be put on prostaglandin to keep the ductus open, and surgery would be later that week. It seemed as if we decided in a matter of minutes. We

Anne Marie Tishka

had no knowledge of HLHS, had never even seen this doctor before, did not even know that Christ Hospital was a major heart center for children, and yet we took what he said at face value.

Anne Marie had the Norwood October 11, 1996, the Glenn March 24, 1997 and the Fontan August 27, 1998. She came through all of her surgeries very well. I have had time to think about my decision over the past months. Would I have picked a different route? No, I am happy with how things are going. This was right for us. I have no regrets, and I thank God each day for my beautiful little girl.

Pioneer Woman

By: Jill Sorensen

When Jeni was born at UCLA Medical Center on June 25, 1985, we were told that there were only three other children in the world who had survived the Norwood procedure. My first reaction was fear, naturally. Jeni was diagnosed with HLHS eight weeks prior to her birth, and I felt that having that knowledge was very much in our favor. Jeni was a very active baby, so I felt she had this in her favor, too.

I had C-sections with both of my sons, so the doctors planned to take Jeni before her due date of July 7th. The doctors did not want Jeni going through the stress of the birth process. At the time we were living in Santa Barbara, California, about two hours away from UCLA. As the time approached, I became nervous.

Originally the doctors had planned to wait a few days to do her first surgery. She looked so beautiful, so pink and normal. She weighed seven pounds, twelve ounces. Unfortunately, it was not long before she started to go into distress. All the plans changed, and she was immediately prepped for surgery. The outcome was a long, nine-and-a-half hour wait. Jeni survived the first hurdle!

To this day I believe that Jeni was given the chance to survive because my gynecologist sent me to a specialist at the Genetic Institute in Los Angeles after hearing an irregular heart beat in utero. From then on, we were able to prepare for her.

I started to use this extra time wisely and decided I should learn all I could about this heart defect. I was determined, and we as a family had faith that we had a chance to beat the odds with God's help. I looked high and low for any information about HLHS, but to my frustration I ran into repeated road blocks. I was told everywhere I turned that there was not very much known or written about this heart defect. Having some nursing training (I was an LVN), I was naturally curious to gain and learn as much knowledge as possible so that I could effectively help our daughter when she eventually came home.

Our social worker finally copied a small paragraph from a medical book that she found. It was not much, but it was a beginning and my "olive branch." The American Heart Association tried to find information on HLHS but without much success. I was not about to lose hope. I remember going to the UCLA Student Book Store, pulling all the medical books out, and sitting on the floor for hours poring through anything associated to heart disease or HLHS.

Jeni came home from the first surgery at thirteen days of age. Unfortunately, she had an infection at the site of her incision, which compounded and lengthened her recovery time because she had to heal from the inside out. I cleaned and changed her bandages every two or three hours her first week home. I even made a color-coded chart to follow so I would not become confused and make a mistake which was one of my greatest fears.

It was a stressful time for me, and I know I could not have done it without our merciful Lord at my side. My husband, Paul, and my family's support were unrelenting at this most crucial time. My mother was a major help to me. She was a nurse, so I felt quite confident in bringing Jeni home. I knew I could call on her for advice, for her opinion, or for help at any given moment. As I look back on it now, I do not think I could have made it without my mother's valuable knowledge, her patience, love, help and understanding. What a blessing she is to me—even to this day!

Jeni is long past her staged procedures. She is a small girl with a big smile and a bubbly personality. At three years of age Jeni had a pace-maker implanted. On December 1, 1994 she had another "new" procedure—radio frequency ablation (RFA). This procedure allowed Jeni to eliminate two heart medications.

Even though we were told that Jeni's chances of survival were very slim, I told the doctors, "I believe in miracles, and Jeni is ours!" I also believe that fear is in the unknown, so I felt the more knowledge I had, the better Jeni's chances of survival would be. We call Jeni our Pioneer Woman. She is a remarkable young lady who reinforces my belief in God.

Jeni and Jill

Special Problems, Special Solutions

Children who have heart defects may have additional special problems caused by the body's response to a weak heart or from the effects of open-heart surgery. Children who have been hospitalized, whether for cancer, heart defects, asthma, meningitis or other serious illness, are at risk for having developmental delays. Children too weak to feed normally or who have surgery soon after birth are much more at risk for developing feeding problems than a child who has never been on a ventilator or been too sick to eat.

Immediately after a baby is born, in some societies, they are put to their mother's breast. Infants are born with a rooting reflex, and they immediately begin the complex task of eating which requires coordination of breathing, sucking and swallowing. Until a child must be "taught" this reflex a parent may not grasp the complexity of newborn sucking techniques. When a mother sees her child turning blue while eating, gagging or tiring after two or three sucks, she realizes that eating is nothing to be taken for granted.

How do mothers handle having a child with special feeding problems? How do you continue to lead a "normal" life when your child is on continuous feeds requiring special equipment twenty-four hours a day? How long must the child use feeding tubes? Will they ever eat food like "normal" children? Is there anything a mother can do to help? Jennifer answers these questions and more.

What about other special problems? Why do children with congenital heart defects also frequently have developmental delays? If our children have problems with their heart, why do they often also have problems with gross motor development? With speech and language?

One of the biggest concerns with open-heart surgery, aside from the obvious risks to the heart, is with the possibility of neurological damage. This is a concern because open-heart surgery is a very complicated and dangerous operation. When a child is put on the cardiopulmonary (heart/lung) bypass machine, the child's heart is not doing its routine job of pumping blood to the body and the lungs. A machine takes the place of the heart long enough for the surgeon to operate without blood flowing through the heart.

In order for the cardiopulmonary bypass machine to work, the child's blood must be heparinized (thinned) so that blood clots do not form. This is where the risk of neurological damage comes in. If blood clots form and travel to the brain, the child can have a stroke causing brain damage. An ischemic stroke is caused by something blocking the path of the blood to the brain such as blood clots or tiny pieces of tissue floating in the blood.

Another potential problem seldom recognized is that of an air embolus causing a stroke. With the heart open, air is introduced into the body. Surgeons carefully do all they can before closing the heart to reduce the number of air emboli and the body eventually absorbs these emboli anyway. But do some of these emboli travel to the brain and cause some neurological damage? There is no way to tell. By the time an autopsy would be performed, the evidence would be gone.

Considering the number of ways problems could develop, it is amazing more children with heart defects do not suffer severe, neurological damage. Do children with heart defects often have speech and language delays? Yes. Do children who have been in the hospital due to open-heart surgery sometimes have motoric delays? Yes. Is it because of neurological damage caused during the open-heart surgery? Maybe.

To blame developmental delays on the open-heart operation alone would be a mistake. In order to understand why some delays occur in some children and not in others, one must look at the whole child, the child's history and the kind of family life the child had before, during and after open-heart surgery.

There has not been any research reported to date analyzing the development of children with severe congenital heart defects. Experience has taught us, though, that many "heart" children do indeed have problems in the areas of speech and language as well as gross motor development. Why do these problems arise?

First of all, parents need to remember that a certain number of children are going to have developmental delays anyway. It is impossible to ascertain whether or not these children would have had developmental delays regardless of their heart defect. Children with severe, congenital heart defects are at greater risk than the general population for some very good reasons.

An in-depth discussion of child development is outside the scope of this book; however, there are certain things that parents should know about how children develop. After birth, a baby is fed, held, comforted when he or she cries, talked to and begins establishing normal routines, including a normal sleep cycle. Babies learn from these different interactions. Babies learn from being carried place to place, and from being put in their car seat, in the swing, on the rug, in their crib. They learn much about the world around them from experiencing their world firsthand. Babies also learn about their world from living day after day in the same environment with the same rituals and caretakers. This consistency helps babies form rules about their world, and the way they can make things happen.

Hospitalizing a baby can interfere with almost all of these opportunities for growth and development. When babies are in the hospital, they will not have the same opportunities for developing routines because they will be monitored around the clock. They will have many different "caregivers" throughout the day and from day to day. Babies who are on a ventilator cannot cry. They cannot affect their environment in a normal manner.

Some critically ill babies are easily irritated when they hear their parents' voices. Their heart rates soar, thus the parents are not permitted to talk to their babies very much until the baby is not in critical condition. Some babies have so many tubes, wires and other paraphernalia hooked up to them, some parents are afraid to touch their children. Most babies are tube fed once the heart defect is identified, and the baby is awaiting surgery. These conditions are not conducive to learning.

Think about the amount of time our babies spend on pain medication and paralyzing drugs. Once again, the babies cannot affect their environment the way a typical baby can. How can a baby be expected to learn under these conditions?

Taking all of this into consideration, it is no small wonder that many children with congenital heart defects are developmentally delayed. Before I would consider Alexander " developmentally delayed," I decided I would do something for him. As a special education teacher I know that early intervention is very important, but I also know the down side of labeling a child. Rather than immediately labeling Alexander, I decided to take into consideration all of the things he had been through.

Children with congenital heart defects often have developmental delays with respect to gross and/or fine motor skills. Occupational or physical therapists can help children use their muscles and move their bodies in space. These therapists usually work with the parents to teach them how to help their children develop the skills they lack. Caroline discusses her daughter's developmental delays and how she has worked with her daughter. She shows how a mother's love and devotion can help a child close the gap between actual skills and potential skills.

Many of our children experience developmental delays or feeding problems as a result of open-heart surgery or from being hospitalized. These problems can be remedied with tender loving care, the attention of skilled professionals and patience. Although the delays can be worrisome, the consequence from not seeking appropriate medical attention is much worse. Fortunately, we live in an age where our children can be saved, although sometimes this means taking an active role in helping them learn what normally develops without effort.

Feeding Problems

by: Jennifer Nachbur

My son, William Michael Farrell, was born on March 7, 1993 and was diagnosed with hypoplastic left heart syndrome (HLHS) within four hours following his birth. To date, William has undergone three open-heart surgeries as well as surgeries to place a pacemaker, to place a gastrostomy tube and to remove a fistula (scar tissue), which resulted from the gastrostomy tube that had been in place for three years. His open-heart surgeries consisted of the routine three stages performed on patients with HLHS: The Norwood procedure, the Glenn procedure and the fenestrated Fontan.

William experienced problems with feeding following his Norwood procedure. Often, babies with HLHS have particularly weak upper respiratory function, and William fell into this category. He was fed through an NG tube and over the course of several weeks never developed the ability to drink more than an ounce during his oral feedings. Usually, he drank half an ounce or less. The healthcare providers suggested that his appetite may have been offset by the fact that—due to a staph infection assumed to have progressed into bacterial endocarditis—he was on a six-week course of IV antibiotics. Often, heavy-duty antibiotics adversely affect appetite. Because William's eating ability did not improve at all during the first eight weeks, he was hospitalized. The doctors told us that he had to get a gastrostomy tube placed before they would discharge him.

Though we dreaded the idea of William going home with a gastrostomy tube, it proved to be a godsend. Giving William medication was no problem since we had a tube and we could feed or medicate him regardless of whether he was asleep or awake. It was definitely a challenge, but we were already used to administering bolus feedings, since we had to take care of that while he was at Boston Children's Hospital. William's oral feeding immediately picked up once we arrived home, since we were more relaxed and he no longer had the NG tube irritating his esophagus.

We used to start each (waking) feeding with two ounces of breast milk/formula/Polycose mixture, and then, if he would not take any more orally, we would feed him the balance of his three or four ounces via the G-tube. William needed to be fed every three hours for about the first six months and often vomited quite a bit of what he had consumed. In order to reduce this occurrence, we consulted with our pediatrician and started adding rice cereal to his oral feedings and spread the feedings apart by four instead of three hours, increasing the feedings by an ounce. He really never stopped the reflux/vomiting until he was well over a year old, but he really packed on the weight! By the time he was ready for his second stage surgery, he weighed seventeen and a half pounds and was seven months old. Without the G-tube, he probably would have been a Failure-to-Thrive baby.

Using a G-tube for round-the-clock feedings over the course of two-and-a-half years really suppressed any natural inclination to eat orally. William never really took to solid food until he was nearly two years old, and oral cups of chocolate milk (Pediasure at thirty calories per ounce) became his staple besides the nighttime tube feedings. Finally in December of 1995, we stopped the few every other night feedings we were administering, and his oral appetite increased. We had worked with an occupational therapist to no avail, consulted with our Department of Health's Child Development Clinic feeding team and did not see strong progress until we stopped the feedings completely. It is a pity that I did not realize what a positive response would have resulted, but I was really too nervous to give it up entirely because I was sure he would stop growing and gaining weight.

I think the existence of the G-tube was more difficult for my husband to tolerate than me. He participated wholeheartedly in nighttime feedings, and once William had his second surgery, my husband was eager to decrease our dependence on the tube. We have an incredible child care provider who started working for us right after William's second stage surgery. She had no healthcare background but quickly learned the ins and outs of tube feedings and administration of medications. She, too, got thrown up on a number of times. None of us made a big deal out of the tube feeding issue, though; it was just a part of our daily life. We fed William through his G-tube at parties, at restaurants, on vacation, in full view of other people. We definitely got a lot of puzzled or stunned looks, but no one ever said anything. Children were more openly curious about William's "button" which they could plainly see when he had on a bathing suit and no shirt. His Bard button was placed after his tube was pulled out when he was six months old.

Weaning both William and *me* from tube feedings were the hardest hurdles to overcome. He had developed a number of weird associations related to food and feedings, including gagging when we opened the refrigerator (associated with getting a bottle for him) and asking for water or milk when he was hungry (because he associated fullness with liquid). Recently, William's gagging has resurfaced, more in relation to foods that he does not want to eat but also sometimes when he is actually very hungry. I get angry with him and raise my voice saying, "No, William, swallow it!" It will probably be awhile before all of these unconscious behaviors are a thing of the past. In the meantime, we feed him things we know he will eat, so we do not have to deal with him refusing to eat entirely or only picking at stuff and then gagging. Certainly a lot of three and four year olds are picky eaters and use eating as a means for establishing independence. William's history just makes this stage of development a little more challenging.

Now that I have eighteen months of proof that William is able to survive without the G-tube, I breathe much easier, but I still struggle with his slightness (since his weight has leveled off) and his paleness. These are physical reminders that he is a fragile being. I cherish him for having survived the current struggle so well. Because we got such great and immediate positive results from the G-tube, it became a symbol of security, progress and growth for me. That is probably why I hesitated to give up the tube feedings entirely.

William is my special child and my first child. I do not give him the most attention, but I am definitely the most protective of him in terms of food, emotional and general health issues. My husband and I continuously argue over my tendency to give into William regarding foods he wants to eat and providing comfort. For example, one evening, he will have refused to eat his dinner only to ask me for something to eat when I arrive home. Much to my husband's chagrin, I will make William a quick tuna sandwich or bowl of Chex. There are only a few types of food that William eats with gusto. I will never forget the first time we actually saw him plow through a bowl of yogurt—what a glorious sight! He recently rediscovered pizza (which he ignored for awhile) and particularly likes tuna sandwiches, tomato, lettuce and cheese sandwiches and good old Kraft Macaroni & Cheese. If he likes it and will eat a lot of it (excepting sweets, of course), I say, "Let him eat it!" Whatever it takes to help my child thrive, I will try it! Sometimes, challenging times create the greatest of life's miracles. That's my William!

Developmental Delays - Physical

By: Caroline Ahrens

We stood over the warming bed and looked upon our four-day-old daughter. Two hours earlier we did not know if she was going to live or die. Her heart had stopped beating, a complication from the Norwood procedure the day before. This was the first in a three-stage palliative reconstruction of her heart. She was born with hypoplastic left heart syndrome (HLHS).

A nurse came out of the intensive care unit to give us news that they had to reopen her chest to get her heart beating on its own. It took the doctors and nurses thirty-five minutes to stabilize her heart; it felt like forever. As we gazed down on our miracle child hooked to monitors and IV poles, the thought of how the cardiac arrest would affect her brain did not even enter my mind. It was not until the pediatric cardiologist (PC) came to talk to us that we began to wonder not whether she would wake up, but what mental faculties she would have when she awoke.

The state of Alaska provides opportunity for an active lifestyle. There is a vast abundance of outdoor activities to be involved in year-round. In Anchorage there are many parks and playgrounds as well as miles of bike trails winding through the city. Being a children's ski instructor, I had always assumed that one day I would teach my children how to ski and develop a love of the sport, as well as the outdoors.

Growing up with a father largely dependent on a wheelchair, a result of a childhood bout with polio, gave me a deeper understanding for the gift of normal physical abilities. Walking is not something to take for granted, yet I never dreamed I would face having a physically disabled or delayed child.

Unless there are very obvious signs of delayed physical development in a young infant, it is hard to determine the immediate presence of such delays. There are small developmental milestones that are consistent to all infants, and there are big ones that should come within a certain range of time. The parent handbooks mark each month with expected development and advise a visit or call to your pediatrician when those developments are not achieved. In the case of a child with a congenital heart defect, many of the milestones are going to be achieved at later dates. Unfortunately there is not a book called "What To Expect When Your Child Is Born With A Heart Defect" or our job of parenting might be a little easier.

When your first child is a "heart" baby, your job of monitoring their developmental progress is extremely difficult, unless you have lots of experience around other growing infants. Hannah is our first child, and I had not had that valuable baby experience. The best I could do was to continually check with her pediatrician and PC for advice.

Hannah's development was expected to be a little bit off mainly due to her cardiac arrest. At the time, a neurologist was consulted for her case and several electroencephalograms (EEGs) were conducted to verify brain activity. The initial results showed abnormal brain patterns common with a cerebral disturbance, meaning seizure activity, for which she was put on phenobarbital. The drug seemed to make her lethargic even at fourteen days of age. A follow-up EEG at ten months showed normal wave patterns and no sign of seizures, so we were able to discontinue the phenobarbital.

Hannah hit many of the small milestones in the early months, smiling, laughing, sucking her hands, rolling over to her back, sitting unaided, holding a cup and spoon, the usual accomplishments. She did not, however, like to be on her stomach at all, and although she sat up, she could not get into a sitting position on her own. Many friends told me that their children hated being on their stomachs, and it was normal. Now that I have a heart-healthy infant at home, I realize all the small things that I missed with Hannah. Her doctors kept saying these things would come in time and to be patient. Pushing her would not help and might make things worse. Figuring their experience was greater than mine, I kept at the normal routine of songs and activities to stimulate her in hopes that I was doing the right thing. She was making progress in some areas but in very small steps. We figured the skills would come when she was ready.

After Hannah turned one we took her to an ophthalmologist to have her eyes checked since they seemed to cross. She was diagnosed with essential infantile esotropia or crossed vision. We got a prescription for glasses in hopes of correcting the problem. Ever try to get a one year old to wear something she didn't want to wear? The glasses were off a lot more than they were on. To make matters worse, friends and family would continually ask if Hannah was crawling or if she had gone straight to walking yet. After a while I found myself making excuses for her delayed development. It was obvious that we needed to have an evaluation done by physical and speech therapists. She was not going to just get up and start to walk and talk one day. This was a big moment for me. After all she had been through just to be alive, I was not sure I wanted a bunch of people telling me about more problems. But we needed professional help and waiting was not going to change that fact.

I contacted a state agency that performed developmental evaluations and provided habilitative services. Hannah had her first evaluation at fourteen months. It took place in our home with three therapists. There was a physical therapist, a speech therapist and an occupational therapist. I was worried she would not want to play with them, but that was not the case.

The comfort factors of being at home in familiar surroundings made things go much easier. They put her through two tests, the Battelle Development Inventory and the Peabody Developmental Motor Scales. There was also an extensive parent interview and observation. As they were writing up their notes, the therapists gave a lot of positive feedback about Hannah's level of progress. That made me feel better because, as an inexperienced mother, I was really worried that I was not doing things right and perhaps hindering her development.

The results placed the development of Hannah's fine and gross motor skills at that of a six month old. My heart sank. The other areas, cognitive development, communication development, social or emotional development and adaptive development all ranged from one to five months behind her age. The therapists explained that the tests are structured to grade on specific activities, so what they see and how the results come out may differ. The recommendation was for physical therapy once a week and a follow-up evaluation in six months.

It was hard to face the facts, but I know we did the right thing. As I held her while she took her nap later that day I cried silently for my baby. It is hard to acknowledge imperfections in your child. We all want great things for our children. I just wanted my baby to walk and talk, to be normal. This was a difficult realization; my baby was different from other children and always would be. In one big rush of acceptance, I was coming to grips with her heart defect as well as her developmental problems. It hurt, but we could now move forward doing whatever we could to make it better.

We worked with a physical therapist once a week, and within three months Hannah was crawling and trying to go up stairs. We had borrowed a big ball that was used during her sessions, and I worked with her on it daily. It was the breakthrough that we needed. I would bounce her on it, which she loved, and then lay her back and have her pull herself up, like doing stomach crunches. The bouncing had two benefits, improved muscle tone and increased verbalization during the activity. We were given weekly assignments of exercises which also seemed to help. She was crawling and pulling up all over the house. It was also recommended that we get her high-top sneakers to give her a better base for standing. She seemed to stand for longer periods with the added stability of the shoes.

Our follow-up visit to the ophthalmologist was at nineteen months. The glasses were not working to correct the crossing of the eyes, thus surgery on the muscles was recommended. After consulting with our PC, we scheduled the surgery for two weeks later, one year from her last heart surgery. It was day surgery, and we could notice a difference in her eyes by the time we left the hospital six hours later. Maybe it was her eyes that were causing her developmental delays not her heart or just the combination of everything. We did not know, but we were doing everything possible to make it better. Another eye muscle surgery was needed two months later to correct the eyes from moving up and down separately, also known as dissociated vertical deviation. Again we could see improvement in her eye alignment within hours after surgery.

I started taking her to a pool for more exercise. One of her doctors said that water activity is one of the best exercises for cardiac kids. We also enrolled in an exercise class at a "Little Gym" once a week. This added physical play and interaction with other children her same age. She watched the others very intently. Six months of therapy seemed to fly by, and the second evaluation was done when Hannah was twenty-three months old. As with the first one, the therapists came to our home for the tests.

The same two tests were performed but changed to be age appropriate. The parent interview and observation periods were also done. Because she was not walking, the motor skills test placed her at the eleven to twelve month level. And her speech skills were not up to her age group either. When mobility is lessened it can hinder speech development. Again it seemed we were at the small-step progress point.

Her therapy was put on hold until after the completion of her final heart surgery, the Fontan. Two months after Hannah's Fontan, she started back with the therapy and also started attending a speech therapy playgroup. Her babbling increased tremendously, and we started adding some signing. At meal times she now sits and holds court giving us the run down on all that she did that day, although only her baby sister can understand her. At least she is using verbal skills to try and get her point across, and we do pick out a word now and then.

One thing that was noticed during both her evaluations and during therapy is the complete dominance of her right side. It is common for a two year old to have a left or right preference, but not to this extent. We discussed this issue with our pediatrician, and he referred us to a neurologist who comes to Alaska every three months. I could not figure out how a neurologist would be able to diagnose problems without tests such as a CAT scan or MRI, but we scheduled the appointment anyway.

He confirmed what we already knew but had never said aloud. Hannah's brain "took a hit" at one point in her life, most likely during her arrest. He pointed out that her skin was more mottled on the left side, a sign of poorer circulation, and that her arm and leg were smaller in muscle tone. He watched her walk holding my hand and tried to put things in her left grasp while restraining her right hand. He said that heart babies who have oxygen SATs below the normal 100% are much more susceptible to brain trauma during cardiac arrest.

The doctor agreed with our current course of treatment, therapy and speech playgroup with additional physical activities. We were doing the best things possible for her right now. I really needed that affirmation. What surprised us was his insistence that we emphasize her speech therapy over her physical therapy. After he explained the importance of communication in daily life this made sense. We just had not thought that far ahead. We had already noticed some frustration in Hannah's face when she tried to get a point across or wanted something and we did not know what she was saying. As we were leaving his office, he reminded us that time with a therapist is important, but the parents are the real therapists for their children, and an enriching environment with lots of stimulation was crucial to her development.

I cannot say that it is not a difficult road we are walking down. It is not the course we would have chosen, but we are here and doing what it takes. This includes pushing her out of her comfort zone, a very hard thing for a parent to do. Hannah really likes all the activities that she is involved in, including her therapies. She has progressed greatly over the last six months, and her therapists see small improvements weekly. It does get frustrating when we are around normally developed children, and we see how far Hannah has to go. But we also see how far she has come and know that we are blessed for what we have and know in time she will get there. Of that, I am positive. A few years from now when I am chasing a screaming Hannah down the aisle of the grocery store with a bag of cookies or down a ski slope yelling for her to slow down, I will look back on her delayed start and wonder what the big deal was.

Hannah and Caroline

Developmental Delays - Speech and Language

by: Anna Jaworski

"Uh, uh," Alexander said pointing to a row of goodies.

"Do you want the cookies or the crackers, Alex?" I asked pointing to each box in turn.

He pointed to the cookies and said, "Uh, uh!" starting to get upset.

"Oh, you want the cookies? Say 'cookies' Alex."

"Uh, uh," Alex said throwing himself on the floor and beating it with his fists and feet.

I felt a lump in my throat. My baby was having a temper tantrum because he could not make himself understood, and nothing I was doing was working. I grabbed the cookies and seeing that he was getting what he wanted he stopped the tantrum and came to the table. I hugged him and spoke ever so gently to him and kissed the top of his head.

Alex was not a baby. He was a toddler—a two year old. And the only word he had was "uh," which he used for everything. No matter what I did he was not picking up any new words, and I was crushed. Over a year ago he was saying, "Mama" and some other "words" which were not as clearly identifiable but words nonetheless.

Over a year ago he had his second open-heart surgery. He suffered some complications which erased all of the speech development he had gained. Due to the surgery he came home with a partially paralyzed diaphragm and totally paralyzed vocal cords. He came home on oxygen. He could not talk even if he wanted to, but he was ALIVE! He was alive, and I was thankful for that and the fact that his surgeon had combined his last two surgeries. So, at nine months of age, Alex had the last of his scheduled surgeries. The fenestrated Fontan changed the plumbing of his HLHS heart into a functional heart.

Now I looked with despair at my little angel. He had been through so much. It had taken a month for his diaphragm to begin to work, but I had been told it could take up to a year or perhaps it would never work again! I had to believe it would work again, and I was so thankful when we were able to dispense with the oxygen concentrator. Even though I had a thirty-five foot nasal cannula tube, it was not easy to keep it on a little one who is on the move.

Two months after the surgery, Alexander's vocal cords began to work again. It was so odd when I began to hear his first cries. They sounded like a kitten meowing. So tiny, so inhuman. I had anticipated his needs for so long that he hardly had reason to cry, and I was glad. That cry brought back to light all that Alexander had been through and fed my own insecurities and fears about his life. I wanted everything to go back to normal, but that would not happen for quite a while.

My bachelor's degree is in Speech Pathology even though I knew I would someday teach the deaf. Five years after I quit teaching at Texas School for the Deaf in order to stay home and raise my children, I was to see an even greater purpose for all of my training. I never wavered in believing that God had a special plan for me. I prayed for guidance on more than one occasion and did things that I felt led to do by a force greater than myself. It was now many years later that I would come to see the real benefit of my training.

"Honey, we need to talk," I began as I sat with my husband at our kitchen table one night after the children were in bed. I poured out all my worries and concerns about Alexander's speech development. Clearly he understood all we said to him, but he could not make himself understood, and the temper tantrums were occurring more frequently. "He's frustrated because he can't make himself understood," I said to Frank. Frank nodded and told me that he had had the same concerns but trusted me to do what was right. "We're at a crossroads," I said gently. "It's time to make a decision. We're going to have to have him tested by a speech pathologist . . ."

"NO!" Frank erupted. "I'm not going to have him tested," he said as he got up and paced in the kitchen.

My heart ached as I saw my husband so wrought with grief. "Well, I would like to give him three more months before we test him," I continued evenly. "If it's okay with you, I want to try something a little radical. I think it might work. It worked with some of my students in the past."

Frank stopped moving and sat down again. He took my hand and looked into my eyes. "I trust you," he said again. "What do you want to do?"

I was not sure how Frank would feel about my plan, but I knew in my heart I had to give it a try. "I want to teach Alexander sign language," I said. "I'll keep using my voice, too, and encourage him to do the same," I added quickly. "I think he needs something as a bridge. This could be that bridge." Frank looked unconvinced, and then finally spoke aloud his real fear, "What if I can't understand him?"

"I'll teach you and Joey, too," I said. "Besides, you know more sign language than you think."

After much discussion it was agreed that I would try this for just three months, and if there was no improvement, we would get Alexander tested and begin a formal program of speech therapy.

The next morning I woke the boys up and got them ready to start their day. We all proceeded to the kitchen, and I told them both that we were going to start something new. I was going to teach them sign language. I told Joey that I had started signing with him when he was a baby and that he had signed, too. As I said that, I realized I had not signed with Alexander simply because we had been going through so much emotional turmoil with the open-heart surgeries and doctor's visits. It had really been over two years since I had signed much at all.

I knew I would be rusty, but I was only going to start out with some simple words and phrases. I spoke and signed 'cereal,' and Joey copied perfectly! Alex watched us with keen eyes. Then I showed them the sign for 'milk' and 'more' and many more words. Joey copied everything I did and encouraged Alex to do the same. To my delight, before breakfast was over Alex signed 'more' and 'milk.' What surprised me, though, was not that he signed, for I expected that, but what surprised me was that he voiced, "muh." It was not "uh" like he had been doing for months. It was "muh." He was starting to say something different! He was trying to say a different word.

By the end of the day Alex signed "love you," and I cried tears of joy. My baby was "talking," and he could make himself understood. Within a couple of days, he was putting two words together—more milk, more cereal, love you, love Joey, love daddy, love mommy—his vocabulary exploded! Even Frank could not believe the difference in Alex's speech.

Almost immediately Alex stopped having temper tantrums. I remember that first day he started to throw a fit, and I took his hands and showed him how to say what he wanted. He stopped getting upset, clumsily copied my motions and hugged me. I remember sending up a prayer of thanks for that and many other special moments those first days.

It is now a year later. Alex almost never signs anymore, unless he does so in response to something I sign to him. He really did not sign for very long. He signed and spoke from the very beginning; somehow the sign language unlocked his voice. It was not long before he realized he could communicate with voice alone. And communicate he does!

Yesterday he said to me, "K.C. loves me because she's my dog." Well, now it was not quite that clear. It sounded more like, " K.C. wuvs me 'cause sees my gog," but at least I understood what he meant! He holds conversations with people and even has conversations with his imaginary friends. He sings his ABC song and other songs throughout the day. He is really a very normal three year old.

Frank and I both agree that teaching sign language to Alex was the best thing we did for his speech development. It gave Alex the tools he needed to communicate clearly with us until his speech caught up. It gave him confidence and showed him how much we valued what he had to say.

There is value in getting help from a licensed speech pathologist, and it is best to get help early rather than to wait too long. It is especially important to get help early if a child cannot communicate or understand what is said to him. We knew there was nothing wrong with Alex's hearing, so I knew his lack of speech development was not caused by a hearing loss. Many children do not develop speech due to frequent ear infections and a fluctuating hearing loss. That was not the case with Alexander.

Do you have to have a degree in speech pathology or deaf education to teach your child sign language? No. All you have to do is use some simple signs for common words which you can make up yourself or find in a sign language dictionary. There are even some good sign language books for children. Your goal is not to make your child fluent in sign language, but to do something to help your child communicate until he is able to enunciate clearly. Some of our children may need speech therapy, but before going that route, you may want to try some simple signs and a lot of love and patience.

Guidelines for Parents

1) When evaluating your child's speech remember to subtract the number of weeks your child was in the hospital, allowing for reasonable recovery time from each surgery (six to eight weeks), days spent on oxygen, and so forth. Use the charts included in parenting manuals but only after subtracting these days.

Example: Alex's age when I started to use sign language was two years and three months; I subtracted two months because it was two months before his heart defect was identified, and all he did that two months was sleep. I subtracted two months because of his hospitalization and recovery from his first surgery; I subtracted four months because of his second surgery and recovery from his paralyzed vocal cords and arrived at the age of one year and seven months. By age one most children have about ten words. Alex did not, so I knew it was time to do something.

Please keep in mind that "normal" children have a steady progress of development. Most children are not hospitalized, intubated, sedated and put on paralyzing drugs. It is normal for children to have setbacks after surgery and for months thereafter. Normal children have day after day of repetition and practice. Our heart children do not have this. They have hospitalizations and doctor's visits. Some of our children are not permitted to get too upset because it is bad for their hearts. These are not "normal" circumstances for speech development.

2) When evaluating speech development in your child, you must take into account that the speech does not have to be crystal clear. The big questions are: Can you understand what your child is saying? Can other family members understand what your child is saying? Lastly, can strangers understand what your child is saying?

Example: Right now Alex is saying 'gog' for 'dog,' and this is normal for a three year old. I understand what he means. His father and brother understand what he means when he says that, and most people who have had children or been around children would understand what he means given the context of his sentence and the fact that he just finished petting the dog when he said it.

Initially you may be the only person to understand your child. By the time your child is three years old, though, even strangers should be able to understand some of your child's words and sentences.

3) Your child may continue to have some unusual speech mannerisms; that is to be expected. Try not to draw attention to those mannerisms. Ignore them and continue to model good speech.

Example: Alexander has pretty fluent speech, but occasionally when he is counting, he speaks on an incoming breath. This sounds very odd; my husband asked me if he were gasping for breath. When I explained that Alex was trying to speak while he inhaled (we speak on exhaled air), then it made sense to Frank, and he agreed that was what Alex was doing.

At first I was alarmed when I heard Alex counting, and one, two and three were spoken on an inhalation. I remembered that was something that stroke patients often did. In my voice class I learned that some stroke patients "forgot" how to speak, and you had to remind them and reteach them how to breathe and how to speak. I wondered how I would do this with a child.

The best thing I have found is to involve Alex in a lot of activities which utilize memorized speech. We sing the same songs over and over, count, recite nursery rhymes and play silly games that Joey and I make up which over time are quite predictable. This vocal practice encourages fluency.

4) Another thing to consider is your child's voice quality. Alexander's voice is "husky" especially for a three year old. I suspect that when he was first getting his voice back, the lower frequency sounds were easier to produce, and thus he used a lower tone of voice than most children his age. He is easy to understand, but his voice is different. If this were ever to be a problem, a speech pathologist could teach Alexander how to raise the pitch of his voice.

5) The last thing to consider is your child's nonverbal communication. Does your child try to communicate at all? Alex was obviously distressed that he could not communicate with us. He had full-blown temper

tantrums out of frustration from not being understood. Some children, though, avoid eye contact and do not even attempt communication. If your child falls into this category, then you will want to seek help from a professional early. Nonverbal communication develops even before clear speech and language do.

It is quite common for speech pathologists to teach children sign language as a bridge to verbal communication. As Caroline shared with us in her essay, Hannah was also taught sign language. For Alexander, sign language unlocked the door to his voice. As he gained confidence in his ability to communicate, he spoke more and signed less. But it still feels great when he signs "I love you."

Alex signing, "I love you."

The Heart of a Mother

"Never consent to creep when you feel the impulse to soar."

- Helen Keller

**upport**

The largest portion of this book is about support. The following essays are written by mothers of children with a wide spectrum of heart defects. Once again, however, it is not the label on the heart defect which causes one to understand these essays. It is the overwhelming need to support and be supported by others that is understood by those involved with special children.

In this section of the book you will find essays by a variety of mothers including grandmothers, single mothers, a stepmother and adoptive mothers. You will also find stories by mothers around the world, military mothers and mothers in the hospital. Two very special chapters deal with education and advocacy and how mothers can influence not only their own children's lives, but the lives of countless others.

How can a mother survive the devastating news that her baby has a life-threatening heart defect? How can a mother make it through her baby's hospitalizations, surgeries and, in some cases, her baby's death? In a word—Support. The only way to overcome these situations is through support by loved ones, friends and our religious communities. But perhaps the most healing way of surviving is to support someone else. By reaching out to others and helping them through their crises, we turn our own tragedies into opportunities for growth and love. Each person we help is just another friend we had yet to meet.

"I do not know what your destiny will be, but one thing I know,
the only ones among you who will be really happy
are those who will have sought and found how to serve."

- Albert Schweitzer

The Life Givers

Being the adoptive parent of a child with a CHD has unique and special problems. There is usually no information about the child's birth parents, grandparents, or other relations. There may not be information regarding the pregnancy, the child's birth experience or even the first days of life. This information can be very helpful when the child's doctors see him for the first time.

These essays all demonstrate the depth of unconditional love a mother can have for a child. They also show how a woman does not have to give birth to a child to be a mother. It is not simply giving birth that makes a woman a mother. What really matters is the unconditional love she freely gives and the joy for life she shares. Because the mothers love these children, they have all lived far beyond any professional's expectations.

My Special Son

By: Karen Brandle

I have been asked many times to write Daelan's story, but I was never ready or maybe I just did not have the courage. My husband and I always wanted to have a family and tried for years. In 1986 we adopted our first son, Nicholas. We tried to adopt again right away, but adoption in Alberta, Canada is a slow process. Then in 1991 a wee baby boy was born on April 3rd at midnight. I knew the mother and was fortunate enough to be in the delivery room.

The delivery was normal, and everything seemed fine. The young mom was not sure if motherhood was for her, and the next few days proved to be very difficult for all of us. On Daelan's fourth day of life, he was having a hard time feeding. Then his respirations started to climb, so he was transferred to the Intensive Care Unit (ICU). The next day he was transferred to the University of Alberta Hospital Neonatal ICU. Things were happening so fast, we could not quite digest all the information. All we knew was that there was concern about his heart.

On day six he had surgery for a coarctation and PDA (patent ductus arteriosus), and we were assured he was on the road to recovery. In the meantime Daelan's mom decided that this was more than she could handle and asked us if we would take care of her baby. We did not have to think about our answer, because we knew in our hearts that Daelan was our new son.

Little did we know that over the next few years Daelan would test our commitment to ourselves and our family. He stayed in the NICU for two months, due to feeding difficulties, in spite of using an NG (nasogastric) tube. His heart also was not functioning the way it should, and a catherization was inconclusive. We saw so many doctors that I could not remember who was whom. Daelan's physical appearance indicated that he had some sort of genetic defect. Apparently he looked as if he may have Fetal Alcohol Syndrome, but no one gave us any answers. We took him home after we realized that the medical staff was at a loss as to whether or not he would actually survive. He was labeled "Failure to Thrive" and did not grow even with twenty-four hour continuous feeds.

The next year was our own personal roller coaster ride. We never knew what was in store for us from one day to the next. Every time we took Daelan to the doctor, there was something else to worry about. During his first year he saw a pediatrician, a cardiologist, a geneticist, a neurosurgeon, a plastic surgeon, an opthamologist, an audiologist, a physiotherapist, an occupational therapist and a speech and feeding team. Some were optimistic; others were not. We believed that if we took care of Daelan to the best of our ability and loved him, he would make it.

When he was four months old, we took him back to the cardiologist and found out he needed to have surgery again. This surgery was to remove a sub aortic stenosis and religate the PDA. He was very sick when we took him back to the hospital, and there was not much hope that he would survive the surgery. He apparently had been in congestive heart failure for over a month and had not gained much weight since his original homecoming.

At the time we did not understand much about heart failure; he was considered a good baby by all because he slept all the time. It is extremely hard to feed a baby who doesn't know how to suck, swallow and breathe at the same time. So, we fed him with one of his syringes only to have him vomit most of his feed moments later, and then we started all over.

In spite of the fact that he was so small, the surgery was successful, and he was discharged six days post-op. Daelan cried from this day forth and never slept through the night again until he was four years old.

After a very trying week of feeding, crying, endless laundering and trying to keep up with a very busy five year old, a friend suggested that maybe we bit off more than we could chew and had made the wrong decision in keeping Daelan. I lay in bed that night crying, waiting for the babe in the next room to start his nightly screaming episode; my husband asked what was wrong. I laid there in the dark and asked him if we had had a choice. His answer was, "No, he's our son." Since that night we have continued without ever looking back.

We thought things would change once Daelan's heart was fixed, but we were in for a huge disappointment. He still did not thrive and at times was so unresponsive except for the almost nonstop crying that there was now major concern about his head and brain size. "Small head, small brain" was one comment, and the question loomed over us: "Was he going to be a viable child?"

Year one was over, and I felt a million years old; I had existed on about two hours of sleep a night and never left the house except for a doctor's appointment or when Daelan's dad was home to give me a break. In his first year, we coaxed many smiles, and he could also now lift his head up while lying on his stomach—not much of a milestone but one of many obstacles that we have overcome.

In our second year, we just tried to cope with Daelan's many needs. We had mastered some sort of feeding routine, mostly force feeds. I know it sounds inhumane to force feed, but I had no other options, and we were not ready to let go. I knew if I could get him to eat, he could survive. The doctors had no advice for us, so we blindly went down our own path. We did not go to many doctors' appointments now, as I found them time-consuming and wasteful, especially considering we lived forty-five minutes from the hospital. With my husband overseas for a year and Nicholas in first grade, I seemed to have more time to just do nothing. I finally had a chance to rest and get back some of the energy I had lost the previous year.

I did take Daelan to the rehab hospital in Edmonton and the staff managed to help me get on my feet again. An early intervention worker came to work with Daelan, and a homemaker looked after Daelan while I got a much needed break. I never thought I needed that sort of help, but I wish now that I would have found that kind of support from the beginning.

The most frightening behavior Daelan displayed in this year was crying so hard that he would turn blue and pass out. The first few times I was afraid he was dead. I then realized he was doing this for attention, but over the next twelve months, I was able to help him discontinue this behavior.

He gave us another scare when he had an allergic reaction to his antibiotic and went into anaphylactic shock. I was driving with him by myself when he turned blue, and I rushed him to the emergency room. He was given a couple shots of adrenalin and some steroids, and we spent the night in the hospital since we lived too far away to drive home.

By this time I knew I needed more help, so my husband quit his overseas job to stay closer to home, a move we have not regretted for a moment. Daelan's major milestone for that year was learning to walk, in spite of the fact that we were told he never would.

As Daelan approached his third birthday, we realized that it was time to break out of our cozy cocoon and introduce him into the big, bad world. In the fall he would start school, an Early Entry Special Needs Program. My baby was not only growing up—he was leaving me! I had never left him before except for a few hours when he was with his dad or caretaker. In just a few months, our skepticism turned into hope, even though we had been told there was not much to work with. Now there was hope that Daelan could be educated in some way. He said two words when he started school "Dad" and "Mom." They were his version of these words, but that was okay as long as they had meaning.

We also discovered that he has a ridge along his hard palate and is tongue tied. This was clipped but had little effect on his speech. This first year of school went without much gain and the only plus was that he would actually stay there without me. We worked on his speech, feeding and social skills which seemed like an endless task; however, this year he could actually say a few words and would feed himself pudding or yogurt.

There must be some magic in the number four because Daelan began sleeping through the night in his fourth year of life. This was a year of many changes for us. It was as if a door or window to the world had just opened for Daelan, and the past was easily put on a shelf for safekeeping. I need to examine the past every now and again to appreciate how good life can really be.

My little boy is thriving (I still feed him, mostly soft food). He is talking, running, laughing and he cannot seem to get enough out of life. We went to Disneyland and weren't sure how he would react. It was a good thing that the park was not busy because we could not go from one ride to the next fast enough. His only response was, "More Dad, more!" Wonders never cease. Daelan's successes are our own. His eagerness to learn has renewed our faith in ourselves as parents and as teachers. The milestones were many for all of us this year, as Daelan began talking a blue streak and eating most foods on his own—even trying to chew a morsel or two. He became a social butterfly, and there was no stopping him!

Daelan started Kindergarten when he was five. I wondered if he would really fit into a regular class of five year olds. His teacher was always very optimistic. We have been fortunate over the years to have come into contact with some very dedicated, caring people. Daelan always surprises us with his willingness and his drive to be like everyone else. When he wanted to play soccer, we thought this was out of his league, but in fact, we were the ones who had the problem. He now plays soccer, swims, skates and is trying to master a bicycle. We finally realized that he will set his own limits, even if they are sky high. When I think of earlier milestones, I am amazed at how far we have come in the last few years. Daelan's biggest accomplishment at age five was being toilet trained; we finally had Daelan out of diapers during the day.

On April 3, 1997 Daelan turned six. We are still wondering what the future holds for our little boy. We enjoy him for who he is and for what he brings to our family. When people refer to my special son, they are talking about his needs. But, when I refer to my special son, I am talking about Daelan. We still see many doctors because Daelan still has a long way to go. He is losing sight in his right eye, so he wears glasses and a patch. He has problems with his heel cords and hamstrings; some days he cannot put his feet flat on the floor. He takes medication for reflux which should have been diagnosed when he was a baby—the reason for Daelan's endless crying. Daelan has recently seen cardiology, and his echo showed that his mitral valve regurgitation is causing his left atrium to enlarge. He also has aortic valve regurgitation. We keep him as healthy as possible and take him to regular checkups.

Now that Daelan is six, he can go to grade one which he thinks is great! I am scared. Daelan will go for a complete neurological assessment before he starts school, and we will try to insure that he gets the best education possible.

Karen holding two month old Katrina, Daelan and Nicholas

The Heart of a Mother

Hope In Tomorrow

By: Bonnie Munden

I answered the phone on a seemingly normal day; little did I know how my life would change after that phone call. "Mom," my son began, "I have something to tell you, but I will have to call you back because I'm at work, and I can't talk right now." Knowing my son as I did, I knew this was something BIG. The forty-eight hours it took him to get his courage up resulted in a phone call which would change my life forever.

"Son," I asked with concern, "has something happened?"

"You might say that," my son replied. "Remember the girl I met last summer?" he asked hesitantly.

"Yes, Son," I replied.

"Well, Mom, she had a baby, and I just found out that I'm the father."

"Oh, my God," I said with a catch in my throat.

"Mom," he continued, "It's not just one baby. It's two; it's twins, Mom, and one of them has a real bad heart."

"Oh, Lord," I said—the first of many prayers I would say concerning my granddaughters.

The first time I met the twins, they were seven months old—only one month after they were introduced to their father. At the time, they were two tiny babies in light blue outfits, with two white blankets, two pink teethers, and two big smiles. Adriane and Caitlin looked exactly alike, except Caitlin bore a large scar down the center of her chest from open-heart surgery when she was a few weeks old. She was given only a 50% chance of survival at the time of surgery. I fought the tears knowing that had I known about her, I could have been there for her. I felt excitement that I was a grandmother, and yet uncontrollable sadness at the same time.

As daily life went on, things seemed to level out for the twins. I saw them as often as possible and was always informed of upcoming tests and catherizations. I would always visit at the hospital and offer my support. Caitlin had one of the most difficult heart conditions the surgeons had ever seen. This would make the chances of a normal life a little more challenging. Even though I didn't really understand the terms of the heart condition, I realized that she needed a lot of TLC, and I was more than willing to give it.

My first visit to the cardiologist was overwhelming. I was told she had pulmonary atresia, ASDs, VSDs, transposition of the great arteries, and heterotaxy. This meant she had no connection from her left lung to her heart. She was born with two chambers instead of the normal four.

The ASDs and VSDs meant she had holes in her septum. Transposition meant that her two major arteries (the pulmonary artery and the aorta) were switched. Heterotaxy meant a lot of her organs were not in the normal anatomical position.

The twins came to live with me when they were two years old. The rooms were filled with two of everything—two cribs, two car seats, two teddy bears, two high chairs. I was seeing double. The closet looked like a store's baby department.

Nights out for dinner by candlelight with my husband and soaks in the spa were a thing of the past. Our main objective was to get the twins healthy and prepare Caitlin for the surgeries ahead. I felt that I had to watch everything she ate to make sure it was healthy for her. She needed to be strong for the upcoming surgery. The doctors were depending on me to make it happen. I tried to keep her germfree. No visits were allowed by other children who had colds or were sick. I watched her intensely at the library, McDonald's, or anywhere there were other children, while trying not to be overprotective.

Caths would be scheduled only to be rescheduled due to a rash, cold, or some other illness. I found out that having a "heart baby" meant our life was subject to change at any moment. We lived on edge. Our world centered around Caitlin and the surgeries. Keeping our sanity and trying to act normal was a challenge. I kept telling myself I could smile even though my heart had such a heavy weight on it.

What would tomorrow bring? One morning I asked the girls what should we do for the day, and Caitlin said, "Go to the doctor?" Trying to hide my tears, I said, "Wow, look at that bird by the window!" Since Caitlin had other health issues, numerous appointments were a normal routine.

We had frequent visits to the cardiologist because surgery would be scheduled when her oxygen levels were in the 60s. I never stopped looking at her blueness, even though she never knew what I was looking for. Caitlin was two-and-a-half when she was finally ready for the second surgery, the Glenn shunt. I remember snapping her picture in my porch swing with her lace dress and bonnet on, clicking the shutter, hoping it wasn't her last picture. The thought of losing her was overbearing. With a lump in my throat, I left for the hospital to check Caitlin in. Her sister, Adriane, had spent the night out, so it would be less traumatic for all of us when the hour to leave approached.

When the Glenn shunt surgery was completed a nurse came in to tell us that Caitlin had come through the surgery great. We were thrilled! We began calling our family and friends to share our joy. The same nurse came back to the surgery waiting area to tell us there was a complication. It was serious. Caitlin had turned a deep purple. They rushed her into the cath lab for answers. Her oxygen levels had fallen dangerously low, into the 30s. Five cardiologists, two surgeons, the social worker, and the chaplain called us into a private conference room. If her oxygen levels continued much longer in the thirties, we were told she would have brain damage. I told the surgeon that would not happen. He looked at me, and I knew what he was thinking. . . I was in denial.

Caitlin lay sedated on a slanted board in intensive care. The blood needed time to follow the new route. The doctor said I could take her home in seven or eight days. I looked at him and behind me. He couldn't be talking to me; I was too scared to take her home. What if something happened? What would I do?

Each day she became stronger and stronger and more like a normal toddler. Her oxygen level rose to the 70s, not ideal, but much better. Several other caths were done, trying to find the problem. "Why couldn't they find what they needed to find?" I thought angrily! She would need some coil immobilizations which were a very tedious and serious procedure.

Once again, we waited and prayed in the surgery waiting area. We were the last people in the waiting area, even the clean-up crew had taken out the trash. Stale coffee filled the air. Finally, the procedure was finished, and she would spend the night in the Intensive Care Unit. The next morning, I noticed she had a fever. The cardiologist was afraid she had an infection from the coils placed in her heart to block off random bloodflow to other parts of her body, and we were told the infection could be fatal. Caitlin stayed in the hospital for two weeks while they gave her blood tests to check for every infection possible. When the IV therapist would enter her room, Caitlin would try to crawl out of her crib. Finally, it was discovered she had a bladder infection and bladder reflux. We added urologist to the list of doctors. Several more times, she was scheduled for coil procedures. We found out the average number of coils for children was five or six; Caitlin now had fifty. The coils would redirect the blood flow, and were necessary in the plan of her staged surgeries.

I was at the point that I didn't want people to ask how she was. It seemed as if that was all they wanted to know. I was angry! She was my granddaughter, why couldn't they ask normal questions? Why couldn't they understand why I didn't want them to come over if their child was getting over a virus, or had a cold? Didn't they realize it could set the procedures back if she were to get sick? I wanted to scream, but knew I had to keep my composure.

I was involved in the support group at the hospital. All the families in the group had children with a heart condition. I was in constant touch with three of the mothers and we shared a lot of information and tears. I knew being a grandmother should feel differently than this. My days were spent figuring out how to entertain the twins without exposing Caitlin to too many germs. Everywhere we went, people were fascinated with them and always wanted to touch them. I felt like making a sign that said "Don't Touch Me." The most difficult part was feeling as if I had to explain every decision I made. I prayed everyday for the Lord to get us all through it. There was hope in tomorrow.

The pressure was building. The equipment wouldn't show what the surgeons needed to see to plan her final surgery. They had a conference once a week to discuss her upcoming surgery. The cardiologist sent us to Johns Hopkins Hospital to have an MRI done. We were all for this, as we were sure the answers would be known. We were called into a conference room once more.

"We're sorry," the doctors reported. "Caitlin is fine, but we were unable to get any pictures."

The coils restricted the MRI equipment from recording any information. Weeks passed with the surgeons and cardiologists comparing and planning, trying to find another child who had similar defects. She was so complex, they were baffled. What if they proceeded, and it was too late to turn back and change what they started?

In July, when Caitlin was five years old, the surgeons attempted the Fontan. I laid one last angel by her pillow before her surgery. I started making jewelry when the girls moved in. It was my way of relieving stress. Each procedure would prompt me to design a special angel for her to take to the hospital. For each admittance, she was given a hand-stitched bear from the volunteers in the surgery waiting room. I saved the bears, sewed them together, tied pink bows on their paws and lined her entire bedroom. For each surgery, I cross-stitched a design on her underwear. I was obsessed about everything being perfect.

While in the waiting area, we would make the normal small talk and jump every time we heard footsteps. Would she be all right? Would something go wrong? Could we hold back the tears when familiar faces of nurses and doctors came in? Could we act normally? I was getting used to hiding my feelings. Here we sat, waiting for news about our granddaughter's future.

When the nurse came in to talk to us, her pager beeped. She informed us she would be right back; they needed her in the OR. I swallowed hard and told myself there was more than one OR. I started to panic when the nurse didn't return right away. We were about to get some bad news.

Caitlin had a cardiac arrest and was unresponsive for five minutes. She could have brain damage. She was in the Intensive Care Unit. I was numb, in a total daze. I don't remember walking to the ICU. Caitlin looked like a wounded angel with tubes going everywhere. The surgeon sent me in to see if she could talk normally.

"Grandma, I have a tube up my nose, and I don't like it," she said defiantly.

I was never so glad in my life to see a tube! I held back the lump in my throat and the pain in my heart and said, "Hi, Honey, did you just wake up?" In a few days, she was transferred to the Progressive Care Unit. She wanted french fries. My husband went out in the middle of the night to a drive-through.

Ten helium balloons floated atop the mailbox. Eight-foot banners decorated the den. A new Minnie Mouse comforter and curtains brightened her bedroom. Tons of stuffed animals from well-wishers lay, waiting to be loved. It was a wonderful day! She was alive! I couldn't tell her she would have to have more surgery. She had to wait six weeks for the scar to heal. She sat on the side of the pool with a water squirter that the doctor gave her to squirt her sister. Her days were brightened by her teacher coming to homeschool her.

Three months passed. We lived everyday as if it could be the last. What fun things could we do? Have a picnic in the yard? Play kitchen? Play dress-up? What would it be today? How would we pass the day? Would we go one more time to Wal-Mart for pictures, thinking it might be her last?

At last, we were given a surgery date. We counted the days on the calendar. I was back in the I-wish-you-could-understand mode. Back to wiping the handle on the K-Mart shopping cart. Back to just-leave-me-alone-and-don't-ask mode. I never realized being an actress was so difficult!

The time came when she was ready to go through the OR doors once more. She looked at our favorite nurse and said, "Let's go." We all laughed through our tears and sat down on the familiar sofa in the surgery waiting area.

The nurse came in several times to give us a report. Everything was going well. She was off the heart-lung machine! The surgery was a success! Eight days later she was ready for her own bed and to see her cat, Jessie. At the post-op visit, I informed the cardiologist I was really concerned about her cough. He ordered a nebulizer from the pulmonary department. Her airways were opened, and she felt much better. It was determined she had asthma. We were sent home with our own nebulizer, and we decorated it as a doll. It had long, curly hair with a bow to match Caitlin's. Caitlin named her equipment Pauline. She was able to go trick-or-treating in a decorated wheel chair. She was happy!

A few weeks passed, and she began to stagger and slur her words. It was Christmas Eve. She was admitted. She loved Santa filling her room with every toy she could think of! She had a rare disease called chorea. It could last a few weeks or forever. I thought the Lord was really testing me. Thank goodness, it left her after two months. She was homeschooled again. She looked forward to her teacher coming in the afternoons. By now, she had every kind of "-ologist" you could think of.

Before the girls came to live with us, we traveled to exotic places:

Hawaii, St. Thomas, Bermuda, but our most fabulous trip was approaching. We were taking the girls to Disney World! We prayed for the day when Caitlin could meet her idol, Minnie Mouse. Minnie held her arms out to her, and I turned around and cried. If Minnie only knew. . . Caitlin rode around the park in a wheelchair. She could get to the attractions faster, and we all had a blast!

The twins have been featured on the cover of the hospital magazine, and several newspaper articles have been written concerning Caitlin's complex heart condition, and the fact that we are raising them. After returning from Disney World, we enjoyed a photo-shoot for an article in Woman's World Magazine, where we were featured in the August 1997 issue. We have appeared several times on the Children's Miracle Network Telethon with Caitlin and Adriane. The doctors say Caitlin is truly a miracle child. The two of them are our miracles and our special angels.

Who would ever have thought my husband and I would be sitting at a PTA meeting wondering if we were the oldest people in the gym? Life is good.

Adriane, Bonnie and Caitlin

My Son, Heart and Soul

By: Jeanne Imperati

Adoptive parents are not saints, nor do they earn a spot in Heaven because they adopted a child with a CHD. They are only what birth parents are—parents. The only difference is that their child grew in their hearts, not in their womb.

An adopted child is as loved as any other child. Upon learning that their precious child has a heart problem, most adoptive parents go through the same emotions as birth parents—fear, denial, anger, depression, acceptance and hope. One difference, though, is that they have no answers to the many questions the doctors need answered.

Do-gooders often ask, "Why keep him? He is sick," adoptive parents are told, "Send him back." "Why put yourself through this?" "You are not being fair to the other kids, family members and friends."

Then adoptive parents hear their own voices, "Should I?" "Can I?" "Will I?" "I wanted a healthy, normal baby. I wanted a perfect life. Why is this happening to me?"

Then they really listen to themselves and answer, "He is ours. We love him." My answer to others was, "If I had given birth to him, would you be asking this of me or would you stand by my side and help me fight for his life?" In my son's case, his first adoptive parents chose to walk away. He was not the perfect child, but how very wrong they were . . .

In November of 1986, Matt was placed in our home as a foster child. It was to be for only six weeks, and he would move on to his adoptive home. He was just the most adorable baby I had ever seen. He had a tiny little heart-shaped face, huge eyes that dominated his features, a button nose, a tiny mouth and big ears! "How lucky his new parents will be, and how sad his birth parents will miss out on his life," I thought as he was placed in my arms. I could feel his little heart beating so fast, so hard, right through his snowsuit. I wondered if he felt fear. Never in my wildest imagination, would I have thought that something could be so very wrong.

Within a couple of days, I called my pediatrician. Something was wrong here, but I was not quite sure of what. Matty was the best infant I ever had. He slept all night, ate every four to five hours and never cried. The perfect baby. The doctors heard a murmur and sent him for X-rays. They came back looking normal. But to be safe, an appointment was set up for the day after Thanksgiving with cardiology.

We were sent home, and I remember walking in the door thinking about how I was overreacting; he would be fine. The next thing I knew, the phone was ringing, and I needed to bring Matty to the ER immediately. The PCs wanted to check him. I packed his diaper bag, called into work and called my husband. My sister-in-law and I started out the door to what would be the most trying time of my life. The hardest part at the time was I had no information for these doctors. I could not give a family history; I did not even know how much he weighed at birth! I called home as he was being examined by numerous doctors telling Ron, "How bad could it be? We'll be home shortly."

Matty was admitted to PICU, and a cath was ordered. A nurse asked me, "Do you want a priest?" I just sat there numb, not understanding why this was happening. My sister-in-law became Matty's godmother two hours after admission. He was baptized and given his last rites within a short time. The PCRN was great. I lost it at one point, hysterical that there was never a picture taken of this baby. If he died, there would be nothing of him. She found a camera and took two pictures. We titled them, "A Fight For Life."

As upsetting as all this was, I still did not have a strong bond with Matty. After all, he was leaving soon to be adopted, and I was just his caretaker for a short time, his foster mother. The cath was done the next day. I was alone in this. I believe it was the fear of bonding and then losing Matt that kept my friends and family away. The PC came out to talk to me about what a sick little guy this baby was. He had complex heart problems. The left ventricle was hypoplastic, he had a coarctation of the aorta, a large ASD with left to right shunt, absence of left-sided forces with AV block, and more, just too many problems to list. They started him on prostaglandins. Surgery was scheduled.

I had no idea what I should do. I was already falling in love just watching Matt cling to life when there was too little of it. I called the social worker. She in turned called the birth mom. During all of this, I was lost with no way to find a path out. Should I go home? Thanksgiving was two days away, and there was so much to do!

My answer came from the birth mom. Matt's birth mother, the social worker and I sat in the waiting room crying and praying while he had his first surgery—a PA banding. The more we talked, the more I realized just how much this child meant to me. When the surgery was done a nurse from ICU called for Matt's mom; he was back from surgery. He made it!

Each of us waited for the other to make the first move. The birth mom looked at me and said, "You have been his mom for his short life; you need to be with him." I ran to my son.

The adoptive parents backed out when they learned Matt was not the normal, healthy child they wanted. Thank God. I never could have given him up to them; he was mine, heart and soul. This was the start of a long and difficult journey, dealing with all of Matt's heart defects, hospitalizations and surgeries.

Up until the age of five months, my husband refused to form any attachment to Matty. He was in total denial and was protecting his kids and himself. He could not protect me, Matt was already mine. How could we possibly even think about adopting another sick child? We already had adopted a handicapped child. And besides, this one was too sick, sick enough to die. No way—never!

Matt's first two surgeries were a PA banding and an angioplasty repair of the coarctation. He spent a few weeks in the hospital with no end in sight. We were alone in the ICU; there were no other "heart" parents around. We were told our child was unique. My friends and family still stayed away. They all believed that Matt would die and did not want to love him. My sister-in-law was the only one to stand by me. I finally brought Matt home after many fights with the doctors. "I could spend more time with him at home," I reasoned.

Finally Matt was allowed to come home, but not until I asked my family how they felt. I told them he might die but they were understanding. "We know you love him," my older children said. I would sit for hours and feed Matty with an eye dropper. I found the most caloric formula and foods I could. My husband worked and helped take care of the rest of the children. My two birth children, Fran and Michael, added their help. Still, I felt so alone and scared.

Matt had to be weighed every other day and have his vitals taken. I spent more time with my pediatrician, than my own husband! Matt was often back in the hospital for RSV, tubes in his ears, and other problems. Matt's second surgery soon followed, repair of primum ASD, and repair with a pericardial patch with secondary closure of ostium secundum, and repair of a mitral valve cleft. This time I was not alone. My husband and our family and friends were by my side.

I watched as Ron and Matt bonded. How could you not love such a little fighter? We sat in awe as he made more strides. One night stands out in my mind. Ron and I were in bed, and Matty was in his crib. He was only a few months old, but he looked at Ron and said, "Dada." Ron looked away but then looked back and saw two big eyes staring at him. "Dada!" Ron got up and took Matt in his arms. He was caught; his heart was captured.

Now our family was complete. We were in this together. But there were more problems on the horizon. Our insurance would not cover Matt's problems because they were preexisting before adoption. We ended up adopting him as a special needs child, with the state covering him with Title 19 until he reaches the age of eighteen. Without this, we never could have afforded his medical bills.

The third surgery came all too soon: a resection of the subaortic obstruction. Matt came through with flying colors. Life seemed to go on as normal aside from his regular cardiology appointments and caths.

For the next six years, Matt had gone unchanged in his health. He was still on digoxin and Lasix. We would see the PCs faithfully every six months for echos and EKGs. Matt did so well that he was enrolled in the United Studios School of Self Defense and was one belt away from his junior black belt. He was self-limited in exercise and attended school fulltime. He appeared to be the picture of health. One would never know, by looking at him, just how many heart problems he actually had.

Then the bad news came. Everything had changed. My pediatrician got a letter from Matt's cardiologist which began, "As you know, Matt is a ten year old with complex left-sided heart defects. . . " and ended with a nightmare. Matt needed another a cath. The results of the cath showed that Matt needed surgery. This was a complex surgery because of severe subaortic stenosis. His mitral valve also had problems which could not be fixed surgically, and so it had to be replaced with a mechanical valve. That meant Matt would have to be on Coumadin for life. The worst part was that Matt's surgery did not do what the doctors had prayed it would. Now instead of being better, he was worse than before the surgery.

Ron and I felt totally helpless. The doctors looked at Matt in dismay. They had failed. The surgeries they had performed had only made him worse, and now even more difficult decisions needed to be made. Would Matt need a transplant or a Konno? A Konno! I didn't even know what that was! Then I learned that a Konno was a very complicated procedure that required more changes to Matt's heart. And while this was perhaps one of the most difficult times in my life, it could have been far worse.

In 1996 I used my computer to get online and found that I was far from alone. The Internet was full of other parents of children with severe congenital heart defects! While I could not find another child exactly like Matt, I did find parents who knew the same fears, had the same nightmares and cared about me and my son. It was these "strangers" around the world who became my support group.

I was at a low point in my life. I found myself feeling resentful of the doctors who had treated my son. They had chosen nontraditional means of saving Matt's life and now they didn't know what to do; meanwhile, Matt had led a relatively normal life, and we were horrified that it could all be taken away. It was my online support group that came to my rescue, sending me messages of support, love and hope.

Matt was such an unusual case that his doctors had trouble agreeing on what would be the best treatment for him. There was not another child like him on the books. There was no precedent. Matt soon byecame the topic of conversation between many pediatric cardiologists and cardio-thoracic surgeons around the country.

I wasn't prepared for what was yet to come. As angry as I was at the doctors who had treated Matt, I still trusted them. They had helped him to have ten wonderful years, and I was grateful they had saved his life. The consensus of the doctors, though, was that Matt needed a miracle, and there was only one man to perform that miracle—Dr.

Edward Bove, in Ann Arbor, Michigan. I had never traveled that far from home before for Matt's surgeries. It would not be possible for all of my friends and family to be with me. I was resistant to the idea. A second opinion from yet another cardiologist confirmed the consensus of the group.

I did research as best I could. There was not much to be found. What I did find made Matt's chance for life look bleak at best. I decided that I had to make every moment with Matt count. We went camping to get away from it all and to come to peace with the next big step Matt would have to take. I tried to concentrate on making wonderful memories with Matt, but in the back of my mind I found myself thinking about his funeral. It was all so much to deal with. Meanwhile letters from friends around the world were filling my online mailbox and prayers were being said in Matt's name with each passing day.

The surgeon decided that the Konno was Matt's best chance at life. Like it or not, we were going to Ann Arbor. Getting on the plane was so hard for me. I fear planes as it is, but knowing I might be coming back without Matt was more than I could handle. I cried, threw up and cried some more. Thank goodness Matt thought it was all because of my fear of planes.

My poor husband! I never once gave thought to him that morning. He was dealing with this on his own and trying to help me. Matt was pretty quiet, too, not asking too much. He knew this was a big surgery. He didn't want to know anything else. My two older children flew out the day before the surgery to be with us. My brother came out to be with us, too. Even with all of this love and support surrounding me, I still felt alone in a world of darkness.

The thing I remember most from the morning of Matt's surgery was kissing him one last time before he walked away with strangers to the OR. As the doors were closing and separating us, he turned back and smiled. I never saw fear in him, only hope. Hope that this was the last one. Hope that he would be okay. Hope that he would soon wake up and it had just been a bad dream. I had no thoughts, no words; I was just numb. The only thing I had was the image of my son smiling back at me. As the hours passed, I wondered if that would be the last image of him to be engraved in my memory.

Finally, we heard that the surgery was done and the doctor was on his way out to talk to us. I asked the nurse about Matt, and she said, "The doctor will talk to you." Now I was sure; I had lost him.

The doctor walked in smiling! Matt was fine. He did really well and was on his way to the PICU. It was not as good as he said though. Matt had a lot of problems. At one point they thought he had had a stroke because he could not wake up. I called our PCs back home so many times that day. Matt slept for four full days! He just would not wake up. I guess his body was just so tired from the past year. He did not have a stroke.

When we got home, we took him to our hospital, and they did all kinds of tests. Matt was fine. The surgery was a success. We went home with a guarded sense of relief.

We do not know what the future holds for Matt, but we do know that he is a fighter and a survivor. Matt could not be more a part of my family, my life or my heart had I born him myself. My husband says that I may not have given birth to him, but I gave him life. All I know is that my life wouldn't have been complete without him.

Matt Imperati

Editor's Note: Matt is one year post-op and still doing fine.

Love never asks how much must I do, but how much can I do.

More than a Mom

Any time a marriage has to deal with unusual stress, whether it be from demanding jobs, family problems or medical problems, the health of the marriage itself is at risk. What happens when your child has a medical problem so severe that you must take off time from work to deal with it and face life and death issues for days on end? Oftentimes those marriages end in divorce. The stress is just too much.

Men and women handle stress differently. I saw over and over again in the hospital how men and women tried to come to grips with the seriousness of their child's situation. I saw both men and women crying as well as stoic men and women, unable or unwilling to share their emotions for the time being. I saw couples cry on each other and couples who could not touch. I saw parents who were there constantly for their child and couples who could not stand being in the hospital.

The women in this chapter, with the exception of the last essay, deal with divorce in addition to their heart child. The first two women had to deal with the stressful situation of having a child with a congenital heart defect requiring surgeries—without the support of their husbands. They had to go through the surgeries, hospitalizations and days of worry without the help and support of a spouse. They dealt with special equipment, doctor's appointments, and insurance, as well as, the daily maintenance of a single-parent household. Although they did this without a spouse, they did not do it alone. The last essay, written by the stepmother of a child with a severe CHD, shares special insight into the importance of treating our "heart" children as normally as possible. With love in their hearts for these special children, each of these women are more than a mom.

The Heart of a Mother

Taking Care of Things

by: Anita Moreno Marcelo

My life as a single mother began when my oldest son, Jaime, was four years old, and Gabriel was only ten months of age. The fear and uncertainty I felt just making this move away from my husband was compounded by the fact that Gabriel had a very serious and severe group of heart defects. Gabriel would need open-heart surgery at twelve months of age This meant I had to face Gabe's big surgery while adjusting to the separation, getting through the holidays (Christmas) and Gabe's birthday all within about five weeks time.

Gabe had been diagnosed with tetralogy of Fallot (TOF) and atrioventricular septal defect (AV Canal) and had a Blalock/Taussig shunt when he was three weeks old. He was plagued with "tet spells" throughout that first year of life which were horrible to watch. He would turn blue when he cried, then his face would show the strain from the lack of oxygen; it was as if he were suffocating right in front of his brother and me. His arms and shoulders would pull in toward his chest, as he instinctively conserved his oxygen for the organs that needed it most. The "spell" would last a minute or so, and then Gabe would take about half an hour to recover. The frequency of these spells varied from once every three weeks to three times a week. By the time he was eleven months old, he was having as many as five a day, and I was falling apart each time. I was also worried that he might not come out of one. All the while, my four year old was right in the middle, taking it all in.

With his surgery in early January (it had been delayed three times), we were relieved to see the end of these spells. Unfortunately, the repair the surgeon had planned to do was not possible. Upon opening Gabe up, the surgeon discovered that he had a single ventricle, so he decided to try something new, a hemi-Fontan (it was new in 1991). The surgeon was elated at the success, and I became very worried because I could not find anything in writing about a hemi-Fontan. We were truly thrown in at the deep end, and it was a whole new outlook for my son. I felt very insecure. Even the information on the Fontan did not ever discuss operating on young babies. Happy that my son was alive, I still felt as if the rug had been pulled out from under me. Instead of being repaired, Gabe was awaiting another surgery to complete the Fontan, and I had no idea what that would mean for him.

Exhaustion was my greatest enemy during this time, but it was so much worse because I really did not know many people for support or relief from the boys. My family did not live near me, and the kids and I could go for weeks without seeing anyone but the clerk at the grocery store. Gabe did not sleep well and was up at least four times a night. I propped my eyes open each morning with the strongest coffee I could make. It was a terrible time, and I tried to think very little about each day, just looking ahead to the future. I figured that we could keep up this pace for a few months. The months, however, turned into years.

While concentrating on the future may have been a survival mechanism, it set me up for a lot of disappointments when plans did not materialize as I thought they would. Gabe went on to have learning disabilities, a stroke, and impulsive and distractible behavior due to low oxygen during that first year. As each of these problems hit, I added them to the mix but never left open the possibility that anything else would crop up. Of course I wanted to be positive, but without knowing how much he was at risk, I was finding things out in piece-meal fashion and did not know how to prepare myself for what was happening.

I also failed to find the energy to really enjoy much of that time. It was as if I waited for the next surgery to fix everything, and then we could get on with life. Well, life was right then and there, but I could not see it for all the worrying and trying to achieve the outcome I wanted. I was really tired and irritable and desperate for another adult to share coffee with me. My mother started coming up for about two weeks at a time. She really helped with the kids and allowed me the freedom to get some things done that I just could not do with the kids. Best of all though, was her presence. She was there in person, listening, sharing and hugging. It also made me realize how much it meant to have someone there, in person.

If exhaustion was my enemy, the phone was my ally. I attended the cardiology support group meetings at the hospital and made some very good friends as a result. They were wonderful. We talked on the phone as often as possible, and it was like speaking a language that other people I knew could not understand. They knew exactly what I felt when I learned about Gabe's condition, worried that he might not make it or felt unsure of myself in the mother-as-nurse role. They were also concerned about his "tet spells" and how my oldest son and I were doing. They understood medications and surgical procedures. It was incredibly refreshing to really open up about coping with a child with a CHD. I may not have always had someone with me, but I made the most of these phone relationships.

I knew very few people outside the support group because we had relocated due to my husband's job transfer. The people in the support group became like family to us. We visited each other's homes, went to the zoo, picnics and other excursions whenever our children were all healthy at the same time. We shared in the work to improve and enhance the support group and I found that giving support back to parents who were new to the group was very healing for me. I began to see the difficulties of our life as more than just a personal ordeal; they were something we were all in together.

There are no simple solutions to the isolation that comes with single parenting a child who has special needs. Over the years, one of the hardest things I had to learn was to ask for help. Asking for help meant you had to know how much you really needed it and what would help you most. I often thought I was letting others know what my needs were but was uncomfortable asking and did not know how far to go.

After Gabe's Fontan surgery when he was two-and-a-half years old, he came home from the hospital after nearly six weeks of battling pleural effusion (fluid build up in his lungs). He was on IV meds, and we were both truly exhausted. I was walking into walls, disoriented upon waking, and he was screaming in lieu of talking. Now I was to give his meds three times a day and do a sterile dressing change every other day as well. With no one else at home to help me, I was told at the hospital that I could tie his hands to the furniture so that he would not contaminate the site around his Broviac line! I could not do that and instead substituted fun and games. His older brother, Jaime, would alternately hold his hands and sing and dance for him while I worked on his Broviac line. We turned out to be a pretty good team, but I was worried about that tubing so close to his heart.

During this time, my five year old started kindergarten. For the first week of school, we were to take our children to the door of their classroom and pick them up there in the afternoon until they got oriented to the school. Gabe was on a severe fluid restriction and high dosage of Lasix. Twice a day we had to pass a drinking fountain on the way to the class, and Gabe would scream hysterically trying to get at the water. Everyday it was a constant challenge to keep Gabe's mind off that water fountain. The other parents probably wondered why I would not let my son have a drink. I had tried to get someone from the school to understand that I needed help getting Jaime to class so that Gabe would not have to go through that, but I guess I was not convincing. On top of that, I really wanted my oldest boy to have a good start and lots of attention during this time. He had really sacrificed a lot while Gabe was in the hospital.

Today, if we had to go through that same situation, I would have found a better way. Time and experience have taught me to be less reluctant to bother others for help. I have also found that I have to spell out what I want to have happen and exactly what I want someone to do.

Grief from a broken marriage, the loss of my son's health and the loneliness and isolation that came with living in a new place without family and friends played an important part in how well I did or did not cope during those times. I certainly could not know what would happen to Gabe, but the support group really was an important part of our survival. They have been there individually and as a group.

Many gray hairs and added pounds later, I do wish I had done a better job of taking care of myself. The usual suggestions for stress relief, taking a relaxing bath or reading a book, just did not work with my two high-maintenance boys. Even now, it is challenging, but any effort to take care of me benefits them, and we are all better for it.

Gabe and Jaime

Never More Than You Can Handle

By: Brenda Vignaroli

The call came in at 3:30 a.m. on the maternity unit where I had undergone a tubal ligation earlier that morning after the birth of my second daughter, Jessica. Ironically, it was this procedure that kept me in the hospital an extra day and may have contributed to saving my daughter's life. One of the nurses on duty that afternoon discovered Jessica's breathing had become shallow, and she was showing signs of blueness.

The hospital brought in a team of doctors from UCLA to transport my baby daughter to their medical center where her needs and an evaluation could be best accomplished. We waited for the results that would change our lives forever and place us in a situation where we had to decide the fate of our daughter's life . . . a decision no parent should ever have to face.

"Mrs. Vignaroli," I heard a kind voice say on the other end of the phone. "This is Doctor Santulli. I am calling to let you know about the situation with your daughter. It seems she has a very complicated problem with her heart. The name of this congenital heart condition is known as hypoplastic left heart syndrome; do you remember Baby Faye?"

I knew in an instant who he was talking about, as I had found her story fascinating. "Yes, the baboon-to-baby heart transplant?" I said.

"Yes, Mrs. Vignaroli, and I must tell you that her situation is one that has a very high mortality rate; 100% if you do nothing and just take her home. I must tell you a lot of parents have chosen this route."

"What is my other option?" Immediately I wanted to dismiss the option of doing nothing. I wanted my child to live. I wanted them to do everything possible, even if it meant another experimental baboon procedure, anything to help her survive.

It was decided that my daughter would have a Norwood procedure, the first in a three-staged surgical procedure to reconstruct her heart. It would be a wait-and-see procedure in that it was experimental and had a 1% survival rate, but I was desperate. My husband and I learned very quickly how delicate this situation was and that there was the possibility our daughter may not survive.

We had to leave as soon as the doctor released me from the hospital that morning in order to make the hour-long drive to UCLA and see our baby before they took her into surgery at 11:00 a.m. Time was precious, and the team of doctors were so gracious and understanding towards two parents who were about to view their baby for the first time in the ICU. I was neither expecting nor prepared to see my daughter in such a swollen state with tubes everywhere. Her beautiful, black curly hair had been shaven off on one side where an IV was sticking out of her head. She seemed to be struggling, but the morphine had begun to settle in, and her eyes were dilated.

"She is a very sick little girl," someone said to me. "We need to get her into surgery right away, so if you don't mind, you can say good-bye to her now, and you will be able to spend more time with her later."

We kissed her on the forehead as they rolled her down the long hall towards surgery. "Be strong, Jessica. Mommy and Daddy love you so much!" I cried.

Waiting for Jessica to come out of surgery was grueling and emotionally draining. I would imagine that even the strongest mind would be tested. In our case the first surgery was close to eight hours— a lifetime.

In the days that followed, our emotions were running high. Jessica survived the surgery, and our darkest hours finally started to brighten. Soon joy filled our hearts again. Our Jessica was alive! I could not wait to bring her home so that my three-year-old daughter, Cara, could finally see the baby sister she had been waiting for. We had to make several trips between the hospital and home so that Cara could be assured that everyone was all right.

In the weeks that followed, Jessica's stay in the hospital was filled with test after test, X-ray after X-ray, and a lot of prayer. She had suffered what was thought to be a seizure following surgery, so the concern shifted to the possibility of brain damage. This would have to be watched closely; therefore, a neurologist was assigned to run a series of tests to determine if she had had a seizure. The doctors explained to us that sometimes babies just twitch after birth, but to be on the safe side she was placed on phenobarbital even though she did not show any more signs of seizures. This continued for the following year along with several EEGs, and finally it was determined that she may have indeed suffered some minor brain damage to the center of her brain, which may or may not affect her motor skills as she gets older.

Every step was a major event, and four weeks later our baby was finally coming home. I remember telling my husband, "Everything around me seems so trivial; the problems and complaints I may have had before seem so small. The only thing that matters to me is having our family together and cherishing every moment. Life is so important." What I did not realize was that my life had taken a very significant turn, and I would be forever changed.

My family was all that mattered to me. God had blessed me with two beautiful little girls and a husband who worked hard to keep things together. The months were very busy with doctors, hospital visits and trying to keep up with the medication schedule. Jessica was on eight different medications at one point, and to complicate matters she had forgotten her instinct to suck. So, she was fed through a tube inserted through her nose which ran down into her stomach. This procedure, known as the Gavage method, was used in the hospitals for patients too weak to feed themselves. I had to learn this procedure while Jessica was in the hospital before they would release her to come home. All of this and a demanding three year old kept my days busy, my priorities straight and my faith in God strong. Someone along the way had once told me that God never gives you more than you can handle. This saying stuck with me and helped me get through some of the tougher days.

When Jessica turned two, we noticed that her breathing was becoming more difficult. Her tiny body was not strong enough for her to make any attempts to walk; therefore, she got around by scooting. She was beginning to show signs of blueness around her mouth and fingers, so her second surgery was scheduled—the Glenn shunt. This procedure proved to be beneficial to her strength and growth. Almost immediately she mastered walking; her breathing was back to normal for her condition, and she was beginning to blossom.

This should have been one of the happier times even though we knew another surgery would be required later; however, my husband was beginning to show signs of stress, and our communication was waning. Some nights he would come home and unwind with a glass or two of bourbon. Over time this amount increased to a bottle a night which continued for several months. The months turned into years, and once again, I found myself facing a dilemma that I was not quite sure how to handle. I knew his drinking was becoming more of a problem. Alcoholism ran in his family, and now our world was beginning to crumble.

His drinking became intense, and his behavior became abusive towards me. He was in denial, and it was not long before he quit his job (which he had held for ten years), forcing me to take a job that paid half of what he was making just so we would not lose our medical benefits.

My concern was how to pay for Jessica's next surgery. I was away from my daughters during the work day, and it was tearing me apart. My husband was not handling things as easily as I had thought. I had read earlier that some parents just cannot handle the stress of having a child with severe medical problems. I had no idea it would hit so close to home.

The abuse turned violent, and I knew I had to remove my children from this situation. My concern revolved around Jessica and her needs. She had been through two open-heart surgeries by now and would soon require the third stage. There were decisions to be made, and from here on we were on our own.

My parents have been our biggest support since my divorce in 1991. I honestly do not know how I would have handled everything without them. It is tough being a single parent when you have a child with special needs. The emotional support is what gets you through.

My divorce became final in June of 1991, and Jessica's last surgery was performed in the same month. By this time Jessica's father had fled the state of California leaving behind all of his responsibilities and, sadly enough, his two daughters who have not seen or heard from him since.

I know in their hearts they are hurting because their father chose to stay out of their lives. Of the two, Jessica is the one who still asks about him every now and then, and my heart aches for her.

Jessica is now eleven years old, and she has given me so much. She has endured more in her short life than most adults could in a lifetime. Strength, courage, undying love for life, these are the things that she has taught me. She is so sensitive to other people's feelings.

After the third, and hopefully final surgery (known as the Fontan procedure), Jessica continues to grow on a slow scale for her age. It was decided after the Fontan to implant a pacemaker as a safety net, and personally I am glad it is there. It eases my mind, and Jessica thinks it's pretty neat too, as do some of the kids at her school. It amazes me how other children become so protective of each other when they know that one of their classmates has a medical condition. Her teachers have been wonderful in explaining the situation to the other students, and they have responded in a loving way. This is another hurdle that weighs heavy on the mind of a parent with a child who requires a little special attention. I am so grateful to her friends and teachers.

She is physically the size of a seven year old, so petite and fragile. At times she loves to climb up in my lap to cuddle and squeeze my neck. It is usually at times like this that her sense of humor overwhelms me. "Mom, don't squeeze me so tight! My pacemaker might pop out!" she teases me.

There have been times, in our serious moments, that she has asked about her father. She does not remember how he looks, since she was only five when he left. So we take down the family photo album, and she stares at the pictures, sometimes with a little sadness. I assure her that her daddy loves her and Cara even though we have not heard from him in over six years. I think it is important for her to believe this; and hopefully in time, she will come to terms with the fact that some people just do not deal with life as easily as others.

This may be something she never understands given the fact that she has fought so hard to live, and she gives it her all because she loves life with such a passion. She is a survivor, and everyday to her is a blessing, just as it is for me.

Jessica Vignaroli

The Heart of a Mother

A Stepmother's Story

By: Karen Pritchett

I am happy to share that for the past eight years I have been in Julie's life, I find I constantly need to remind myself that she even has a heart problem! To look at her, you would not know that she is the oldest living person of a major medical breakthrough. She has a very healthy appearance. She has no special diet and only a once-a-year checkup that seems as routine as a sports physical for school.

It is my conclusion that the doctors give gloom-and-doom attitudes because they are understandably baffled, and with no scientific answer to read from a textbook, they guard against giving false hope. But the best advice I've ever received was from Maria Wallington, one of Julie's doctors. Having a child with a congenital heart defect was new to me, and I wanted to know what I was supposed to do. Her response to me was, "Other than watching her salt intake because she has a tendency to retain water, treat her like a normal person."

IF (the big word) we could go back and do anything differently, it would be not to "spoil" her in her younger years. She is now a teenager, and had Julie learned the meaning of the word NO, her life would be better today.

Julie is the oldest living survivor of the Norwood procedure. Because her prognosis was totally unknown when she was a baby, everyone around her spoiled her. Every procedure was new and experimental. There were no statistics, nobody to compare Julie to. It is no small wonder she was given whatever she wanted and permitted to do as she pleased.

I married Julie's father when she was nine years old. She had already been through life-saving procedures. She had recovered from long hospitalizations. Her father is the one who made all of the trips from Alaska to Boston or to Philadelphia. He waited in the waiting rooms, paced the hallways and lived through the hospitalizations with Julie. I came into their lives long after these emergency procedures were done.

Because of all of this, I was able to bring to the family one thing they had not had—normalcy. I brought my son and daughter into their family, blending to make a five child home. I expected the same from Julie that I expected from any of the children. This was a first for Julie.

As I became frustrated with certain behaviors Julie exhibited, I discovered things that she had been permitted to do for many years. It was in analyzing these behaviors that I began to understand how Julie had become the person she was. I still struggle to guide Julie into behaving by the same rules and expectations of anyone else in our society.

In earlier years Julie had learned that all she had to say was, "I don't feel good," and homework was a thing of the past. She became accustomed to using her heart defect to get out of doing anything she did not wish to do. One day, though, she was in for a surprise!

Julie decided she did not want to do her math, so she went up to the teacher's desk, showed her chest scars and said that she had a heart problem and did not feel like doing math. What Julie did not know was that her teacher had had polio as a child. Her teacher's response was to pull up her pant leg, showed her scars and said, "So? I had polio, and you need to sit down and do your math."

Another thing Julie discovered in her earlier years was that people would do whatever she wanted because they did not want to see her get upset. Everyone was afraid of what stress would to do her heart. This meant that when Julie was with a group of friends, either at a birthday party, Girl Scouts or school and they were playing a game, if Julie decided to change the rules, she expected everyone to go along with her. After a while Julie ceased to be invited to parties or functions.

Another result of having everyone give in to all of Julie's whims is an attitude of impatience. When she wants something, she wants it immediately. She would do whatever it took to see to it that she got what she wanted, too!

Julie was not disciplined like her siblings were. Because everyone was so afraid of how fragile she was, she was never spanked. Julie witnessed her siblings receiving spankings for their misbehaviors, but she never experienced it herself. Finally, when she was ten years old, she got her first spanking. Julie's eyes were wide with disbelief! She never cried one tear; her mouth simply dropped open, and she stood there in amazement.

Perhaps one of the most challenging behaviors for me to deal with as a stepmother was that Julie's siblings had become wise to using Julie's condition to their advantage. They would convince Julie to take the blame for their misbehaviors because she did not get punished! I was amazed to see how the children had come to use Julie's heart defect to get what they wanted or to get out of anything they had done wrong.

The funny thing is that we never thought we were spoiling her at the time. We thought we were just loving her and giving her the happiest days we could. But in essence we were hurting her future. We came to realize that we had to concentrate on when Julie would get older rather than if she would get older.

Just the other day I was talking with Julie, and she is now grasping how she can be anything she wants to be. In fact at the top of her list is to start a newsletter geared toward communicating with HLHS parents and children. Julie loves to read, write and has a naturally caring attitude, perhaps from her days in the hospital surrounded by caring nurses and doctors. She also has a vivid imagination, so we have been encouraging her towards becoming a children's author.

Julie will not be able to pull a forty-hour week like most because she does tire faster than others, and because employers are reluctant to hire people with medical problems. So perhaps she should look into being self-employed as a writer, or working in a hospital in the counseling department; maybe she could work with the American Heart Association!

Julie can ride bikes, roller skate, swim, hike, and go camping and fishing. She likes acting in plays. She loves talking on the phone and shopping at the mall. She is just a "normal" teenager.

As a non-biological parent who was not present during the hard times, it is easier for me not to reflect on the child in the recovery room. This can be good. I feel I have been able to bring situations back to reality quicker than a biological parent who is caught up in the emotion of the moment. I think my greatest frustration in raising a stepchild with a CHD has been that even though I want the best for Julie, she needs to want that for herself as well. I want Julie to think about how her behavior affects others. I want her to acknowledge my feelings as well as her own.

Julie and I have grown closer over the years. I have watched her grow from a little girl into a young woman. I think that in spite of the frustrations, Julie has been a very special person for me to get to know. The more we grow together, the stronger our bond becomes.

Military Moms

Having a child with a heart defect is difficult, but military life makes things even more complicated. Whether the husband, wife or both parents are in the military, certain things are expected—namely, that the family lives wherever the United States Government deems necessary; that one or both parents can be separated from the children for certain periods of time requiring some type of childcare; and that a family can, at any given moment, pack up and go, if necessary. These are only samples of expectations on military life.

These "givens" do not necessarily work when you have a child with a heart defect. First of all, not all medical facilities are equal. The local hospital may not be equipped to deal with the surgical intervention needed to save your baby's life. While surgeries are sometimes planned, it is not uncommon for children's surgeries to be postponed more than once for one reason or another.

Perhaps one of the biggest challenges military families face is separation. Few people realize what a tremendous sacrifice men and women in the United States Armed Forces make to safe-guard our national security. These men and women often drop everything to fulfill their obligations, even if it means a year or longer separation from their families. More commonly, soldiers train in the field, requiring days or weeks on end when they are not permitted to be home.

How can a family with a child with a congenital heart defect fulfill their job commitment when they also have the burden of caring for a critically ill child? How can they be there for their children and still maintain the rigorous schedule required by the Armed Forces? How does the military work with families with special needs?

The following chapter is written by three mothers involved in different sectors of the military—the Army, the Navy and the Air Force. These mothers share their stories to answer these questions and many more. Read on to see if Uncle Sam wants you, even when you have a child with a heart defect.

The Heart of a Mother

In The Navy

By: Gabriele Stiltner

When I was eleven years old, my dad joined the Army for the second time. I knew then that I wanted to be in the military just like my dad. I turned eighteen in May 1983 and joined the Navy four months later. My husband and I met on recruiting duty in southern Indiana where we dated on and off for two years. We were both facing a transfer in December of 1992. I had chosen orders to Hawaii, and only by luck so did he. We married in February of 1993, and our first child was born also that year on August 19, 1993.

My husband's submarine, the USS Kamehameha, had not yet arrived in Hawaii, so my dearest friend, Dawn Tourville, supported me through the birth of John Loren Stiltner. Four months later I found out I was again pregnant. We had another beautiful red-headed boy on September 19, 1994. Aaron Lee Stiltner, exactly thirteen months after we had our first son. We were not planning on having more children; two was enough.

I knew that I would have to transfer to sea duty in December of 1996, and my husband would be transferring to shore duty at the same time. Since we were a dual military family, the military must keep one of us on sea duty while the other is on shore duty. Sea duty for me would mean packing up all the squadron gear and going to a remote island in the Pacific for six months out of every eighteen. Since my husband was already on sea duty, the boys were used to him being gone, home for a few months, then gone again. I was sort of looking forward to getting a break from the boys and giving my husband a chance to bond with them, but in February of 1996 I found out I was pregnant again. Our third child was due October 28, 1996, the same time my husband was due to go out to sea for eight weeks. My transfer date changed to March of 1997 since Navy policy prohibits a female to transfer to sea duty until four months after the baby arrives, allowing mother to bond with the newborn child.

All went well throughout my uneventful pregnancy. The baby moved all over and always had a good heart beat at our prenatal checkups. I made arrangements with Dawn once again to be at my side for support when the baby arrived. My husband went out to sea as planned on the fourth of October.

I continued my job as Supervisor of the Tire and Wheel Shop, where we disassembled and reassembled aircraft and helicopter tires for the Navy's P-3 Orions, H-60s and H-3s stationed in Hawaii. Always short-handed, I helped in the shop throughout my pregnancy. The upper echelon wanted to take me out of the work center and put me in an administrative job when they found out I was pregnant. I told them that I would not sit behind any desk and push papers for nine months. I stayed in the work center and performed flawlessly with both of my other children, and this one would not be any different. Since I was the supervisor and did not have much strenuous work to do, the Navy let me have my way.

On October 22, 1996, I went to work and had contractions all day about thirty minutes apart. I told everyone that I would not be at work the next day because I was having the baby that night. By 3:30 a.m. on the 23rd, my contractions were five minutes apart. I called Dawn and told her it was time, and I would be over with the boys right away. I woke Loren and Aaron and told them we were going to Auntie Dawn's because I was going to have the baby. I got to Dawn's house, left the boys with her husband, Brian, and we were off to Trippler Army Medical Center. I registered at the hospital at 4:15 a.m. Aimee Leilani was born an hour later. A message was sent to her father off the coast of Korea that he had a healthy baby girl and mother and daughter were doing fine. Aimee was taken to the newborn nursery, and I was taken to recovery. When I got to the OB ward, I went to the nursery to get Aimee; however, because she was such a fast birth she had wet lungs and was put on oxygen. I never got to bring Aimee to my room because she was still on oxygen at 10:30 p.m. when I went to feed her.

The nightmare began the next morning at 5:30 when the pediatrician who was in the nursery came in and asked for my consent to do a spinal tap on Aimee. She had started breathing fast. They did blood work and chest X-rays and wanted to do the spinal tap to rule out anything else. I gave consent. At 7:30 a doctor from the NICU came in to get my consent to start a central IV in Aimee's belly button and told me that Aimee had turned blue from the waste down. This IV would allow them to administer a drug to keep the ductus arteriosis open so that blood would continue to flow through to the lower portion of her body. After transferring her to a civilian hospital (because the only pediatric cardiologist on staff was out of town), Aimee was diagnosed as having an interrupted aortic arch, a large ventricular septal defect and an atrial septal defect.

Meanwhile my husband thought everything was fine. He called me via ship-to-shore telephone, and I told him that I was taking Aimee to Children's Hospital in San Diego because she needed open-heart surgery. He told me that he would make arrangements to be there.

The MEDIVAC Department at Trippler made arrangements to fly us to San Diego at 1:00 a.m. Friday morning. My brother made arrangements for my mother to fly to Hawaii on Friday morning from Indiana so she could stay with my boys while I went with Aimee. My friends, neighbors and fellow shipmates assured me that my mother and children would be taken care of during the time she was alone with the boys. This was the first time I had ever been away from the boys for more than twenty-four hours.

My husband finally made it to San Diego on the 26th of October. We met with the surgeon on Sunday to review Aimee's heart defects and how he was going to fix them. He also discussed her chances of survival, which were pretty good. That afternoon we had a priest come in and baptize Aimee. Two days later, she went into surgery and did not come out until 1:00 p.m.—these were the longest five and a half hours I have ever lived through. Surgery went well, and all her defects were repaired. She had some complications that night, and for several days after surgery, she suffered uncontrollable seizures. Once the seizures were under control, Aimee started shedding tubes and IVs quite regularly. Because her VSD was so large, after the repair she went into complete heart block. After twenty-four days she had another surgery to insert a permanent pacemaker. This surgery was on the 21st of November and went very well with no complications. My husband made arrangements to return to Hawaii, as he was running out of leave time. Of course when he made the arrangements he thought that I would be right behind him in a week or two. I was on official orders from BUMED allowing me to stay with my child so I was not burning up any leave time and could stay as long as I needed.

I called home every couple of days to talk to the boys. They were very excited about their baby sister, and wanted to know when we were coming home. Instead of coming home a week or so after my husband, it ended up being almost a month. We were learning to feed Aimee, and slowly she was weaned off the oxygen. This was very time-consuming because her lungs kept collapsing. Once she was off the oxygen, feeding got better, but she still was not eating enough by mouth.

When the doctor mentioned Aimee was ready to go home, I contacted the MEDIVAC Department at Balboa Naval Hospital to check on the next flight. To my surprise there was one on December 17, 1996, but if we were not on that one, the next flight was a whole month later. I reported to Children's, and they immediately started making arrangements for Aimee's transfer back to Trippler for follow-up care for her feeding problems.

I thought the day would never come when we would leave the hospital and head for home. I was in tears. We took an ambulance to Miramar Naval Air Station and sat on the runway for two hours before we were told that the plane was diverted from Arizona to Travis Air Force –Base because of high winds. Back to the hospital we went. What an awful feeling having to return because our plane never arrived! I was in tears! Just the thought of having to stay there for another month and being away from my boys devastated me. Had it not been for the support of several other mothers from Hawaii, I do not know what I would have done. The hospital let the military play around one more day, then the Heart Association paid for a commercial ticket for Aimee and me so we could get home in time for Christmas.

While we were in San Diego together, my husband and I had a lot of time to discuss our options about my sea duty in March. Scott never pressured me and let me make my own career decision. I had five months left on my current enlistment. It was not hard for me to decide what I needed to do. During Aimee's surgery, the surgeon discovered her thymus was absent, and she tested positive for DiGeorge Syndrome.

The thymus gland develops an infant's immune system. By puberty the thymus shrivels up, since it is no longer needed by the body. With the absence of this gland and Aimee's pacemaker, daycare could be a problem.

In Hawaii daycare is very expensive and difficult to find for a special needs child. The Navy regulates the home daycare program in Navy Housing and stipulates that providers caring for special needs children can only have three children total in their care. In addition, the provider must have permission from the Commanding Officer of the Base to care for each child. The provider that I had caring for the boys was leaving in July of that year. This meant I had much to consider regarding whether or not I continued my military career.

I returned to work on the 20th of December and requested thirty days of leave. I also spoke with my division officer and told him that I was going to put in for a hardship discharge. He took me to see the assistant department head to let him know of my plans. After several hours of discussing my intentions, they asked me to think about my decision while I was on leave. When I returned they would support my decision. I already knew what I was going to do. While I was still on leave, I spoke with the department career counselor and got the information I needed to start my hardship discharge package. I wrote a letter explaining why I needed the discharge and got supporting documents from Aimee's doctors. Aimee's cardiologist wrote a wonderful letter in support of my decision.

Two weeks before I went back to work, I turned in my discharge package. This took about a month to get through my chain of command. Once it went through, there were no questions asked, and my request was quickly granted. After having the required medical and dental exams and attending the required discharge seminars, I was released from the Navy on February 28, 1997 after thirteen years, five months and twenty-eight days of service.

The first month was very difficult for me. Having always worked, I was accustomed to a schedule and particular regimen. I awoke everyday not knowing what to do with myself. Besides being depressed, I laid around the house tired most of the time. I was not sure if I had made the right decision. We went from a dual to a single income household.

I really lost it the day I called the unemployment office because I had not received my first check yet and found out my claim was still pending. I must have cried for hours wondering how I would make the house payment in Indiana plus pay the rest of our monthly bills. I knew that I should have just stayed in the Navy. What had I done to our family? I was very angry at myself for being so selfish and getting out of the Navy.

Then one day John Loren told me a secret. He came close to my ear and whispered, "I like staying home with you, Mom!" I stopped dwelling on what I had done and started moving forward to enjoy the time I could spend with my children.

We started going to an organized play morning and doing crafts at home on rainy days. I suddenly realized how much I had missed by working rather than being at home. I never remembered the boys first teeth, but I was able to watch Aimee's first two teeth come in. I got to see Aimee roll over all the way and start getting on her hands and knees learning to crawl. These were things I just took for granted before, and I never realized just how wonderful it was being a mom.

I now have no regrets about getting out of the Navy. I have started a part-time job that allows me to take the kids along with me. We volunteer at a children's waiting room once or twice a week at our local medical clinic. I have found direction in my life and am sure I am going the right way.

To help me understand Aimee's situation, I belong to two support groups through the Internet. One is the PDHeart list and the other is a VCFS/DiGeorge Syndrome list. Without these two lists, I think it would be a lot more difficult to move on. I still fear the unknown with regard to Aimee's future, but these lists help in dissipating some of that fear.

I have learned so much about being a mother since I had Aimee. I now revel in the accomplishments of all of my children. I feel stronger and better informed about children's health issues—something I used to take for granted. But, perhaps one of the most significant changes in my life is that I have found God again and have started incorporating Him into our lives. I know in my heart that with God all things are possible.

The Army Way of Life

by: Lou Anne Wright

Nicole was born at 7:52 p.m. on March 14, 1996 at Darnell Army Community Hospital on Fort Hood, in central Texas. Nicole is our third child but only our second experience with childbirth in a military hospital. Despite the fact that Darnell and many other military hospitals have bad reputations, I cannot complain about the care I received. It was not quite as nice as the civilian hospital where my eldest child was born, but maybe a little better than some small town civilian hospitals.

Nicole's birth was my easiest delivery. I could not believe that I made it through with no pain medications at all. It helped that she was about one pound smaller than my second child, weighing seven pounds, thirteen ounces. We did not even make it to the delivery room. While the doctor and mid-wife were preparing me to go to the recovery room, a nurse took Nicole down the hall to bathe her. The nurse brought Nicole back into the labor room, so I could see her again. Then my husband, Doug, and the nurse took her back to the nursery.

Doug came into recovery to tell me that it might be a while before they could bring Nicole in to nurse. She was having some kind of problem, but he did not know what. He thought they had said something about her body temperature, but now I think it must have been her oxygen saturation (O2 SAT). Doug then left to get us something to eat. Neither of us had eaten since noon, and it was now after 8:00 p.m. I waited in recovery for the nurses to bring me my baby. Finally after what seemed like an eternity, one of the on call pediatricians came to talk to me. He said there was a problem with the oxygen levels in Nicole's blood, but they did not know why. I was told the neonatologist would meet with us after he had the results of some tests.

At about 9:30, I got a call from the lobby. A sergeant who worked with my husband wanted to know how things were going and said he had brought some food for Doug. Since Doug had gone to get us food, he decided to wait. Just after Doug's arrival, the neonatologist came into the recovery room wanting to talk to us privately.

In a room down the hall, we were told they thought Nicole had a congenital heart disease known as transposition of the great arteries. The doctor told us they could not be sure. Darnell did not have the proper equipment to give a definite diagnosis. The doctor had already called for a dust-off (medical evacuation) helicopter to come from Wilford Hall Medical Center at Lackland Air Force Base in San Antonio. He explained the dangers of the flight and gave us the papers to sign. The doctor then went on to explain transposition of the great arteries, which is when the aorta and pulmonary arteries are switched. The oxygenated blood from Nicole's lungs was being pumped back to her lungs, instead of going through the aorta and out to her body. We were told that the only thing keeping her alive were the typical newborn holes in the heart which close shortly after birth. They put her on prostaglandin to keep these holes open. We asked if we could see her. The doctor then escorted us to the Neonatal Intensive Care Unit (NICU). We were there only a short time when we were asked to leave so that they could do a shift change. The doctor said that they would bring her by my room before transferring her to San Antonio.

When we left the NICU, the sergeant was waiting in the hall. Doug told him what was happening. He said he would contact the unit first sergeant and let him know about Nicole. When the recovery room nurse called the ward to get me a room, she made sure they gave me a private room. Most of the postnatal rooms at Darnell are dual rooms with mothers having their babies in the room with them. Normal hospital policy also requires the husbands to leave the ward by 10:00 p.m., but Doug was allowed to stay until Nicole left the hospital.

Sometime around 2:00 a.m., the doctor introduced us to the pediatrician from Wilford Hall and the two nurses who would escort Nicole to San Antonio. We were told that there was a change of plans. The dust-off helicopter had been grounded due to weather conditions in San Antonio. Nicole would be making her trip down to San Antonio by ambulance. I felt that this was for the best because it removed the risk of damage to her lungs due to the flying altitude. Driving did mean one more hour outside of a hospital. At that time a nurse came in and stated that I could not leave the hospital until six hours after birth, but highly recommended I stay until morning.

I received a call around 6:30 a.m. from San Antonio saying Nicole was safely at Wilford Hall and would receive her echocardiogram in a couple of hours. Sometime after 8:00 a.m. a midwife brought my release papers, and someone from the Red Cross came into the room. I really do not remember what they said; all I wanted was to be in San Antonio. When Doug arrived he said he had talked to the first sergeant who gave Doug permissive temporary duty (TDY) to go to San Antonio so he would not have to use all of his leave. This meant that we would have to wait around town for a while so the paperwork could be signed by the chain of command. We then went home to pack and wait.

At home I noticed my mom had already packed for my other children. My mom, grandma, and great aunt were all ready to go with us. I grabbed some clothes for myself. Not knowing how long to pack for, I forgot a few important items. I tried very hard not to think about that empty bassinet sitting next to my bed, and if I was even going to use it.

A neighbor from across the street came to give some words of encouragement and said she would keep an eye on the house. The sergeant from the night before was also there trying to get to know the dog so he could come and feed him. Finally around noon the papers were all signed. Doug just needed to go to the company and get them. Doug was only able to get ten days TDY and would then start using leave. The first sergeant tried to get us a guaranteed room in the Lackland transient lodging facilities (TLF) but was told it was first-come-first-serve basis. We called Wilford Hall to let them know we were on our way and would be away from the phone. They confirmed the diagnosis of transposition of the great arteries. They said Nicole needed to be transferred to University of Texas Medical Center in San Antonio for surgery, and they needed permission. Doug gave them oral permission so she would be at University by the time we got to San Antonio. He was also given University's phone number.

Upon arriving in San Antonio, we got rooms and called for directions to the hospital. It was after 6:00 p.m. when we finally got to the hospital; I thought we would never make it. The first place we went was the NICU where we were shocked to discover that not only was Nicole not there, but they did not even know who she was! Then another nurse said she was probably in the Pediatric Surgical Intensive Care Unit (PSCU) at the other end of the hall. So off we went in search of our daughter.

When we got to Nicole's room, she was no longer on a respirator. A pediatrician and cardiologist were waiting to talk with us. We were told that Dr. John Calhoon, who would be her surgeon, felt there was no big rush to do her surgery; it could wait until Monday. Nicole would be having an atrial switch. Dr. Calhoon wanted us to have the weekend to get to know her. I was given the opportunity to nurse Nicole for the first time; however, she was not interested in eating at all. The next morning she was back on the respirator. Nicole had some apnea, a side effect of the prostaglandin.

Sunday, all those who had come to San Antonio with us visited Nicole. I know more family would have liked to have been there for us, but being in the Army means family is not always close. The reason my mom and grandma had come was to take care of Winona and John while I was in the hospital.

We were restricted to only one visitor at a time. Winona, our oldest, was very happy she finally got to see her baby sister but was upset she could not hold Nicole. We did not take John up to see his sister. John, an active two year old.boy, would not be quiet or still enough even for a short visit. Both Winona and John visited Nicole when she was post-op.

Monday was Nicole's big day. We decided Doug would get up and go to University to meet with the surgeon and sit with Nicole until the anesthesiologist came to get her. I stayed with the older children so they could sleep and have some time with me. After Nicole was taken to surgery Doug came back and picked up the whole family. The rest of the family would wait in and around the van while we waited in her room for news. While waiting we watched as the nurse set up IV after IV. I think this was good, as it helped prepare us a little for how she would look, thus we were not shocked by all the tubes. I remember getting only two updates saying the surgery was going well.

Sometime after noon we were told Nicole was on her way up, and we would have to leave the room until she was stabilized. A nurse gave us a place in the hall to stand, so we could see Nicole, as they rushed by to her room. Ten minutes later Dr. Calhoon came and took us to see Nicole. The first thing he said was, "I bet you have never seen her so pink." All I could think of was to thank God she made it and to pray for her recovery. Her little face was so puffy it looked twice its normal size. The nurse said it would probably get worse before it got better. We stayed with Nicole for about half an hour and then went to call Doug's parents to let them know she had made it through the surgery and was doing great. The doctors and nurse said she would be sedated for the rest of the day. We went to the van to let the others know Nicole had come through just fine. They did not think the news could be good because we had been gone so long. Everyone was relieved.

Now, as hard as it was to leave our little baby, we had to make a quick run back to Ft. Hood. My grandma had to get her car from our house to go home. We had asked my sister if she could come and help mom with our two children. We would meet her, and she could follow us down to San Antonio. When we got home, there were a lot of things we had to do in a very short time. We had to call CHAMPUS (Civilian Health And Medical Plan Uniformed Services) because there was a message on our machine. Then we needed to contact the birth clerk at Darnell so we could complete Nicole's birth certificate form. Next Nicole needed to be registered with DEERS (Defense Eligibility Enrollment Record System), otherwise the military would not cover her medical costs. We also decided to enroll her in Tri-Care Prime (a private company working under contract with CHAMPUS). Tri-Care assures timely medical care even with military providers. It was mid-afternoon the following day before we were able to head back to San Antonio.

When we got back to the hospital I expected to find my baby's face still puffy and swollen. Instead she was beautiful and looked better than before her surgery. Wide awake, Nicole's eyes were open for the first time since she had left Darnell. Recovery went quickly, and there was only one small setback when Nicole developed some fluid on her left lung and had to have a chest tube for a few days.

It seemed as if the doctors and nurses liked to play guessing games. Every day when we arrived, they would ask us what was different about Nicole. We would quickly answer with what various IV lines had been removed. Finally only the oxygen had to be weaned in order for Nicole to go home. The doctor wanted Nicole's O2 SATs to stay in the mid 90s, without additional oxygen before we left. By Sunday night, six days post-op, Nicole's oxygen was turned all the way down. Every time Nicole's oxygen was turned off, her O2 SATs would start to drop into the 80s within twenty minutes, necessitating the use of oxygen. The next morning when we arrived at the hospital Nicole was not in her room, and they were obviously getting it ready for a new patient. My first thought was panic, but a nurse quickly told us she had been moved to an intermediate room.

Around noon we were told Nicole would be released that day. We had already been given instructions on infant CPR; all we needed was instructions for her medication. Our baby, who had just had open heart surgery eight days before, was going home on just one medicine, Lasix. We needed to bring her back to University Hospital for a follow-up with Dr. Calhoon on Friday and start her normal well-baby checkups.

Nicole's pediatrician was great. I chose him as her regular pediatrician, one of the benefits of Tri-Care Prime. With Tri-Care, children with special needs could have pediatricians assigned to them. Nicole's pediatrician is Army Captain Timothy Hart. He coordinated her first follow-up with her pediatric cardiologist at Wilford Hall. Nicole's pediatric cardiologist is Air Force Colonel John Brownlee.

Nicole was taken off Lasix at her post-surgical follow-up at University. She has not been on any regular medication since. Nicole's weight gain was very slow at first with a few slips backwards at times. We were making weekly trips to the doctor, but things have greatly improved. She now weighs over twenty pounds and is not due to see any doctor until her eighteen month checkup. Nicole sees a cardiologist every six months.

All during Nicole's pre- and post-surgical hospital stay, we ran up phone bills by keeping family up-to-date. That's one of the hardest things about being in the Army—you rarely get to live near family, making it difficult to lean on them for support. We were lucky to have my mom nearby, she only lives 500 miles from Killeen. Doug's parents were unable to make the 1,200 mile trip from their home, but they did help us a great deal with some of the finances. Even with the great military insurance coverage, the cost of room and board is not covered. There have even been times when I have wondered if the insurance was going to cover everything. After a year, and many phone calls to both University Hospital and CHAMPUS/Tri-Care, the bills have finally been paid.

It would have been nice to have known about The Fisher House, a military program similar to the Ronald McDonald Houses. The Fisher Houses are located next to major military medical centers and some VA Hospitals. The cost for staying in the Fisher House varies depending on its location. It would also be nice if military hospital personnel could talk with the parents of newborns who have unexpected problems and are being transferred far away. The support person could inform parents of programs like the Fisher House. This person could also help coordinate things like TDY and special TDY pay, something else we learned about a little too late. Sometimes it seems the Army includes just about everything in its "Don't Ask/Don't Tell Policy." Parents who do not have advanced warning need someone to tell them these things without question.

The scary thing is Doug is being transferred to Korea for a year on a remote tour. We have decided it would be best for me to move to my home town to be closer to my mom. Mom can help when I need someone to babysit when Nicole has appointments out of town. So far all of Nicole's cardiology appointments have been in San Antonio, making child care difficult. I have talked to the pediatrician at McConnel Air Force Base, the nearest military facility to my parents home. I told her I would hate to change cardiologists for just one year. The pediatrician agreed and said they always have the option of referring to a military provider, but I may have to cover the transportation myself. That means a 600 mile drive for a checkup. Military life means constant changes, it would be nice to maintain some stability for Nicole.

Lou Anne and Nicole

Overseas with the Air Force

By: Shiloh Hanshew

In 1995 my husband was stationed at Pope Air Force Base in North Carolina. He got orders to RAF Molesworth, England in April. Our family would arrive in October. In June I returned to our home town of

Corvallis, Oregon, where I found out I was pregnant. I went to my doctor in August and remember how relieved I was when I heard the heartbeat, healthy and strong. I already had a son who was a little over a year old at the time. He weighed nine pounds, ten ounces when he was born, so my biggest concerns were for my weight gain and the baby's weight gain. I was afraid it would be eleven pounds or more!

We arrived in England on October 2, 1995. At the time I had still only been to the doctor that once and remember feeling an urgency to get a doctor just to be sure all was well. I wondered if something might be wrong, but felt confident that the baby was healthy.

I went to an Air Force doctor within the month and found out I had to decide whether to deliver at the Air Force hospital, a long drive from our location, or at Hinchingbrooke, a local civilian British Hospital. I decided on Hinchingbrooke.

The Air Force, as I have been informed, has a general policy of not doing ultrasounds unless they feel a medical need for them, but because Hinchingbrooke required them of all delivering mothers, I was scheduled for one. I went for my first ultrasound on November 8th. Everything seemed fine, but I was told that the baby was in a bad position to view the heart clearly. I went back in two weeks only to be told the same thing. I started to feel a little nervous. They took me into another room to a more advanced ultrasound machine. I watched and still remember looking at the heart as the technicians studied it. I thought maybe something wasn't "right" about the way it looked but felt eased when they reassured me that the baby was in a difficult viewing position. I was again told I would have to come back later for another attempt. I felt annoyed that I had to return if everything was fine like they told me. I was confident that it was fine and saw no need to keep doing this if indeed all was well.

The Friday before Thanksgiving weekend, I received a call from the head OB at Upwood, the Air Force clinic, saying that I had to go to Great Ormond Street Children's Hospital in London on Monday. Throughout the weekend I feared for what could possibly be wrong. Luckily we'd made many friends in the short time we'd been in England and were reassured by them that all was fine.

I remember the day so clearly that it all seems like a nightmare happening to someone else. We left our son, Joshua, with a sitter, and my husband, Scott, and I rode the train, leisurely enjoying our ride and trying to refrain from letting our imaginations run wild. When in London, we decided to walk to the hospital. We went to the normal prenatal clinic for the ultrasound but found we were scheduled with a pediatric cardiologist. I was starting to worry a little but trying to hold myself back. The doctor had been called to an emergency, so we were told to come back in about half an hour. We went to the cafeteria, ate a little and returned feeling the need to find out what was happening.

The Heart of a Mother

I can still picture the sick heart babies that were hooked up to machines passing by us while we waited. I remember thinking or saying how happy I was that I was having a healthy baby.

When the doctor was studying the echocardiogram image, we could tell he was looking for something specific. It seemed that he knew before we even came in the hospital what the diagnosis was. He told us he would answer questions after the echocardiogram.

In his office he informed us our child had a serious heart defect. "The baby has tricuspid atresia, meaning absence of the tricuspid valve. Its heart only has three chambers." I was in shock. I couldn't believe he was serious. He drew us a diagram. I remember little about the heart from studies in school, but I remembered it had four chambers. How would this child possibly survive with only three? What about the valve? Maybe they could build a chamber and a valve? Would this baby need a heart transplant? What did I do wrong to make this happen? So many questions raced through my mind.

The doctor told me it was not a result of anything I did. That as far as they know, there is no known cause. He told us there are palliative or alleviative surgeries but no cure. They strongly suggested we terminate the pregnancy.

It was explained to us that the baby's quality of life could be good if it survived everything. All I could hear was "if it survived." He continued to tell us that the baby would require at least two surgeries before the age of two. He gave us some statistics: an 80% chance of surviving the second and most serious of the surgeries (which we've come to know as the Fontan), an annual increase of 5% that the child would die from complications, and a 50% chance of surviving to be a teenager after the surgeries were completed. I felt totally devastated. I couldn't believe that they were putting the decision of my child's life into my hands. After hearing all those numbers and considerations, I really didn't know what to think.

We were asked to make our decision within the week. If we decided to keep the baby, we would need to return for an amniocentesis. He told us that there are often other defects in a baby with a heart defect and that if the baby had other problems it would have less of a chance for survival or quality of life.

We left that hospital as different people. We walked in thinking we had a healthy baby but now had to decide if the baby would even be born. I am without words to describe the weight I felt on my shoulders and the pain it brought with it. As we walked back to the train station, I watched moms with their babies and thought how lucky they were to have healthy babies. How lucky they were not to have to make a choice about whether their child should have to live a life of possible suffering or whether they should spare all parties involved of the tragedy that may lie ahead.

I have been a Christian as long as I can remember and had thought I had the abortion issue clear in my mind. My ideas were challenged that day. Our future had already been changed forever, whether we chose to continue with the pregnancy or not. How would we afford the hospital trips to London and child care for our son? Would the Air Force even let Scott have time off to go to London? What kind of life would this child have? What if it had other health problems? Would it be right for me to keep it alive, possibly causing the child suffering in the end anyway? Would it be better to protect it from the pain and suffering now, or give it a chance? I felt confused.

When we picked up our son, I cried and said, "At least we have Joshua." We went home, and I called the Family Advocacy nurse who visited me previously for support. She called the base chaplain, with my consent, and he called to tell us he would come over that night.

The chaplain gave me the best advice I've ever been given. He assured us that no matter what our choice, he would be there to help us through it, but that first we should educate ourselves the best we could so we could make a well-informed decision. He also suggested we get a second opinion, even if we had to return to the United States to do it.

After he left we felt like we could think clearly. We had a mission: get as much information as we could in a short period of time. We decided to keep the baby. I was sure I'd feel guilty if I were to terminate. We felt throughout the pregnancy that the baby was a gift from God and that God should decide when the baby should go. But I had a new respect for parents that decide otherwise because I knew that for us to keep the baby was a gamble.

In the following days, we called for further advice from the head OB at Upwood. Our calls were unreturned, but we had to make decisions quickly. Scott's first sergeant stepped in and had the doctor call us. When he did call, he was not supportive and said, "No matter what you decide, you have to go to London." I wasn't going to just take that as the final word. I told him to send his report about me to Dr. Nelson at the Molesworth clinic, as I would be seeing him for further care.

I didn't even know Dr. Nelson but had heard his name from a friend at our church in Oregon when I was there earlier in the year. We called him, and he saw us the next day at closing so we would have his full attention without interruptions. He answered our questions as best he could. When we asked about getting a second opinion, he got us up to the head OB at the Air Force hospital in Lakenheath, who had us on our way to Wilford Hall Medical Center, an Air Force hospital in San Antonio, only a few days later.

Military flights don't work the same as civilian. We flew to Germany, where we spent the night. The next day we flew to Andrews AFB in Maryland, where we were to stay in the hospital for four days until the next flight to San Antonio came through. Luckily, one of Scott's former co-workers lived near enough to let us stay with his family until the last night. Finally we went to San Antonio. All of the flights were primitive in comparison to commercial airplanes. The C-9s were nice, but we sat backwards from commercial flights. The C-141 we flew in over the ocean was loud, stripped of internal lining and uncomfortable.

At Wilford Hall we saw Dr. Barth, who did an echocardiogram, and then had Dr. Brownlee, the pediatric cardiologist, come in to see what he thought. He confirmed the diagnosis but informed us the odds we were given were outdated and had been improved. Although we knew we had no promises, we immediately felt hope was renewed.

While we were there, they also did an amniocentesis so we could prepare ourselves if there were any other problems. We were relieved weeks later when we found out all else was fine. I was advised to stay in San Antonio until delivery so they could take care of the baby after birth.

Out of leave time, Scott had to return to England. With help from his supervisors and the doctors, he was able to get an Exceptional Family Member Program, or EFMP, reassignment. Within a month he was reassigned to Kelly AFB in San Antonio. I was in the Temporary Lodging Facility for three months, one of them without my husband, although our son had been with me the whole time. We had no car privileges and had to depend on an unreliable base shuttle for transportation.

After Scott got his reassignment, we were sure we would have out-of-turn base housing on Lackland or Kelly so we'd be close to the hospital for our baby. We were misled. We fell between the cracks, the same as it seemed we had done so many times before. We couldn't get base housing on Lackland because we were at Kelly. We couldn't get on Kelly because they only had a clinic, and we had to have need for the clinic over the hospital. Lackland housing told us they might consider us if we went through the application process at Kelly and brought evidence of rejection to them afterwards. That was only for us to be considered, not approved. My doctor wrote letters advising that we be near Wilford Hall. We never got base housing.

The last months of my pregnancy, I worried if my baby would survive. Instead of anxiously awaiting the birth of my baby, I feared it. I felt that as long as the baby was inside me it was safe, but there was no way of telling how the heart would work after birth.

On March 19, 1996, after only four and a half hours of labor, Megan EmmaLee Hanshew was born weighing six pounds fourteen ounces, measuring twenty inches long. Though her delivery was treated as a normal delivery, she did have her own pediatric staff on hand through the birth. She seemed to be fine from what I could hear across the room. After only minutes, they took her away, stopping only to let me peek at her a second before they left for the Neonatal Intensive Care Unit. It was a bittersweet moment.

Megan remained under observation for three days before I could take her home. Wilford Hall allowed me to stay in the hospital until she left instead of releasing me right away. I appreciated that. Soon after release we went to see the cardiologist and were told that Megan would go into congestive heart failure (CHF) in a few weeks. He told us she would have a shunt put in by Dr. Calhoon when she went into CHF.

When Megan was three weeks old, we took her to the ER at Wilford Hall, and she was admitted. She was eating only one or two ounces every three to four hours and breathing eighty breaths a minute. She stayed at Wilford Hall for a week and then went to a civilian doctor and hospital for the specialized care she needed. A couple of days before the surgery, we were told the plan changed and that they would do the pulmonary artery (PA) banding instead of the shunt. The doctors debated about it and decided on this because they felt she was too sick to do the shunt. I always heard the PA band was riskier because it wasn't an exact science. They put it on and hope it's tight enough but not too tight. The banding would be done by Dr. Rouse, a doctor I'd never heard of before. I was confused but trusted Megan's doctor.

To top it all off, Tri-Care, the military HMO, was telling us it was an elective surgery. My daughter was in a hospital bed dying, and they were telling me the surgery was elective. They approved it but canceled it somewhere between that day and the next when Megan had her surgery. We had to make a lot of calls to get things worked out, and it took a long time. I know now to write down whom I talk to, when I talk to them and what is said. I keep detailed records of phone calls.

Megan's surgery went well. Pastor Boatrz, from our church, and my Aunt JoAnn sat with us through the surgery. They also visited us while Megan was in the hospital. We only had five visitors while we were there. I wish we had had more friends and family nearby.

The only complications were during the first night and the next morning. Megan seemed to have a bad reaction to morphine in the night, and they had to counteract it, leaving her without pain relief. They gave her a dropper of over-the-counter Tylenol. She had been extubated soon after returning from surgery but cried all night from the pain, leading her to be reintubated the next morning. She grew stronger after a few days and was able to be extubated again. We took her home a week after the surgery.

Dr. Rouse couldn't have done a better job. Megan grew well until she was about six months old when her growth tapered off. It was time to talk about the bi-directional Glenn, her next surgery. Although we were grateful to Dr. Rouse, we couldn't stop thinking about how much we heard about Dr. Calhoon and decided to go to him for following surgeries. She had her bi-directional Glenn done on December 3, 1996 and didn't even need to go on the heart-bypass machine. She had problems getting off the respirator like before, but she was still home in a week.

We worked hard to get things done early with Tri-Care before her bi-directional Glenn, and again, it was approved one day and canceled the next. We are still trying to work that out with them. It doesn't seem right that anyone going through something like this should have to fight with an HMO, too. I dread having to go through that again after her next surgery. One of the hardest parts of being in the military is being away from family, especially when things are going rough and you feel like you need support. I've felt alone through a lot of what we've been through, and last year I decided to turn that loneliness into something positive.

I tried to start a support group at Lackland for parents of children with heart defects, but in the military, there is so much red tape to go through that I decided to search in the civilian world. Brenda Seidel, one of Dr. Calhoon's nurses, got some hospital staff together and helped me start Thumpers Support Group. I am determined to do what I can to help other parents, especially military parents. Many military families get uprooted from wherever they are to go to a place where they don't know anyone, and then have to muster up the strength to get through a recent diagnosis, surgery, or death without the support of family or friends. I decided to provide the kind of moral support needed for these military families and civilians, as well.

Megan has nice round, healthy arms and legs. She started walking recently and does everything in her power to keep up with her three-year-old brother. My biggest concern are cyanotic spells, where she turns a little blue for a few minutes, then returns to normal. *

I have a lot of hope for her future. I think back to when the doctor in England gave us the choice to terminate the pregnancy. We've had an abundance of trials since then, some of which I've only touched on here. I've seen my daughter balance between life and death, but even after all we've been through, I can't imagine life without her. If she were to go tomorrow, I would still be thankful for what I have had.

*Editor's Note: Megan went home only four days after her Fontan and now, a year later, is still doing well. She still appears cyanotic with her SATs usually 80-85 (but sometimes in the high 70s).

Megan Hanshew

Grandmothers' Stories

As a child, my vision of a grandmother was an American stereotypical myth. I thought grandmothers were supposed to be white-haired little old ladies who baked cookies, hosted tea parties for their granddaughters and filled their houses with handmade afghans and knickknacks in every nook and cranny. Grandmothers had sweet dispositions, big soft hands and bodies and smelled of powder and love.

As I grew older I soon discovered that many of my preconceived, romantic notions were just that—preconceived. My own grandmothers defied the myth, debunking my idealistic fantasies. My grandmothers are actually very young and both had daughters close to my age. I now know that I will not really understand the role of Grandmother until I become one myself. The same is true for becoming a mother. As the mother of two boys, I find my opinion about motherhood changing as I mature and grow. Undoubtedly the same will happen with my views regarding the status of Grandmother.

One thing I have learned already is that being a grandmother is not just about spoiling grandchildren. It is not about retiring, getting old and baking cookies, either. Being a grandmother is much more important than that. A grandmother is often the one person who knows everybody's birthday, who remembers special things often forgotten, whose hands can cool feverish foreheads and whose heart helps mend her children's sorrows—no matter how old they are.

Our mothers have an often unappreciated ability to provide love and support in the most desperate of times. With a baby in the hospital facing open-heart surgery, I was beside myself with worry and fear, but my mother was by my side the entire time. Without even speaking she knew how to calm me; with only a look she could comfort; and with the gentlest of spirits she willed my baby to live. As mother and grandmother she played numerous roles to me, as well as to my baby, her youngest grandchild. She did it seemingly without effort, but that is part of the beauty of the situation. I know what a challenge it was for her to be there and to remain the constant source of strength she was.

When a baby has a heart defect the situation touches many more people than just the parents. The grandparents are often deeply affected. The following four grandmothers' stories share insight into that special Grandmother role and exemplify how the best do it right. This book is dedicated to my own mother and mothers everywhere who strive to protect and love their children. A grandmother's hug, a mother's touch, a baby's laugh—these are the gifts that make life bearable. They make for our happiest memories.

Part of the Team

By: Carol Self

I do not know where to begin with this story, only where it ends. Our story is one of encouragement. Ben is our miracle boy considering when this happened and the mind set of that time.

My daughter and I come from a long line of one child, daughters only. We were thrilled to find that she would have a second child, a boy.

My grandson, Ben, was born in Orlando, Florida in April of 1987, and what a beautiful boy he was. It was an uneventful pregnancy and normal delivery . . . no indication that anything might be wrong. Within hours of his birth, he became blue and was diagnosed with HLHS. He was placed on life support, and we were told that nothing could be done but that they would like to send him to the University of Florida, Gainesville. Ben was airlifted there, and we were again told he had HLHS and that nothing could be done. They suggested we take him off life support and allow him to die. One doctor, as an afterthought, mentioned that Dr. Norwood in Philadelphia was doing some experimental surgery on these HLHS babies but that he was not getting good results, and if Ben did survive the surgery, his "quality of life" was questionable.

I cannot begin to describe how I felt to see my only daughter in so much pain. She and her husband were numb with grief. My ". . . and they lived happily ever after" dream for them was collapsing. I felt so helpless. I could cry with her, but as her mom, I could not make the pain go away.

Because I was the grandmother of a child with HLHS I think things were doubly traumatic for me. I wanted to protect my daughter from life's injustices. I wanted her pain to go away. I felt every pain she suffered and added my own as a grandmother.

Well, they threw us a bone, and, of course, we elected to send Ben to CHOP (Children's Hospital of Philadelphia). After another airlift, Dr. Norwood himself operated on Ben for Stage I, the Norwood procedure. He had no complications and came home after about a week.

There was only one pediatric cardiologist in Orlando who supported and believed in the procedure, and he was great to us. He had never treated a post-op HLHS patient, and we became partners to prove this could be done. Ben's post-op Stage I was uneventful, and he had a heart cath at twelve months (we sure did a lot of traveling back and forth to Philadelphia from Orlando).

About this time my daughter's marriage failed, and because her insurance company went bankrupt, she also lost any insurance coverage for Ben. She, Ben and his older sister, Ashley, moved in with me and my husband to help make ends meet and to help pay off the huge debt from the Stage I surgery and catheterization.

At this time my role as "Grandmother" changed. I felt my role became one of co-parent because my daughter and her children lived with me. I also became my daughter's cheerleader, financial advisor, confidant and more.

At age eighteen months, Ben's condition started to deteriorate, indicating it was time for Stage II, a modified Fontan. Because we had no insurance, the hospital wanted $100,000 up front! Local and state agencies turned us down for assistance because she had a decent job, as if she could ever pay that amount of money in her lifetime! As Ben's condition worsened and we searched even more for some financial help, a local television station began coverage of our story and a local state representative became involved. The story affected the governor of Florida, who agreed that this story was ridiculous. He made a few phone calls, and suddenly, the very agencies who had turned us down were calling and vying to see who was going to help us!

Within days we were on a plane to Philly for the dreaded Stage II. At that time there were only two surgeries done, and the second one was the dreaded surgery, the one most likely not to be survived. Complications post-op could be stroke and fluid accumulation around the lungs and/or heart. At the time of Ben's Stage II, Dr. Norwood was experimenting with tapping the fluid and replacing a certain percentage of it with IV albumen.

Ben did well during surgery but of course got the dreaded fluid post-op. At one point the doctors tapped the most fluid from around his lungs that had ever been taken from a patient. They told us to prepare for a three-month hospital stay but Ben, all of a sudden, stopped producing fluid and went home in about thirty days!

Post-op he was immediately pink and much more energetic. And he has not lost any of that energy yet. Our cardiologist checks Ben every six months, and we laughingly say that he checks Ben and treats us. Ben has had no complications over the years and is on no heart medications.

About that "quality of life" issue: Ben did not walk or talk before his Stage II surgery. At birth he had some seizures, and I understand some of the medications they gave him also could potentially cause some neurological/developmental problems. When we returned to Orlando after Stage II, Ben was tested and showed developmental delays and was placed in an intervention program with a United Cerebral Palsy Clinic. He does not have CP, but they have wonderful therapy programs including physical, occupational and speech therapy. He stayed in that program for about a year and a half and then went into the Orange County Public School system program for physically impaired children. Because Ben's condition was so rare, the school did not know what to expect from him medically and felt he would benefit from the daily medical monitoring and the therapies offered there, again physical, occupational and speech. What a wonderful program!

Ben is definitely delayed, testing a steady two years below his chronological age but making steady progress. At age ten he is testing at age eight, and at this age, it is fairly noticeable. At age thirty, testing at age twenty-eight won't matter.

He has been diagnosed with attention deficit/hyperactive disorder (ADHD) and takes Ritalin. Because of the medication, Ben's appetite is poor and he is a rather tall, thin boy. He has no physical limitations related to his heart and goes from sun up to sun down. He makes good grades and loves the computer and Nintendo games.

To look at Ben, you would have no idea there is or was anything wrong. He has a zest for life, and all who come in contact with him fall in love. He has dimples and a quick grin.

It took several years for us to get over what we had been through with him, but now we seldom mention his problem and tend to forget that he is a cardiac child. He is just a normal little boy—a pain in the neck sometimes.

I love Ben more than anyone could every know, and I love my daughter for being strong and making it through this tragedy. When a parent finds out their baby has HLHS, they are understandably frightened. I feel that the role of the grandparents at this time should be one of support and understanding, as well as providing the same sense of stability given to them as a child. As a team we should all love the baby, spoil him and just take it one day at a time. When a complication arises, just move ahead. We saw kids overcome every complication conceivable and survive. God does not give these children to people who cannot handle it.

We have seen so many changes in the field of pediatric cardiology since Ben was first diagnosed. Now there are centers all over the world doing the Norwood procedure and saving more and more children's lives.

I feel that we grandparents are an important part of the team necessary to help our children and grandchildren survive. Together we can make a difference.

Ben Agosta

Editor's Note: Ben is now twelve years old and continues to do well.

Allowing Jane to Focus on Marcus

By: Clarice Warrick

I am a registered nurse. I married Francis Bewley Warrick, M.D. who is an internal medicine physician, partly retired. I have worked in physician offices, a small community hospital, a county health department and for the past twenty-two years in hospital infection control and education. I have seen sick, malformed, retarded, and dying children throughout my career, so I think I had more preparation for what was about to happen to my daughter than many other people.

Shortly after her son Marcus was born, Jane called to tell us (Grandpa Bewley and me) that he had arrived, his weight and length, hair color and that the nurse had heard a murmur during the initial assessment. She explained to Jane that murmurs are not unusual and not to worry. When Jane told me this, my nurse's instincts went on alert. I know that many newborns have murmurs that are meaningless, but no one in my family or Bill's family had been born with a newborn murmur.

A few hours later, Jane called back in tears. She said that when Marcus was circumcised, he turned very blue. The pediatrician, ordered an echocardiogram, consulted with a Scott & White Hospital cardiologist, called Children's Hospital in Austin for another consultation and made arrangements for Marcus to be flown to Austin for evaluation and care. The two older boys, ages two and six needed immediate care because Jane and Bill were driving to Austin, about an hour away. The boys had seen Marcus, and they had also seen how upset their parents were. We immediately made arrangements to fly to Texas to help everyone: Jane, Bill, Justis, Lucas, the other grandparents, and all of Jane's friends in Temple. Fortunately, Jane and Bill have friends who took care of the boys until we arrived.

My personal feelings were multiple. My first concern was for Jane, my child. She was so distraught and intense and sounded as though the possibility of a bad outcome—death—was more than she could bear. Understandably she wanted life for the older boys to go on as normally as possible. I felt inadequate to give her all the comfort, support and encouragement she needed. I could only reassure her, based on the very good prognosis Marcus' physicians had given her, that Marcus might have a rough time but that he was a strong baby and had excellent chances of doing well. I also kept telling her that we would do whatever had to be done. I took as my primary role in this crisis as caretaker for the older boys.

Jane was concerned that I could not take time from my job to stay with the boys until Marcus could come home. Again and again I reassured her that I would do whatever she needed. My job was less important than her situation. Fortunately, my boss supported and encouraged me to take care of my Texas family first, then my job.

Grandpa Bewley was a real trooper and a rock for all of us. He ran a zillion errands—to the grocery store and to school to pick up Justis. He cooked, washed dishes, helped with homework and watched the boys play. Everyday I felt grateful that he was a part of the team.

My second concern was Marcus. I did not have a strong emotional attachment to Marcus yet, but I wanted the very best for him. I was prepared for the worst short-term scenario as well as the long one ahead. My primary concern was "being there" for Jane, Bill, Justis and Lucas, especially if Marcus should have serious complications or die.

Since I work in hospital infection control, I was keenly aware of the infection risks as well as many other complications associated with being in a hospital and having surgery. My husband (Grandpa Bewley) supported us with his medical knowledge and provided emotional support for me. He, too, prepared to deal with whatever happened to Marcus.

The most difficult thing for me was watching all that Jane was going through. She is very intense about her babies and their well-being. In addition to the situation with Marcus, she wanted to continue nursing. The breast pumps she used were not strong enough to prevent nipple clogging. She developed mastitis, ran a high fever and was put on antibiotics. Finding an adequate breast pump was an adventure, following directions in suburban Austin at night. The lactation specialist at Children's Hospital was a lifesaver.

I suppose that because of my medical background, I did not have any great difficulties understanding what was happening to Marcus. Keeping up with two boys, cooking, laundry, minimal housekeeping and getting enough sleep were my biggest challenges.

I am very grateful for the medical expertise and surgical skills that made Marcus able to live a normal life. We were told early on that with the planned procedures and no major complications, he could expect to live to be a grandfather. As he grows and develops, his pediatric cardiologist discusses physical limitations and suggests specific sports for Marcus. So far, he is a normal four year old. Marcus has some color changes when he is cold, but Jane and Bill are easy about letting him experience the activities in which he is interested.

My fears regarding Marcus are very much the same as the fears I have regarding all of my grandchildren: major accidents, illness or injury that could result in physical or mental handicap or death. As long as Marcus is on an anticoagulant, hemorrhage is a reality. I know that he has risks of carditis (infection in the heart) because of the surgeries, but I do not have what I would call extraordinary fears about him.

This is the first major birth defect I have experienced in my family and in Jane's father's family. Seven other grandchildren were healthy newborns. Only my profession gave me any preparation for any kind of congenital defect and fortunately Marcus' is not of a genetic origin.

The rest of Jane and Bill's family were concerned, but because of the distance between Indiana and Texas, they worried at home. Jane's father and Bill's parents and sisters called Jane at the hospital or me in Temple. Bill's stepmother is also a registered nurse. When I talked to her I could use medical terms, and she would interpret to her family.

In the end I think it was helpful that some of Jane and Bill's family members had a medical background. We were able to explain and understand what was going on with Marcus. We were also prepared to help Jane and Bill regardless of the outcome of the surgeries. I feel, though, that my medical knowledge was not as important as the knowledge I have being Jane's mother. I knew my daughter, and I knew how to help her. By taking care of my other grandchildren, Jane was free to be with Marcus and focus her care and attention on the child who needed her most.

I am lucky to have had a job where my employer supported my

decision to be with my daughter. Because we have weathered this crisis together, we are bonded in a whole new way. I have a very special relationship with my grandchildren, and I am delighted to see how advances in medical science have given Marcus a chance to share his life with us.

Clarice and Marcus

Supporting a Mother's Love

By: Linda McAdam

My grandson, Tyler Andrew Prior, was diagnosed with hypoplastic left heart syndrome two weeks before he was born. His parents,

Christine and Mark Prior, went in for a routine sonogram. All prior prenatal examinations were normal and the prior sonogram was unremarkable. During the last exam, they found out the baby's gender— a boy. My son-in-law, Mark, was so proud that he was having another son. During the exam the technician spent a great deal of time examining the heart, but the parents were so overjoyed at seeing their baby boy that they did not notice.

Christine called me at work so happy and excited. She told me they were having a son. I shared her happiness. We went from referring to this new person as "the baby" to "Tyler."

About two hours later, our secretary came to get me in the courtroom (where I am a court reporter) to tell me I had an emergency telephone call from my daughter. When I got on the phone my daughter was crying and distraught. She told me their pediatrician, Dr. Righter, just told her that the baby's left ventricle was not formed. The left ventricle was necessary to pump the blood from the heart into the body. My daughter cried and cried. It broke my heart to see her heartbroken. I tried to encourage her by focusing on the miracles of medical technology and the assurance that Tyler's problem could be fixed.

I immediately told my supervisor and applied for Family Emergency Leave to be used when the baby was born. My supervisor was wonderful and told me I could have all the time I needed.

Christine saw a cardiologist, Dr. Patel, before the baby was born. He examined her, looked at the sonogram, then told Christine and Mark of the three options they could choose from: (1) compassionate care, (2) three-stage operation, (3) heart transplant. He sent them home to discuss the situation before their next appointment. Christine and Mark decided to go with the three-stage operation that day.

Christine's father, Jim, is a big computer buff and he got Christine looking on the Internet to find out what she could about HLHS. Well, through the Internet she found out so much about this condition and shared it with the rest of the family. We all learned together. She eventually met Anna, and then we all had a real person who had experienced the same situation and could share our trials..

Christine researched and found Dr. Bove and the University of Michigan Hospital; he had the best survival rates for performing the three-stage surgery in our area. I was so proud of my daughter for putting her grief and despair aside in order to look for the answers to save her son's life.

Eventually the day came when Tyler was ready to be born. Christine called me at 4:45 a.m. to tell me she was leaving for the hospital. I got up, called my supervisor to let him know I would be off indefinitely, packed my bags, left a note for my neighbor to start feeding the cat, turned down the heat and left.

When I reached my daughter the baby had been born. We all went down to NICU to see him. He was beautiful! To look at him you would never suspect that there was anything wrong. He looked perfect. The next morning a helicopter was sent to pick Tyler up to take him to the University of Michigan Hospital. Christine cried terribly when they whisked her baby away. She was afraid she would never see him again. We assured her that everything would be fine. How difficult for a mother to have to let her baby go! She and Mark left in the car and drove to the University of Michigan Hospital.

Two days later Tyler had the Norwood procedure. It was amazing how much we as a family had learned about the heart and the operative procedures our little one would go through. It was so sad to see him afterwards on a respirator and not be able to pick him up and rock and cradle him. But eventually the respirator came off, and we were able to hold him.

He came home two days after the respirator came off. What a joy it was to take care of him at home. He came home with a feeding tube, two diuretics and baby aspirin. Within two days he was off the feeding tube and fit right in with the family. It is amazing how quickly babies improve when they come home. Hospitals are good when they need specialized care, but nothing can take the place of a mother's love.

When Tyler was three months old, it was time for his second surgery. We were all surprised because he was not expected to have the second procedure until he was six months old. He had outgrown his shunt and needed surgery earlier than expected.

The surgery itself was successful, but Tyler had many problems afterwards. He was on a respirator for over a week, slept for a week, and his head was so swollen because of the increased pressure that he could not open his eyes for a week. We were told that after the second surgery, babies suffer terrible headaches until they become used to the extra pressure in the upper portion of their bodies. Eventually, after two weeks, he was able to come home. We all thought he would progress as well as he did the first time.

When Christine and Mark brought Tyler home, he cried continuously for two days. Christine called the cardiologist on call after the first day, and he recommended Tylenol with Codeine thinking the baby was probably experiencing severe headaches; however on the second day, Tyler was still crying. He had not slept in two days. We were all exhausted and extremely concerned about his well-being. Christine called the cardiologist on call again who said to bring Tyler to the hospital.

Tyler was taken to the children's hospital in the city where he lives. It is a wonderful hospital that is known for its care of sick children; unfortunately, it is not so well-versed in the care and treatment of a child with HLHS. Many mistakes were made in his care until finally my daughter and her husband contacted the University of Michigan

Hospital and talked with the staff. Then, after receiving permission from the insurance company, Tyler was sent by ambulance to Michigan.

The doctors determined that Tyler was going through morphine withdrawal. He was put on Methadone and weaned down a little every day until finally he was weaned completely. After a week and a half, Tyler came home to finish the weaning process. This time he was our normal Tyler and progressed wonderfully.

Tyler is the joy of all our lives. Now seven months old, he laughs, coos, loves his brother and his dogs, recognizes his family members and is typical for his age. Amazingly, sick children are so compassionate and have such loving dispositions. They are a lesson to all of us. They bear their burdens and show such joy and happiness to the world around them.

As the grandmother of a child with HLHS, I can only say that it is very important to be available for your child in any manner necessary during this trying time. They will need your encouragement; they will need a shoulder to cry on; they will need financial help. They will look to you for approval for their decisions; they will need help with their other children; they will need your faith when theirs is almost gone.

The greatest gift we can give is to serve one another. What a privilege it has been for me to serve my daughter, her husband, and my two grandsons. When I look at my grandson, Tyler, I see the promise of a beautiful life, a wonderful future and all the joys that any grandparent shares in the development of "our" babies. Share with your children whatever decision they make concerning their HLHS baby—through thick and thin. That is what makes a family and gives us our strength.

Being Strong for Teresa

By: Joanne Clarkson

My grandson, Matthew, is the greatest gift in the world. How I love him! And when he holds my hand or gives me a hug and kiss, I cannot even begin to describe the feeling!

We arrived a few hours after Matthew was born. I remember going to the hospital and holding him as he slept. Teresa had asked me to go in with him during his circumcision to hold his hand. I asked the doctor why Matthew's feet and hands were so blue. She said it was common. I had never seen this in any of my children or the children I had seen delivered before, but I let it pass because I did not want anything to be wrong with my grandson. He was already jaundiced, like his mother had been when she was born.

Teresa and Jim brought Matthew home from the hospital, and we were so excited. He did not awake the whole day, and as we were eating dinner, Matthew became very restless and began breathing rapidly. Teresa called the pediatrician, and as we waited for her call, Matthew began to labor in breathing and was getting cold and clammy.

Teresa called the pediatrician again and was told to bring him in. She called and told us that the doctors were going to check him for an infection. Later in the night she told us about Matthew having heart trouble. I could not believe what she had told us. I remember praying that it was not true. I immediately called all of Teresa's siblings and grandparents. They were very upset and were ready to make plans to come out to be with Teresa and to see Matthew.

At this time we did not know if Matthew would survive the night. Never in my wildest dreams could I imagine this happening to our family. Teresa's sister-in-law was also expecting in January, and Matthew's condition was very upsetting to her and her husband, as they now began to worry about their unborn child.

When Teresa and Jim came home from the hospital that morning, they told us about Matthew's options. I knew right then and there that I wanted the heart transplant without a doubt. Matthew was my grandson, so it was not my decision to make, but Teresa knew in her heart how I felt without asking. I was heartbroken watching my daughter going through the anguish of seeing her child being connected to all the tubes and monitors. I wanted so much to help her, but the only thing I could do was be there for her.

Waiting for Teresa and Jim to choose Matthew's treatment was very difficult. I know they had to look at different options and determine what was best for him. I have a tendency to be optimistic.

One afternoon Jim's parents, my husband and I were sitting at the table discussing Matthew, and they asked me how I felt. I told them I would go along with any decision that Jim and Teresa made concerning Matthew, but I also told them that I wanted Matthew to live. I wanted to hear him say "Grandma" and hold my hand. I could not let him go. The tension in the house was very high. I guess the fear of the unknown made our days very hard. Megan, Teresa's two-year-old daughter, kept us all going with her talking and wanting to do things.

After several days Teresa and Jim told us that they opted for the heart transplant at Children's Hospital in Denver. I told my daughter that I would do anything to help her. We decided that I would live in Denver with them to help with Matthew's sister, Megan, and also with Matthew.

Richard, Teresa's father, knew that I wanted to help and went with me to Colorado to find a place for us to live. When Teresa, Megan and I moved in, he returned to Florida. Having Richard in Florida and Jim in Kansas was very difficult because they both wanted to help, too.

Teresa and I took turns going to the hospital with Matthew and staying home with Megan. I believe that the time we spent together brought us even closer together. We do have a very close-knit family, and we kept close contact with each other during this time. Family members would come out and see Matthew and stay for a while.

When we first arrived, the doctor said we may not receive a heart until December, and here it was the first of September! I told him that he was crazy and that Matthew would have his heart by the end of September. But it did not happen. Everyday I would visit the hospital and hold and rock Matthew not wanting to put him down. He would sleep on my chest, and I would sleep with him. I would tell him that we would grow old together, and I never thought of him dying. I knew in my heart that he would live and get his heart. I would read to him and sing little songs. I cried and prayed so much that I wore out the cross on my rosary. To me Matthew always looked strong even with the medication he was taking to keep his heart going. Little did I know that he was getting worse.

Matthew always sensed when we were in the room with him. There was great bonding between Matthew, Megan, Teresa and me. We would bring Megan up to see Matthew quite often. Sometimes it would be longer than she wanted it to be. She would get up in the morning dressed and say, "I'm going to Matthew." There was not any way to stop her, so we took her. Satisfied after seeing him, Megan just wanted to make sure that he was all right.

Matthew finally received his heart after three months and eleven days, the longest three months that I have ever endured. The wait, the tears, the anguish, the weight loss came to an end on December 11th. When the nurses wheeled him into surgery and we all kissed him and prayed that he would be all right, I again knew in my heart that he would be okay. His strong will to live outweighed his will to let go, and I refused to let him give up. The care he received at the hospital and the care and love that we gave him during his wait, combined with the skillful doctors that did the transplant caused him to fight harder.

Finally, we brought Matthew home after surgery and his week stay in the hospital. What a great feeling! The surgery and wait was behind us. We lived in Colorado for three more months to make sure his heart was not rejecting. This was a difficult time because Matthew also had to learn to suck and be given several medications at certain times.

The weather was still cold, and Teresa would have to bundle him up for his weekly visits to the hospital and lab, which took a lot of patience and time. I will always marvel at how Teresa learned to administer all of Matthew's treatments. She should have been the nurse, not me.

After three months, Teresa took Matthew in for a checkup, and the doctor told her we could take Matthew back to Wichita. Teresa's father and brother just happened to be in town. We called them, and they immediately brought the motor home and packed up all of our belongings. The next morning we drove to Wichita.

What a joy it was to finally be home and put Matthew in his room, which he had never used before. I could see the joy and happiness in my daughter's face. We had done it, and Matthew was doing so well with no rejection.

I always worry that he will forget me because we live in Florida, and they live in Kansas, but he knows who I am when he sees me. When he kisses me, gives me a hug and holds my hand—it is the greatest reward. I am still waiting for him to call me "Grandma," but I know the day will be soon.

I pray a lot for Matthew, as I do for all my children. Now that surgery is over, I want to spend time with him and all my grandchildren, as much as possible.

I love them like they were my own and wish they were. To look at Matthew you would never know he had a heart transplant. He is a normal twenty-month-old child. He does all the things that any child would do and maybe a little more since he has a big sister to teach him.

Everyday I remember one of the nurses saying to me, "This, too, will pass." How right she was. Without the help, compassion and support of the nurses I really do not know what I would have done.

Teresa used to say to me, "It's okay to cry. Don't always try to be the strong one." I always wanted to be strong for her; she was going through so much. If I could have traded places with her I would have. No mother wants her child to endure the worry and hurt she was experiencing.

Joanne, Matthew and baby brother, Colton

A Tribute to My Mother

By: Anna Marie Jaworski

Growing up, I was obviously a "Daddy's Girl." My father was a teacher, and from an early age I knew I would be, too. I remember walking next to my father and trying to match my footsteps exactly to his. I adored him.

It is difficult for any wife to win in a situation like that. In my eyes my mother was to blame for any fight or disagreement. I remember feeling that my mother was not supportive enough of my father's ambitions. I remember feeling angry with her for her lack of understanding. My father and I thought so much alike I could not understand why she did not agree with our "reasoning."

After I went to college and took some child development classes, I began to see that my mother was much smarter than I had given her credit for. There were many things she had done " right" in raising my sister and me. This realization changed my relationship with my mother. Sometimes I went home from college and shared with Mom my new appreciation of her life's work—raising my sister and me.

Before long I found myself being closer friends with my mother and seeking out her companionship. Suddenly I felt unusually protective toward her. I began to wish to repay some of the things she had given me as a child—self-confidence, education, little kindnesses which meant so much. I erroneously thought she needed to be taken care of.

When my baby was diagnosed as Failure to Thrive and admitted to the hospital, I was distraught. For two months my husband and I had taken our son to one doctor after another saying something was wrong. For the first two weeks of my baby's life, my mother stayed with me to help. She watched Joey, my older son, while we took the baby to the hospital for his appointments. After every visit she would assure me that everything would be fine.

After she went back home to San Antonio, the boys and I began to have a normal routine. We played and laughed, took walks and even took food to my husband at the hospital where he worked. Every time I went to the hospital, Frank would pull aside a different doctor and ask him to look at Alex. And each time Frank was told that Alex was fine.

He wasn't. But at first we did not know what was wrong. I called my mother in San Antonio and told her when Alexander was admitted for Failure to Thrive. She was very calm and told me that everything would be fine, but I would probably have to stop breast-feeding him. He probably just needed to be put on formula. Then she told me that when I was a baby, I had been admitted to the hospital, too. For some reason I was not gaining weight like I should. Apparently a lot of tests were run, but the doctors never discovered anything wrong. "We just switched the formula you were on," my mother stated simply, "and you were fine."

I hoped it was something that simple, but something deep down told me it had nothing to do with my breast milk.

Alexander had a number of tests run. I went to check on the results of every test to see if they were positive or negative. All I knew by 2:00 a.m. was that it was nothing simple. The blood work had all come back negative. Alexander was scheduled for a "sweat test" early in the morning. The pediatrician suspected cystic fibrosis. But the X-rays the doctor showed me the next morning revealed something totally different. Alexander's heart was huge, and there was something seriously wrong with it. After viewing the X-rays, the doctor told me that this hospital was ill-equipped to care for a baby so sick. We would have to be transferred. Where did I want to go?

I decided to go to San Antonio and told the doctor in charge. Before long I was on the phone with my sister and then with my mother. My sister agreed to meet me in San Antonio later that day. My mother and father would meet us at the hospital.

I remember wondering how my mother would handle all of this. My mother hated doctors and hospitals. When I was seven years old, I had broken my arm and was put into the hospital for about a week. I remember that my mother hardly came to visit me at all. I knew she had to take care of my little sister and that was part of the reason. I knew, too, though, that she hated hospitals. Now her grandson was in the hospital with a life-threatening heart defect. How would she handle it?

I did not need to worry. My mother came through with flying colors. She talked to the nurses and doctors. She touched Alex and talked to him. She was very strong. I never saw her cry. She really pulled through, and I know it was not just for Alex; she was being strong for me.

I did not want to leave the hospital. I was so afraid something would happen to Alex, and I wanted to be with him every minute. My mother was raised in a different generation. Her feeling was that he could not be under better care than to be with the nurses and doctors at the hospital. I knew, though, that hospitals are scary and a child needs a parent nearby. I did everything I could to be there for Alex.

My mother and father worried about my health for I was not eating or sleeping enough. How could I eat? How could I sleep? My baby needed me! My mother finally picked a strategy to help me take better care of myself. She gently reminded me that I needed to make good milk for Alex, and I could not do that without eating and resting. I remember numbly following my parents to the hospital cafeteria. I don't even remember what I ate, but I remember my mother encouraging me to get food to make good milk for Alex. This from a person who did not even believe in breast-feeding!

Mom put aside her own personal feelings to care for me and Alex on other issues, too. Seeing that I refused to leave Alex's bedside, she scheduled a personal routine to help me. She came for a few hours every afternoon and helped with Alex. She often stopped at Taco Bell and brought food not only for me, but also for Alex's nurse. She helped me with the breast pump. The hospital had an electric breast pump that was used on both breasts at the same time. The first couple of times I tried to do it by myself, I got milk everywhere! I asked my mother if she would come and help me. Every three hours I had to pump, and it was really nice of Mom to help me as often as she did. She even teased and joked to lighten the heaviness that seemed everywhere in the hospital.

Mom and I watched the physical therapist (PT) everyday when he came to work on Alex's lungs. After many friendly conversations, the PT informed Mom and me that we could beat on Alex's chest and back just as he did. He said these percussions (pounding on the back and chest with a little rubber clapper or a cupped hand) would help Alex's body eliminate the problem causing his lungs to be deflated. After we learned how to do percussions, Mom and I worked on Alex every hour to help make his lungs healthier. Alexander was discharged one week after his surgery and I can say with great confidence that this probably would not have happened if I had not had my mother by my side. This is not to say that we didn't argue. We did. This was a traumatic and stressful time. Both of us were running on too little sleep and too many nerves. We had little spats (mostly her wanting me to rest and spend less time at the hospital), but in the end, we always hugged each other knowing each of us was doing the best we could.

When the doctor discharged Alex, it was with the understanding that we stay in San Antonio for an additional week so we would be close to the hospital in the event of an emergency (we lived over three hours from San Antonio). Without question I went back to my mother's house. My husband brought my older son, Joey, to stay with us, too, because Frank had to return to work. My mother took such good care of Joey while Alex and I rested and recuperated. For the first time in weeks, both Alex and I got sleep. It was heavenly. Alex started nursing like never before. He started gaining weight and looking healthier. At our one week post-op visit there were exclamations from the nurses who had cared for Alex. He looked like a new baby! Everybody was so happy to see the progress he had made. We were given permission to return to our home in Mound.

I left thankful to be able to return to my own home and my own routine and very grateful for the kindness shown to me and my family during this crisis by my parents. My mother was a pillar of strength for me and my family. I will forever be in her debt. Of course, being a mom myself, I now know that is just part of being a good mother.

Now I have two parents up on a pedestal.

Carol Daigneault with grandchildren (l-r) Joey, Megan and Alex

Mothers Around the World

I devoted this chapter to a sampling of mothers around the world who share their heart stories. The Internet erases the barriers of race, religion, socioeconomic status, and dialect giving people an opportunity to know each other through the issues most important in their lives. This allows mothers to communicate with each other on a daily basis regardless of where they live.

The Internet features listservs, daily posts written by and sent to everyone who signs up on a list, for almost any topic of interest. There are special listservs for parents of children with heart defects and bulletin boards where parents can post and answer questions. Anyone can make a web page and post it so that anyone else with access to that server can see it. There are even web rings linking web sites to each other. All of this enables a new worldwide community to emerge.

The Congenital Heart Defect (CHD) community is a special subset of the Internet world. These community members include parents, grandparents, aunts, uncles, friends, doctors, nurses, other care providers and even Adults with Congenital Heart Defects (more commonly referred to as ACHDers). This community has listservs, weekly or special chats (where people assemble in special meeting rooms to talk), pen pals and opportunities to get to know others on a personal basis about whatever they feel like sharing. Oddly enough, many people on these listservs come to know other CHD community members more intimately than they know their own family and friends. Many people even feel that the CHD community is a special family due to the universal bond shared. Because of the intense feelings common to the community, people become so close that they often arrange to meet in person, make hospital visits when possible and have formed geographical support groups as well.

By communicating with others about the fears, trials and triumphs, we have come to know each other, befriended each other and benefited from knowing each other. If it were not for the Internet, neither these connections nor this chapter would have been possible. Every mother who contributed an essay for this chapter belongs to the international CHD community described above.

The following essays are written by mothers in lands other than the United States, but they share the same fears we American mothers have. Unlike mothers in America, however, not all of these women have access to sophisticated, appropriate medical care in their own country. Many of these women have traveled outside their homeland to secure the care needed for their children's survival.

The following essays are written in English; however, you can find some of them written in the mother's native tongue in the Appendix. Regardless of language, though, there are universals. The language of love is the same, no matter where it is spoken. These essays speak of the universal feelings of love, helplessness and determination all mothers feel when their children's heart defects are diagnosed. These mothers all share a common bond—a universal devotion to their children.

A Little Bit of Heaven—Canada

By: Carolyn Thompson

Cody was born on May 31, 1995, an adorable, perfect little boy that was the completion of our little family. We already had a little girl who was the centre of our universe. Everything was right with the world when the doctor said, "It's a boy!" However, that world crumbled in the early morning hours of June 2, when at 4:00 a.m. Cody was transferred to London Sick Kids Hospital due to breathing problems. There, after many hours of waiting and wondering, it was discovered that he had a congenital heart defect called critical aortic stenosis. Cody was a very sick little boy. We were told that he would need some type of heart surgery, but they could not perform it there, instead he would be transferred to Toronto Sick Children's Hospital.

No words can describe the first time I saw my child in critical condition. I replayed everything I had ever done in my life to try and figure out why God was "punishing" me like that. I could not stop remembering the first few moments after Cody's birth when I did not even want to hold him. My emotions were in turmoil, wondering if in some way I had given God the impression that I did not want or love my baby boy enough, and now he was going to be taken from me. My whole world stopped when I realized that there was nothing I could do to make his pain go away—the one thing that a mother should do best. He was so full of wires and IV's that I could barely tell there was a baby underneath it all. He looked so small and helpless that all I wanted to do was pick him up and run, to take him as far away from all the needles and machines as I could. I would have given my life at that moment if it would have spared even a moment of his pain.

I cannot remember all the names or faces of the staff I met, but I do remember the first time when my mother saw Cody in Intensive Care. I pretended to be so strong and reassuring to her, only to run into the washroom and sob my heart out for ten minutes afterwards. I remember sitting in a rocking chair, holding him while I carefully maneuvered around the wires and having my arm fall asleep. But it did not matter, because when I held him I knew in my heart that God would not take him from me. The evening before he was transferred, I went home for the night to spend some time with my daughter. I have never before felt so torn as I did that evening. I did not want to leave my baby all alone in a strange hospital, but I also missed my little girl, Carrie, and wanted to be with her in case she was scared and needed her mommy. When I left Cody that evening, I left half of my heart with him and took the other half to Carrie.

The next day Cody was transferred, and we headed to the big city of Toronto. We got there a couple of hours behind Cody, so they had already ran him through a battery of tests. We got to see him while waiting for the results. I was amazed at how much better he looked. They had most of the IVs covered, and he was coping very well with the meds and oxygen. My hopes soared when a nurse stated that he was a real fighter. I felt that Cody wanted to stay with us. We were in higher spirits while we waited for the doctor to see us; we even arranged our accommodations and ate. When the team of doctors came in the waiting room, they told us they had discovered things were not as optimistic as previously thought.

His actual diagnosis was hypoplastic left heart syndrome, a severe, life-threatening heart defect. The cardiologist gave us three options— all with their own risks and benefits. The first option was a heart transplant, but Cody was so small and weak they did not hold out much hope that he would survive the wait for the heart. The second option was a series of three surgeries, all done at certain intervals, each with its own risks and it was a fairly new procedure. The final option, compassionate care, required nothing but easing Cody's pain until he passed away. We did not even consider this an option. We figured that if our little guy had the strength and courage to come this far, we would see to it that he got any chance there was to go all the way. We were not going to give up on him now.

We talked to doctors, to each other, to our parents and to God. We were to look at both options and decide after hearing all the arguments. First we spoke to the doctor, Dr. Ivan Rebeyka, who would be doing the series of operations. This man was unlike any doctor I have ever met. He explained very thoroughly all the aspects of the first surgery, being very considerate and patient with all our questions. The transplant team came to see us, giving us the impression that there really was only ONE choice when you considered Cody's options. After only a couple of hours, we consented to the Norwood, which was scheduled for June 7 and went extremely well. God was listening to a lot of prayers on that day and answered them. There were no complications, and Cody was released from the hospital two weeks later.

Our son did very well from that point on; the only thing reminding us there was anything wrong with him were the frequent trips to the doctors. He saw his cardiologist in London once a month and his pediatrician in Stratford twice a month. A nurse also came to our house twice a week to check his SATs and vitals. I thank God we live in Canada where there is this terrific health care system. All of our health care costs are paid through taxes that are deducted from our income. We are even receiving an allowance to help with the costs that are not paid for by the Ministry of Health, like accommodations, meals, and gas for the trips to and from the doctor's office. I believe that if we lived anywhere but Canada, we would have been forced to make an entirely different decision.

When Cody was about two months old, I found we had to really watch for colds and infections; what a healthy kid could fight off in a week or so would drag him down and put him in the hospital. In October he was scheduled for a heart cath to determine when the best time for the second surgery, called the Glenn shunt, would be. Apparently Cody's shunt was not operating properly, and he was rushed in for emergency surgery; he had the Glenn (second surgery) two months ahead of time. I remember Dr. Rebeyka rushing in at midnight to perform Cody's surgery and trying to make me smile. He said, "What are you doing here? I wasn't supposed to see you for another couple of months." It shocked me that he not only remembered me by name and face but that he also showed so much concern about me being there alone. My husband returned to work, thinking we would all be home in a couple of days.

This surgery also went well, considering it was unexpected. It was after the surgery that Cody started having problems. The second day that he was allowed to eat, he refused to take any food. He would scream if he even saw his bottle, so we had to continue feeding him via a nasal gastric tube. They ran all kinds of tests, sent in specialists, even tried therapy, but nothing worked. He was in the hospital for five weeks before they decided to teach me how to change the tube and feed him at home. He was at home for a full month before he started to eat on his own again. We still have no idea what caused this to happen, or if it will happen again. With that hurdle passed, though, he seemed to get better. He was slow learning to sit up, but once he started there was no stopping him.

We encountered another mini-crisis; Cody might have come into contact with tainted bodily matter. It was discovered that the person from whom they had gotten some tissue used in Cody had died from a very rare disease called Creustzfeld-Jacob Disease. There is a slim chance that he may have contracted this disease, but there is no way of finding out. There is an incubation period with the disease that can last twenty to thirty years, and once the symptoms start to show, it is too late. I have convinced myself that if by some chance my son has contracted this disease, twenty to thirty years from now medical science will have a cure or some kind of treatment. I cannot afford the energy that it would take to worry about this dreadful mishap, especially since it may not have anything to do with us for another twenty years. One concern I have about the Canadian medical standards is that a person is not permitted to donate blood, tissue or body parts specifically to another person. Once again there are prayers from all over going up to heaven on my son's behalf, and I have to believe that whatever happens, happens for a reason. Cody was put on this earth for a purpose. Maybe he will only stay for a short while; maybe he will live to an old age. No one knows, and there are no guarantees. The only thing I know is that I have been given two wonderful gifts from God, and I plan to consider myself blessed just to have known them.

Cody's cardiologist continues to brag about his progress to other patients. During our January visit, the cardiology informed us that Dr. Rebeyka (Cody's surgeon) had taken a position in Edmonton, Alberta and would not be performing Cody's final stage, the Fontan. I was very upset and wrote Dr. Rebeyka a letter asking about the possibility of coming back for Cody's Fontan. I never expected him to return, but I felt I should try. I was floored when he called the day after receiving my letter to explain that because of provincial regulations he could not come back to Ontario to perform the Fontan, but we could take Cody to him to have the surgery done. He suggested we talk it over with our cardiologist and do whatever we felt in our heart was the best (another thing that I have never ever heard a doctor say). We talked to the cardiologist and found out that we would have to apply to the Ontario Health Insurance to have Cody's medical care transferred to Alberta. After he submitted the application on our behalf, we were told it would be a while before we found out anything, and if we were refused on that level we could apply higher up. About a month after we applied, we got the approval; it seemed to be a sign that going to Edmonton was the right thing to do.

I understand that the doctors here in Ontario are very good doctors, and some people say that I am wasting a lot of money buying a plane ticket when I could have the same thing done within two hundred miles. I really wish I did not have to go so far away from my family at a time when I really need them with me, but I know deep in my heart that taking my son to Dr. Rebeyka is what I really should do. He has helped save my son's life not once, but twice, and he treats my family as he would treat his own. To him, we are real people rather than just numbers on a paper. So as we prepare for another emotional roller coaster, I find myself more peaceful and relaxed than ever before. For even though I stand and stare into the unknown, I know that I am not alone. I am looking forward to many more years of memories with both my children. I want to believe that God has much bigger plans for Cody's life, but if God should decide to take His little angel home, I will know that my world had been a much better place because I have known a little bit of Heaven. I am a better person because through his little life he has shown me how to appreciate all that I have—family, friends, hopes, dreams, laughter and love. To know someone as close to Heaven as a child is an incredible feeling that never goes away.

Cody and Carrie Thompson

Editor's Note: Since this essay was written Cody had the Fontan procedure and is currently doing well.

A Miracle—Germany

By: Beate Lemmer
Translated by: Janet Fendt and Susan Kaser

Mareike entered the world on 29 April 1989, our second daughter.

It was a difficult delivery, and my husband and I were happy that we had a healthy child. Three days after her birth, the pediatricians diagnosed a heart murmur. I was overcome with fear and worry.

After discussing the murmur with my husband and me, the doctors transferred my baby to a cardiology clinic in Cologne. After thorough examinations and tests, we were informed that our daughter suffered a difficult and complicated congenital heart defect known as Fallot's tetralogy, and she would have to be admitted to the clinic.

At that time I did not really know what this diagnosis meant; it was all too new and strange. The one thing I did know was that they wanted to take my baby away from me. I was supposed to hand my baby over to people I did not know. The cardiologist took us aside and explained just how seriously ill our child was, which caused me to break down. First came the shock, and then the gradual dawning realization that we must live with this terrible truth. I thought of our other daughter, waiting for her baby sister to come home, and I wondered how I could it explain this to a seventeen-month-old child. She had to wait six weeks before Mareike was finally discharged.

Back at home a totally new life started for us all. Everything revolved around Mareike. She was not allowed to cry or she would become blue. We could not allow any visitors into our home if they had a cold. Friends who before had been regular visitors stopped coming to see us. My father even blamed me for Mareike's illness. My brother, who became father to a little boy two years later, also somehow managed to blame me that his son was born with a tiny hole in his heart. For us it was very sad to discover that suddenly we were all on our own. But the struggle for Mareike's life was only just beginning.

Every six to eight weeks, Mareike was examined by her cardiologist. As she gradually put on weight, the dosage of her medications also increased. In terms of size and weight, Mareike developed quite well. In July of 1990 the cardiologist referred Mareike to the Heart Center for a heart catheterization. On 1 August 1990 this was carried out, and we were informed that an emergency operation would have to be undertaken because the pulmonary vessels were underdeveloped.

At this time Mareike was sixteen months old. She could not talk, crawl or walk. August 5, 1990 was the date set for the operation. Mareike must have known that something was happening to her because on the way to the operating theater she cried out loudly, "Mama!" Even today I can hear that cry.

The operation went well, and there were no complications. When I saw Mareike again afterwards in the Intensive Care Ward, I was not intimidated by all the technical equipment. I just saw my child. In that moment I thought I had never seen a more beautiful child. Mareike looked lovely. She was not blue any more. Rosy cheeks and red lips revealed how much better she was. I was very happy.

Mareike was discharged on 21 August 1990. Two days before leaving the hospital, she learned to walk. At this time I was pregnant again, but two days after arriving home, I lost the baby. It had all been too much for the nerves.

Mareike began to make rapid progress, and for the first time we all started to take a deep breath. Then on 7 August 1991 she was readmitted to the Heart Center for a heart catheterization. The results determined that corrective operations could now be carried out, and a date was set for 28 March 1992. This gave us a "breathing space" of several months.

In October of 1991 our third little girl was born. The initial problems following her birth, lack of oxygen, cyanosis and suspicion of heart defect, were all remedied within a few days, but I cannot begin to describe my feelings during these days.

I have to thank my husband because I do not know what I would have done without him. Of course he could not be with me all the time because he had to look after the other children, but he was always there when I came home from the clinic in the evenings—when I was desperate with worry. All the worries and fears had turned me into a pessimist. My husband, on the other hand, always remained the optimist. He always used to say, "Mareike's going to be all right."

The operation on 28 March went well, and there were no complications. She recovered very quickly and was discharged on 12 April. According to the doctors, Mareike was "almost well." How wrong they were!

In August of 1993 Mareike started kindergarten. Everything went well. At the end of August, the cardiologist discovered a heart murmur, and at the end of September she was back at the Heart Center for a catheterization. This time they diagnosed pulmonary stenosis (narrowing of the pulmonary artery). The indications, however, were that this was minimal. We were instructed to observe Mareike closely, particularly if she were to become blue again.

Visits to the cardiologist became more and more frequent, and with every examination we had the same anxious question, "What are we going to discover this time?" Mareike was not allowed any exertion; she could not be too active when playing. She had to be constantly watched. When Mareike was in kindergarten, I hardly dared answer the phone for fear that something could have happened to her.

On 5 October 1994 Mareike was readmitted to the Heart Center. Her condition was now critical, and with even the smallest exertion, she became blue. A balloon catheterization was introduced to widen the narrowed area of stenosis. Everything went well, without complications, but it was all for nothing.

Only four months later the pulmonary arteries had narrowed again. Mareike needed another operation. The right side of her heart was getting bigger. It was having to work too hard to pump the blood through the narrow places, and the danger of heart failure increased daily.

On 3 April 1995 Mareike had to undergo another operation. The cardio-thoracic surgeons wanted to widen the left pulmonary artery by means of a patch of synthetic material. The operation was carried out without any complications. Afterwards, Mareike was on a ventilator for two and a half days in the ICU because the physicians had failed to pick up a lung infection during the previous examinations.

Mareike recovered and was discharged on 17 April 1995, following a thorough examination. I asked my usual question of whether or not the operation had brought the expected results, but this time I did not get an answer. The discharge report was to be sent to my home address. This was all very strange, since normally that was given to me before leaving the hospital. None of the hospital staff gave us their good wishes for the future, as they normally did.

Four weeks later we discovered part of the truth. The operation did not have the desired result. It was a waste of time. We were given a new admission date in yet another Heart Center. There they were considering implanting a stent.

We arrived for admission on 20 September 1995 full of hope even though we were very worried. This change to another clinic frightened Mareike. She panicked, screamed and cried, refusing to cooperate when a blood sample needed to be drawn. The staff ignored her and let her cry. I stayed with her as long as I could. When she fell asleep I tried to creep out of the room, but she would awaken and start crying again.

Normally it takes me about one hour to get home by car from this clinic, but in these three days, I kept getting lost and took ages to get home. I just could not concentrate. The cardiologist explained to me then that the stent could not be implanted after all because the pulmonary artery was damaged during the last operation. I could not come to terms with all of these incomprehensible things. Another clinic was recommended for us to seek treatment for Mareike, and she was discharged.

The next examination undertaken by our cardiologist revealed the full truth. Mareike was now considered "inoperable." Everyone knew this, but nobody told us. No one had had the courage to tell us the whole truth.

I began to hate physicians. Our daughter was condemned to die! Hospitals closed their files on her. Other clinics refused to offer any treatment. It is terrible to see a child and know that he or she is seriously ill; it is devastating to realize that your own child will die because no doctor can help her. Just when I gave up hope, a miracle happened.

In January 1997, our cardiologist flew to a medical congress in Geneva, Switzerland and discussed Mareike's case with world renown pediatric cardio-thoracic surgeons. Then the miracle occurred. We were informed by telephone and in writing that there was a possibility of help for Mareike. The letter stated that Mareike could not undergo the classical surgery to one side of her heart, but a stent implantation could be attempted.

This was the most wonderful letter I have ever received. There was someone out there who could really help Mareike. We were given an admission date and our insurance company readily agreed to pay the costs of treatment in another country because there was no possibility of treatment available in Germany.

On 31 March 1996 we flew to Switzerland. I had to fly with Mareike by myself because my husband had to look after our other children. I had never flown before and was very nervous, but I had to do this for Mareike.

The procedure carried out in Switzerland was a complete success. When it was all over and I was waiting outside the operating theater, I suddenly heard a cheer from the doctors and nurses! There was music playing, and the staff all embraced each other. I had never experienced anything like this before. The surgeon came up to me and kept saying, "It's fine. Everything is okay."

I cannot describe my feelings at that moment. Mareike, too, was very happy. She enjoyed the fact that I could be with her day and night. Our beds had been pushed together so that we could be as close as possible to each other. She was not afraid and did not cry. I soon saw that she trusted these doctors and nurses completely.

Three months later we flew to Switzerland again for treatment to the other side of Mareike's heart. This procedure was also a total success, and even more astounding to all was that only four days later she was discharged. When we flew home again, no one could believe it.

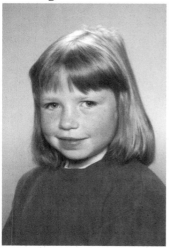

For us this was and always will be a miracle. We are deeply grateful to our cardiologist for not giving up on Mareike. He told us the truth, and he explored every possibility until he found the right specialist in another country to save Mareike. And of course we are especially thankful to a cardiologist and surgeon from America who operated at a heart center in Genolier, Switzerland. Mareike will always suffer from this heart defect, but now with only a few minor exceptions, she can lead a life like a normal, healthy child.

Only three weeks after this final treatment, Mareike started school.

Mareike Lemmer

Chrysanthemums for Paesan—Singapore

By: Helen Ng

Our lives are one long journey fraught with trials and challenges. There is one chapter in mine which pushed me to the greatest test of faith and whose reward has convinced me of God's infinite love.

In November 1994, I made a trip with my husband, Dominic, and our then two-and-a-half-year-old son, Paesan, to Cleveland, Ohio. Paesan was to undergo major heart surgery there. His second.

I spent the nineteen-hour SIN-LA flight praying and thinking. A further four-hour flight from LA to Cleveland gave me more time to recall the painful moments in my life since an ultrasound scan during the pregnancy suggested a "foetal abnormality."

With our three normal, boisterous children, we had looked forward to the addition of a fourth child to fill the sixth seat at the dinner table. But my world collapsed when I was thirty weeks into the pregnancy: ·the obstetrician disclosed that I would give birth to a cyanotic child. A child with heart problems? I could not accept that.

Paesan was born on 12 April 1992 after a thirty-eight-and-a- half week gestation with a complex congenital heart condition. So complex that we did not know where to turn to or what questions to ask. He was VERY blue and deteriorating quickly.

After four months of alternating between blue spells and gasps for life, I had to do something. We were led to the Royal Children's Hospital in Melbourne, Australia to Dr. T. H. Goh, a fine Australian cardiologist who called Paesan "a mixed bag," and whose one question, "How much do you value life?" jolted us.

That August morning in 1992, at the tender age of four months, Paesan went into the operating room blue as a pansy and came out pink as a budding rose. Despite the cost, Dominic and I never looked back to debate his surgery.

I had always thought of Paean, our eight-year-old son, as a little bubble—full of energy and enthusiasm—until Paesan came along. After his bi-directional Glenn shunt in Melbourne, Paesan's life came into focus. My entire perspective of life changed. He walked; he talked, never getting enough of life. His mind knew no bounds. Though he did not walk until he was thirteen months old, he spoke English with great proficiency and had a vocabulary two years ahead of his age. At church, he knew the order of mass and precisely when the bells would ring at the raising of the host.

Paesan loved reading. "Mama, read your Bible," he would say. Books fascinated him. So did CD-ROM. You could find him busy at the PC, "working like Mama" at his next make-believe article. But never could he play ball with the Wing brothers from next door without getting breathless or falling flat on his back—his body's way of forcing him to rest.

The surgery in Cleveland was going to be more complex. Doctors would open Paesan's common pulmonary venous drainage and connect a baffle to redirect the blood flow. He would need a Fontan.

The Cleveland Clinic Foundation is a non-profit, patient-friendly research institution. Its staff is especially helpful and gentle with children. There are children's play areas, children-sized apparatus and the sweetest gowns and pajamas with Bugs Bunny and Tweety Bird prints.

Paesan's operation was delayed for a week because he developed a fever from an ear infection. We forgot to allow for time to acclimatize a Singaporean body from a tropical belt, whose biological clock was set back by twelve hours.

On the morning of November 17, 1994, I carried him to the OR, where he was anaesthetised in his blue Sylvester gown. With tears brimming and trying not to let my voice break, I sang his favourite "Little Eyes," as I watched his own little eyes close. Everything was now in God's hands.

On Day 2, Paesan's pulse shot up to 220, and he developed a high fever. His body was having trouble adapting to all of the changes since his surgery. He developed seizures which the staff were quick to arrest. "We've done all we can," said Dr. Roger Mee, the surgeon who operated on Paesan, first in Melbourne and now in Cleveland. "It's up to his system to adapt. We'll take it one day at a time."

For the first time since our arrival, Dom, who has been my constant shield and comfort, broke down among Paesan's tubes. Fear gnawed painfully inside us. A rosary hung constantly by our son's bed.

In the four weeks following, there would be up days and down days, mostly down. Time with a dispirited child who could never understand why he was bedridden and hurting so much required more than patience. It required infinite wisdom. Watching other patients discharged and their beds occupied by new patients did little to boost his spirit. We played his favourite cassettes, read him his books. We talked about the things we did and things we would do when we got home. We tried balloons. Paesan loved flowers, and Dom found two pots of chrysanthemeums at the gift shop which reminded him of home.

By then, Paesan was getting used to nurses changing the plaster dressing on his chest, and the incessant drawing of blood from his open

IV lines. "Look, Paesan, another tube removed," Dom would say with delight. It was our way of tracking progress.

The weather turned cooler, and folks said it might snow. At noon on Day 6, we saw hail through the ICU window. "Look, Paesan, snow," I exclaimed to my unsmiling child.
"Go away," Paesan said.
"Why?" I asked.
"I don't love you. You are so bad," my baby said. I cried inside and out.
Dom then suggested that I leave the room. When I returned shortly, Dom was leaning over Paesan, gently stroking the boy's hair. There is something poignantly powerful about the closeness of a father and his son. Next, he did something unimaginable—he carried a resistant Paesan who was still connected to tubes and wires off the bed and cuddled him. His eyes met mine as I stood at the door. That cold afternoon, we had our son back.

On Day 8, when the tubes were drying, the hospital allowed Paesan's discharge to the ward. "We've done Fontans before, but none made it out of the ICU in less than ten days," said Dr Sabik. En route to the ward, we made a detour to the chapel where the three of us said our thanks to God. Paesan offered his pots of chrysanthemums.

Aptly on Thanksgiving Day, 25 November 1994, eight days after Paesan's operation, we were discharged on "postoperative home-leave." Everyone had gone home for the weekend. There we were—two lonely Singaporeans and a wobbly-kneed little boy, in an empty ward far from home.
But home was the Ronald McDonald House. We were the only Chinese family at this temporary haven for families of children undergoing treatment at the Cleveland and Rainbow Center hospitals. There is nothing like the equivalent of a Ronald McDonald House back in Singapore. That discharge day called for a celebration: chicken, rice, vegetables and steamed pork in egg. Though the ingredients were American, the fare was far tastier than we have had in a long time. Despite his fluid restrictions, Paesan became bubbly again.

The Bayas family from Ecuador had been staying at the House for over a year before we arrived. We spoke English while the Bayas spoke only Spanish. But families in pain understand each other's crises. Eleven-year-old Robertito Bayas had leukaemia and had gone bald.
It was to be our last week at the House when I met Robertito's mum, Ruth, in the hallway. "Ruth," I said with arms fluttering to simulate wings, "Tomorrow we fly home." She nodded but said in heavy Spanish

something about no remission. A flurry of Spanish followed, and the word "fe" kept popping up.

"You . . . give . . . me . . . faith . . . ," Ruth muttered carefully. I finally understood that "fe" meant "faith" in Spanish.

"No, Ruth," I said, pointing to Paesan. "The doctors said that he would not survive his birth. But he did. He had two surgeries and survived them both. Paesan gives you faith. Trust in God."

"My sees-ter, my friend," Ruth said, as she hugged me with tears streaming out of those brown, Ecuadorean eyes.

I never saw them again. It was to be a year later that a Christmas card would arrive from Ecuador. Below the well wishes for a Joyful and Merry Christmas was signed off the names of Rodrigo, Ruth, Socrates. Under a bold, hand-drawn black outline of an angel complete with halo, the name ROBERTITO was neatly written.

Paesan had lost two kilograms during the surgery. Despite having to be on life-long penicillin prophylaxis and anticoagulation, the pain and the struggle of the past four weeks had been worth it.

Early the next morning, a hospital security car came by and picked us up. As the car rounded the Cleveland Clinic complex for the final turn, I looked at the many buildings which had become so familiar— the H building where the chapel was our daily refuge, heavy with our prayers and thoughts . . . where Dom towed Paesan on a little red wagon to HB6 for his X-rays . . . M building and the ORs, ICU and the wards . . . where on Thanksgiving Day, I had sat alone in the hospital grounds . . . the lounge where our meals were a quick bowl of instant noodles . . . where Paesan's painting is pinned on the wall of the playroom . . . where we picked acorns at the parking lot amid strange stares from passers-by and smelled the crinkling autumn oak leaves . . .

Jesus is my rock, my refuge and my strength. He carried us wherever we were. And if home is where the heart is, I say with full faith that home is where God is.

It wasn't the sun's early rays peeping out from the edges of the buildings that broke my thoughts. It was the beaming faces of my son sitting on my lap and my husband beside me and thoughts of Phaemie, Phaelyn and Paean back home waiting for their baby brother.

After a final turn at the fire station and one last look at the Ronald McDonald House, Dom said, "We'll bring Paesan back to Melbourne and here to show him all these things."

I smiled at my husband for once again he has read my thoughts.

(Back row) Phaemie, Dominic and Phaelyn
(Front row) Paean, Paesan and Helen

Editor's Note: Paesan was born on 12 April 1992 with single ventricle, ambiguous isomerism, systemic situs inversus, primum ASD, bilateral SVC, central IVC, pulmonary venous drainage to left and right-sided atria, common AV valve, pulmonary infundibular, valvar stenosis and asplenia. He also has malrotation of the intestines.

He is now in kindergarten where he enjoys life like any other five year old. The hospitalisation costs of his surgeries at the Royal Children's Hospital in Melbourne, Australia were A$20,000 and in Cleveland Clinic US$25,000 which, for foreign patients, have to be paid in full. The amounts exclude other costs like airfares, accommodations and other incidentals which amounted to US$10,000 for each surgery.

Doctors estimate that six to eight per 1000 live births in Singapore are babies with congenital heart defects. There is a Singapore Heart Centre at Singapore General Hospital. Paediatric cardiac cases are managed by the KK Women's and Children's Hospital and the National University Hospital, the two restructured hospitals in Singapore with tertiary paediatric care facilities. Others are under the management of cardiologists and cardiothoracic surgeons in private practice. Heart Kids, a support group catering to children with congenital heart disease under the umbrella of Club Rainbow, is now available.

Running the Race—Australia

By: Lyn Chappell

Ken and I live in Cairns, Queensland, Australia. Our son, Luke, was born on 12 October, 1984 and weighed eight pounds, four ounces. I could not believe that I produced such a big baby because I am only five feet tall. Anyway, I remember lying in bed looking at this perfectly healthy baby boy and thinking how lucky we were to have a girl and a boy, our pigeon pair; we had only ever wanted two children. Our daughter, Belinda was nearly three years old.

When Luke was about two weeks old, he started falling asleep when I fed him, then he would wake up half an hour later wanting to be fed again. I did not think anything of it and gave him another feed. At a play group he went blue, but we thought he must have been cold and put another blanket on him. He then turned pink again and fell asleep.

At five weeks Luke got a cold and sounded chesty, so I took him to our family doctor. He prescribed an antibiotic, and we were told to come back in two days. On returning, our doctor ordered blood tests and an X-ray. On my way out the door, the nurse remarked that she did not like Luke's colour. We returned the next day for the results. The doctor basically said he was not happy with things and would like us to see the paediatrician.

I expected the paediatrician to tell me it was bronchitis, but he thought that my doctor had prepared me for Luke's heart problem. My mouth hit the floor when he started talking about something being wrong with his heart. It was then he realised that my doctor had not told me anything. By this stage I was crying; I was in total shock. He thought Luke had tetralogy of Fallot but that would be confirmed in Brisbane after tests were done.

The hospital was 1700 kilometres away (a two hour flight). Still in tears, I drove home to see my husband. That weekend we felt our world was crumbling.

A few days later, we were arrived at the Prince Charles Hospital in Brisbane. We could not fault the service and care that the staff and doctors provided. Luke was scheduled to have blood tests, X-ray, ECG, and an echo done. The cardiologist reviewed the echo and decided to do a catheterization.

The catheterization was scheduled for the following week, but Luke was not cooperative. The charge sister told me I could creep up behind her and kiss him on the head as long as I did not wake him or let him smell my milk. She carried him down to the catheter theater herself. I came back to find nurses running back and forth with warm blankets, and Luke on an IV drip. Luke's right leg was black. He had in a drip of heparin in case he clotted—that was 2:00 p.m. About 9:00 p.m., the nurses found a pulse and immediately marked the spot with an X. By morning, circulation returned to his leg.

Luke's diagnosis, a double outlet right ventricle, pulmonary stenosis, and a large VSD was a rare and complex defect. His aorta was attached to the right side of his heart, instead of the left, and he had a very narrowed pulmonary artery and valve. They would have to insert conduits down each side of his pulmonary artery, which would have to be replaced as he grew. The surgeons hoped to postpone corrective surgery until he was four or five years of age, although a palliative operation might be necessary around eighteen to twenty-four months of age.

After I arrived home, Luke started turning blue (cyanotic) which we were told to expect. At three months, he started having cyanotic spells and was put on propanolol three times a day which seemed to help. His weight gains were very slow but constant. He cried often and was a very unhappy baby. Luke hated lying on his stomach, so he learnt to sit up by five months of age.

Luke experienced cyanotic spells quite regularly now, so the doctors decided Luke needed surgery—a classic Blalock-Taussig shunt—at nine months of age. All I could say was, "He's pink! He's pink!" When Luke came down from ICU, my husband noticed that Luke could not open his right eye. The nurses had never seen this before and called the surgeon. He said it was nothing to worry about and that it would correct itself. During that day the eye slowly opened but not fully. Later we were told it was Horner's Syndrome; otherwise, Luke progressed well and went home after ten days.

After Luke's shunt surgery it seemed as if he had a new battery. His only medication was half an aspirin everyday. He started to crawl within six weeks and walked by the time he was fourteen months. He was a very happy little boy.

Around eighteen to twenty-four months, Luke started slowing down and was unable to keep up with other kids. We went down to Brisbane again in April of 1988 for another catheterization. The surgeons were pleased with the results because Luke did not need an extra shunt, as they had feared. His corrective surgery was scheduled for early the next year. I enjoyed talking to others with heart children because we could relate in a way that family and other friends could not.

Towards the end of Luke's first year in pre-school, he started to get blue again. We saw the surgeon in November, and he arranged for surgery the next February or March. Our surgery date finally came, March 28th. We went to Brisbane five days earlier to wean him off aspirin before surgery to avoid complications. My husband, Ken, and Belinda (my daughter) came down the day before. Seeing Luke being wheeled in for surgery was extremely difficult, not knowing if I would ever see him again—I broke down. I found I could be strong at all other times except then.

Luke came through the operation very well, although he did have tachycardia, and his liver was enlarged. During surgery, the doctors put a large outflow patch on Luke's pulmonary artery which meant he needed only one operation. The outflow patch went from the "T" junction of the pulmonary artery down to his right ventricle through his valve. They also put a Dacron patch from the bottom of his aorta to the bottom of the VSD in a tunnel shape so that it formed part of the left ventricle, and they cut away a lot of muscle tissue in the right ventricle. His medications were choltide, and aldactone, and he had to be on a salt-free diet. He stayed in post-op until March 30th. On the 5th of April he went white, losing all colour from his lips. Then he started sweating excessively. We had to change him and his bed twice during the night. The doctor ordered a twenty-four hour holter tape plus blood tests to check his white cell count. There was no answer regarding these spells. His colour to me was still not good. We were discharged on the 10th of April.

Luke continued to sweat at home, and his pulse rate was up to about 120-130 beats per minute (bpm). He was also often out of breath and made grunting noises when he breathed. Although often fatigued, Luke remained active. The paediatrician thought Luke might be anemic and ordered more blood tests. Luke appeared yellow to me. Over the next week his liver enlarged even more, so an echo was ordered. Luke's patch had come undone and was leaking.

We went back to Brisbane with Luke in gross heart failure. In the previous three weeks, the kids' ward had been incorporated into the neonatal unit. This time accommodations were provided for mums and dads, which included a parents' lounge with microwave, television and refrigerator. The hospital used pagers so that parents could relax knowing they would be beeped at a moment's notice. A member from the support group and the social worker host a morning tea once a week for the parents to socialise.

Luke was sent for X-rays, blood tests and another echo. He was put on digoxin, and Lasix. The results of the echo were not clear enough, so a catheterization was scheduled. The results showed the patch had indeed come undone and would have to be repaired. This time Luke's recovery took longer. His tissue was very fragile causing the patch to lift. Luke required more chest drains this time and he was restless and required morphine. His breathing tube was taken out the next day. Luke's pulse rate was still 140 bpm, and his chest rattled. He was taken down from post-op to PICU on Wednesday. His SATs were not good, so he needed oxygen. He also retained fluid, so a catheter was used, and Lasix was given.

That night Luke began having irregular heart beats and started vomiting. Another echo revealed that the patch had lifted in another place. Deciding to wait until he was stronger, the doctors sent him back to post-op where he could be closely monitored. Two hours later, he went into complete failure. We were asked to leave the room, as the defibrillators were asked for. Ken and I broke down. We thought we had lost Luke, but then the door opened, and we were asked to sit with him as they stablised him.

When Luke crashed again, Ken and I were in a total state of shock. We were given consent forms to sign for emergency surgery. We kissed Luke good-bye and watched as they wheeled him to the theater. We felt distraught. Thankfully, the nursing staff was tremendously caring and supportive.

Finally, when we returned to post-op, the surgeon walked in eating an apple, so I knew the surgery must have gone well. This time he overstitched and reinforced the patch. Although Luke lost less blood this time, he was transfused due to low hemoglobin. He also needed a catheter because he would not urinate, but when he ended up with a urinary tract infection, they removed it and put him on antibiotics. On Saturday they noticed that Luke had a pneumothorax, but since it was not getting worse, they just monitored it. Luke stayed in post-op for four days before going down to the PICU.

Luke seemed a little brighter this time. Tuesday morning when I arrived, he was sitting up in bed complaining he was sore. The left side of his chest and shoulder were swollen indicating the pneumothorax had progressed. After taking X- rays, the doctors placed a drain into his side to let the air out. It took a few days for the swelling to go down. Because there was so much air in Luke's chest, he felt like rice bubbles to touch. Over the next few days, Luke was weaned off oxygen and monitors—my security.

After three weeks Luke finally progressed to the kids' ward again. Another echo proved inconclusive. The doctors suspected the patch was once again undone, but because Luke was coping so well, they controlled the leak through medication..

By the end of the week, they decided we could go home. All that Luke remembers of his hospitalisation is the tape ripping his skin as the nurse took out the central line. I wish that were all Ken and I remembered.

Luke returned home on aldactone, chlotride, and digoxin, and slowly we returned to normality. I bought Luke a waterproof S.O.S. medical alert bracelet. He attended preschool a month later part-time before resuming a regular schedule. I had a pager for immediate contact if necessary.

A private adult cardiologist sees Luke in Cairns. He has been monitoring Luke since his operations. Luke started school the following year, but one week into school, Luke was hospitalised with suspected endocarditis. Luckily it turned out to be a very bad, six-week case of tonsillitis.

Later he started getting chest pains while running around at school; his hands became icy cold on exertion. The chest pains continued, and a twenty-four hour Holter tape was recorded. The doctors found nothing wrong, but by the end of the year, the cardiologist prescribed Capoten. It decreased the blood pressure and made the blood flow forward so it took pressure off the patch.

By now Luke was six, and we decided to have another baby. I wrote to Luke's cardiologist in Brisbane and told her that I was pregnant and asked if she would do a fetal scan for me when she did Luke's checkup. She replied in two days with a date for the scan and Luke's appointment. Luke, at this stage, was still often out of breath and had chest pains. The surgeon decided to do a stress test. It was arranged for the same time as my scan. Luke's testing went through out-patient, allowing us to stay with my best friend, the founder of the heart support group. My fetal echo went great, with no major defects identified. Luke's stress test also went great but provided no explanation for the chest pains.

A lot of people asked me if I was scared about maybe having another heart child. My reaction was that I had been there and done that. I knew I could cope and was prepared.

Our new baby daughter was born on 21 November, 1991. Luke wanted a baby brother but had to be content with a sister. Well, a certain little miss coming into our lives took the pressure off Luke. His neurotic mother had someone else to occupy her mind.

That year at school Luke gave me a scare. I told him that he could not run in the annual school race, which the teachers and principal knew; however, Luke participated anyway. No one noticed until Luke came down the finishing track. The principal rang me and apologised. I told him it was not his fault and dealt with Luke after school. I sat down and explained all the things that could have gone wrong. The next year he participated with warnings. He still overdid it and became tachycardic, but the paramedics monitored Luke's heartbeat until it resumed a normal rate. He was fine and had a great time racing. Luke continues to defy his heart condition and lead a normal life.

When he was seven years old, Luke broke his leg. We had just arrived at our holiday destination when Ken took the kids over to the swings. Luke, clowning around on the slide, fell over the edge, landing straight on his chest. Ken kept asking about his chest, and Luke kept saying his leg hurt. Luke finally said his chest was fine. That night Luke whimpered in his sleep, so the next morning we made a doctor's appointment for him. Sure enough his leg was broken and had to go in plaster for six weeks.

At age ten, Luke went in for another catheterisation. The doctor discontinued the Capoten because the hole in the patch seemed to have closed a little, and Luke was doing quite well. I immediately went into panic mode, but the cardiologist at home kept a close eye on him. Thankfully, Luke started to gain weight.

He began to play and enjoy soccer, which is now his passion. He cannot run as fast as the other kids, but he makes a good goal keeper. Luke received a trophy for "Most Improved" a few years ago. So far he has had no injuries, although his hands get icy cold.

At age fourteen, Luke is in grade ten and discovering his own place in the world. We still do not know what the future holds in Luke's life, but then none of us have any guarantees. We thank the doctors at Prince Charles Hospital and Luke's doctors here in Cairns for the care and attention our family has received.

Lyn and Luke Chappell

A Light in my Life—New Zealand

By: Jasmina Henderson-Rauter

My name is Jasmina, and I am from Slovenia. My husband, Darren is from New Zealand. We have two little boys, Mikey born 26 February 1992 and our heart baby, Tjas, born 18 September 1994.

My second pregnancy was much different from my first one. Most of the time I felt sick and tired. I blamed this on having a toddler to look after, but at the same time, I felt worried. I had a fetal scan done during the eighteenth week of pregnancy and "everything looked perfect" yet somehow that did not ease my mind.

I had a feeling something might be wrong, yet I wanted to believe everything was fine. I wanted an ultrasound at the end of pregnancy, but my midwife thought it unnecessary, so I did not push the issue. My labor was very long and in the end required an emergency forceps delivery because Tjas' heart rate dropped to 60 beats per minute. He was delivered "flat" and needed to be resuscitated.

We did not know what was happening at the time. Doctors and nurses took my baby away, and I barely saw him. They rushed him to the Neonatal Intensive Care Unit (NICU). After a half an hour, we got a photo of my little boy. His eyes were open, but he had tubes and wires all around him. At that time we did not know what was wrong with him; we thought it was just stress from the difficult birth.

His APGARs were 2 the first minute, 4 at five minutes and 6 at ten minutes. Despite full mechanical ventilation and an FiO2 of 100%, he remained cyanotic with saturations in the 50's. The doctor on duty told us he had very bad news.

A chest X-ray showed a narrow mediastinum, and an urgent echocardiogram confirmed transposition of the great arteries (TGA) with an intact septum and small ductus.

We did not know what that meant. He drew a picture of Tjas' heart and a normal heart. Then, he told us we would have to go on the first free flight to Auckland (about 1700 km from Christchurch and on another island) because there was a pediatric heart hospital where Tjas would need an operation very soon.

We were very upset. I think I cried. Darren had to go home to tell his parents, pack a few things and get Mikey. The doctor came to tell me they had tickets for us and that Tjas would be transported in an incubator. He was a big baby (3790 g and 54 cm), so he looked squeezed into it.

I went to see Tjas in the NICU, but I was too afraid to take a photo. I was so scared I would lose him. In the room by myself, I could not sleep. I lay there wondering how my baby was doing and what was happening. I waited for the sun to rise. The nurse took some photos of Tjas for me. I was still recovering from giving birth.

In the morning, Darren arrived with his parents and Mikey, a new big brother who could not hold his baby brother. I told him through the pregnancy how he would hold and take home his brother. Instead we all went to the aerport. I did not feel much; I was numb.

The ambulance carried Tjas and a registered nurse. We were ready to go. Darren's parents did not say much. I was afraid to phone my mum; I was scared she would start to cry and that would push me over the edge. I got my father on the phone; he was very supportive, trying to reassure me everything would be okay. I certainly hoped so.

Tjas was in the NICU when we arrived. We arrived by shuttle bus because I could not leave Mikey by himself, and Darren could not leave me since I was a stranger to this country. I was given a room for myself, and we were told Darren and Mikey would get a room in a nurses' home (a short walk from the hospital).

The pediatric cardiologist came to tell us about the operation and that it needed to be done soon (in the first two weeks of life). She drew a picture of Tjas' heart and told us he would need to undergo an atrial balloon septostomy to make an atrial septal defect (ASD) because his saturations did not improve with near maximal prostaglandin E1 infusion.

She said he was listed for the operation the following week. I did not comprehend what I was told; I just wanted to hold my baby and share him with my two-and-a-half year old son and my husband. We had to wait for doctors to perform the balloon septostomy, and then we were able to see him. We took a few photos of Tjas and his brother, then Darren stayed with him while I stayed with Mikey. We set up shifts for day and night.

I slept in my room for a bit on the first night, but I was miserable not having my baby with me while all around me were babies waking up to be fed. All I had was a picture and the hope that he would be okay.

Tjas waited for his operation for months. He got sicker and sicker, catching all the bugs floating around. First he developed seizures after his balloon atrial septostomy (which, unknown to me, was done without anesthesia), and he was put on phenobarbital. Then Tjas got pneumonia, the reason his saturations did not get higher than 50% for first two weeks of life. He even developed all the signs of necrotising enterocolitis, which was discovered in the earliest stages. He needed a lots of IVs which were very hard on him. After about two weeks he stopped fighting and would not move. The cardiologists and pediatrician decided that his brain must be damaged from low O2 and from being flat at birth.

They told me it would not make sense to operate on Tjas if he were brain damaged because he would not survive. We had to wait to see if he would improve and get off the ventilator in order to transfer him to another hospital for a CT scan. He did get better, but en route he got septicaemia. We nearly lost him three times that night.

Finally he was all ready to be transferred 200 meters to another hospital for surgery. That was a big day for me. I was so scared, but happy thinking that once we were there, no one could put my baby off the waiting list. I was wrong. The last night before we were transferred, Tjas' SATs were between the high 80s and low 90s. When I saw 94% on the monitor, I thought it must be miracle and that God decided Tjas would not need the operation after all. I was wrong again.

When we arrived at Green Lane heart hospital, Tjas was on prostaglandin and had oxygen via a nasal canula. His SATs were 80-

90%. Unfortunately Tjas' doctor discontinued the prostaglandin (due to his ASD) after Tjas arrived, but during the night Tjas became cyanotic, so the prostaglandin had to be re-administered. It was Saturday, and the operation was scheduled for Monday morning. I was so afraid something else would happen while we waited. My husband and Mikey, who had to go back to Christchurch after a week in Auckland, came to see us every second weekend, and of course for the operation.

When they arrived, I had to tell them bad news: Tjas' operation was changed to Tuesday afternoon. No one had even told me this directly. I just overheard some doctors discussing Tjas' case. When I burst into tears, no one knew why I was crying.

Finally the day came. We had a family photograph made. Although nervous, Darren had his first cuddle with Tjas. We all believed that Tjas had been through so much he had to survive, but it was still difficult to kiss him good-bye . . . until later. I carried him to the theatre, and I held him close. We had to wait for the nurse to get us. I wanted time to stop.

Darren and Mikey said good-bye to Tjas and waited outside (Mikey was too noisy and lively to wait in the preoperation room). I came out so light; my hands were empty and my heart almost could not cope. Mikey went for one hour to the playroom. We did not want to upset him with our tears. Darren and I went for a walk in the park nearby. We returned asking whether there was any news from the theatre (we knew he had to survive, but on Monday a boy who had TGA died on the operating table, which gave me even more to worry about).

After about four hours we got the good news, Tjas was off bypass. He would soon be in the Intensive Care Unit, and we could go see him!

Darren and I were so happy! We got Mikey and waited for the phone call. Finally a nurse told us to go downstairs to see Tjas. They told us he was still a very sick boy and that the next twenty-four hours would determine his outcome.

I was happy to see him. He was heavily drugged, but he opened his eyes for us. He was full of drains and tubes; he had a central line for all the drugs. But he was alive! Darren and I started doing "shifts" again taking turns caring for Tjas and Mikey. We could not stay there overnight, but the nurses promised to call us if anything happened. I went upstairs to sleep.

In the morning when I saw Tjas, I could not believe my eyes. He was pink! He was so pink. I took a picture of him. I ran to the Nurses' Home where Mikey and Darren were sleeping to tell them. Because of his history, doctors predicted Tjas would have to stay in ICU for at least ten days. Three days after the operation, he was extubated, and we stayed in ICU for four more days just to be safe.

The day we went to the ward, I knew nothing else could happen. We had our own room, and I finally got to take care of Tjas. He still had his pacemaker attached, two drains and his head was in an oxygen box, but he started to suck. He never tried before. I was expressing milk for him all that time. Like magic, the first time I tried to breast-feed him, he took to it. Unfortunately I did not have a lot of milk, so he needed top-offs through the nasogastric tube.

Darren and Mikey had to return home. Darren was training for a new job, and he was about to start. This time it was not so difficult to say good-bye because we knew we would soon all be together again.

Tjas continued to improve so that after a few days the nurse removed the monitor. I protested, but she told me I would have to learn to live without it. The first day or two I was nervous and could not wait for the nurse's rounds to see if Tjas's SATs had dropped. Soon afterward, though, I stopped worrying.

The life on the ward was nice. I met a lot of sick babies and their parents. We had a common bond. There were difficult moments when babies died, or there was little hope, but for the most part I felt secure on the ward.

I was really homesick. I wanted to take Tjas home, but the doctors did not want to discharge us with the nasogastric tube. My milk was slowly coming in, but not quickly enough. Tjas started with formula top-offs after he used my frozen supply, but he did not like the bottle.

After one week on the ward, we were flown back to Christchurch hospital until the feeding was established. I was happy and nervous. We were given first class tickets on the national line, but we went alone without a nurse or doctor. In Christchurch an ambulance was waiting for us.

I dressed my little boy, packed my luggage and took a taxi to the aerport. Of course, first we had to say good-bye to everyone and take as many photos as possible. At the aerport my suitcase fell apart, and I had to give Tjas to someone to hold for a minute while I fixed it. I would never have believed I could release Tjas from my hands even for that small moment.

On the plane I nursed Tjas so he would go to sleep, and I cried with happiness. In Christchurch Darren and Mikey were waiting, and we were reunited. After staying one day in the hospital, we were discharged home.

All this time we kept in touch with my mother by phone. The first phone call was the scariest. I was scared my mum would start to cry, and then I would break down, but she was so strong for me. She reassured me Tjas would be okay, and they all prayed for him. It was difficult for her to be so far away from us. Not knowing English was hard, too (my mum is Slovenien). Yet, she phoned many times, and even when I did not have good news for her, she was so brave. It was hard for Darren's parents too because of the distance. They looked after Mikey when he was away from me. Mikey somehow understood that his brother was sick, and I had to stay with him. He never cried when he returned to Christchurch despite the fact that we had never been separated before.

After we came home, an outreach nurse visited us twice a week. Tjas was on two medications—furosemide (Lasix) and phenobarbital for the first three months. After that he was weaned from both medications. Although we did not need our outreach nurse any more, we saw our PC frequently. I just could not stop worrying about Tjas. Mikey was a great brother during the day but had nightmares while sleeping.

After the operation everything was better for Tjas. We saw his pediatrician every three months, then every six months and now annually. Five months after the operation, we saw a pediatric cardiologist who was very happy with Tjas' development, although Tjas had a murmur. The next time we had an appointment in May of 1997 (two and a half years later) no murmur was heard! Now Tjas does not need to see the cardiologist for another two years!

The doctors do not expect any complications, and Tjas is free to do whatever he wishes in life. He is a healthy little boy (with colds and ear infections, like any other child his age), but he developed asthma when he was two years old, which is pretty common in New Zealand.

Tjas is a very active little boy and in the 90th percentile for height

Tjas (age 5)

and weight. He has a very lovely nature but can be stubborn as well. His front teeth are a little discolored due to strong antibiotics, and his voice is hoarse due to a lot of intubations during his stay in NICU before the operation, and a possibly damaged nerve during the operation. He is developing very well and is very bright for his age. Until recently, he enjoyed looking at the photos from when he was sick. He even wanted to watch a video tape of himself, but when he saw tears in my eyes, he agreed to turn it off.

Tjas really brought light to my life; he gave me faith and love. I am glad he came into my life. He taught me to take nothing for granted.

A Saint for Sebastian—United Kingdom

By: Susanne Mühlhaus

Sebastian was born on December 16th, 1990 in Gibraltar, an overpopulated British colony with bilingual Spanish-English speaking citizens at the southern tip of Spain.

Since I worked and paid health insurance contributions in Gibraltar, my family received free treatment under the Gibraltarian National Health Service. At the time, only straightforward medical problems were treated in Gibraltar, while more complicated cases were referred to British hospitals, where patients were not only treated for free under a reciprocal agreement between Britain and Gibraltar, but also given an open return plane ticket (and in the case of child patients, an accompanying person also). In addition, the insurance provided an allowance towards accommodation costs. This unusual arrangement, unbeknown to me at the time, later proved to be of crucial importance.

We found it difficult to decide on a name for this sweet little baby, but we were finally happy with Sebastian. Little did I know that the image of the martyr St. Sebastian with an arrow through the heart should take on some special significance for my precious baby boy.

Sebastian was a normal healthy-looking boy, our second child. Although I had breast-fed my first child for nine months I was not very successful with Sebastian. The nurses at the baby clinic were not very helpful and appeared to just want to expedite the visit. After a few weeks I changed to baby formula. He started bringing up most of his milk, and he was also a little blue around his mouth; although the lips themselves were red. At the baby clinic I was told that this was normal. Some babies are sick; others are not. In the literature I read, large amounts of "flat" vomiting were not described as normal. I sensed that something was wrong.

When Sebastian was six weeks old, he suddenly suffered from a terrible cough, and the general practitioner (GP) told me that he was admitting him. I was devastated. Rather than going by ambulance through congested narrow roads, I walked the several hundred steps halfway up the Rock, where the Gibraltarian hospital was situated. This gave me time to regain my composure.

By the time Sebastian saw the pediatrician, he had somewhat recovered from his croupy cough in the fresh air, and I wanted to take him back home, but the pediatrician insisted on seeing him anyway. He heard a heart murmur. This already confirmed my darkest fears. Of course, murmurs are insignificant in many cases, but I somehow knew that this would not apply to us. My little baby had to see the chief pediatrician. The intervals from one appointment to another at this stage seemed to be very long—weeks, probably months.

Then Sebastian was put on a list to see the cardiologist from England who came to Gibraltar every few months, but no one knew when exactly he would come next, and I was told to be on stand-by, ready to come into the hospital at very short notice. Several months passed. I called the hospital repeatedly, only to be told that there was no news. The Gulf War was given as a reason for the cardiologist's delay. Doctors were needed in the Gulf. I found that a little strange. Surely cardiologists were not needed there.

All the time the vomiting continued. I tried different formulas, but it did not subside. Sebastian did grow, though perhaps a little less than others. The doctor at the routine checkup and the nurses maintained that vomiting was normal, contrary to information from all the books I had consulted. These were mainly books for parents and nurses, and in fact, a nurses' manual stated that Failure to Thrive can be related to congenital heart disease. But my comments did not elicit a single response from the staff at the baby clinic.

What I found most difficult to cope with during this time was the uncertainty due to lack of information. No diagnosis had yet been made, hence I did not know what the prospects were. The doctors were vague, and the books available in Gibraltar's only book shop and in the public library were, although not of a specialist nature, both daunting and at the same time too superficial in the description they gave of heart conditions.

Finally, when Sebastian was six months old, the phone call came. He had been waiting to see the cardiologist from the age of six weeks. When I entered the waiting area of the hospital, I was instantly scared. Everyone looked so worried. My baby was the youngest patient. The room was so crowded that many people had to stand. We waited more than two hours before the cardiologist arrived. Apparently the plane had been delayed.

A tall, dark-haired figure with piercing blue eyes swished passed the waiting patients with the director of the hospital and several other staff in tow. After another long wait it was our turn. No greeting, no introduction. The cardiologist's breath smelled of cognac. He listened to Sebastian's chest for about ten seconds, and then he told us we could go, immediately resuming his conversation with the hospital director exchanging the latest gossip.

On my way out I apologised, but I really wanted to know what was wrong with Sebastian's heart. To my surprise the cardiologist was not very helpful. He told me that Sebastian probably had a ventricular septal defect or VSD. He confirmed that a VSD is a hole in the heart. He also told me that Sebastian would have to go to a specialist hospital in England for checkups. I had to drag every piece of information out of the doctor because he answered in curt sentences without much explanation.

That was the last I saw of this man. Later I found out his name from the my son's file. Fortunately Sebastian was referred to a different hospital from the one where he worked. And fortunately this first cardiologist's unwillingness to communicate seemed to be rather the exception. All of my subsequent encounters with pediatric cardiologists and surgeons were much more positive in this respect. Indeed they always gave me all the time I needed for clarification.

Another three months passed before Sebastian received an appointment at Great Ormond Street Hospital for Sick Children (GOS) in London. He was now nine months old. His consultant pediatric cardiologist was Dr. Catherine Bull. After listening to his chest, she said that he probably had a hole in his heart that might either close on its own or require surgery.

After the echocardiogram, she said that he had aortic stenosis and a bicuspid aortic valve. I was not prepared for this. I had read up on ventricular septal defects in the nurses' manual, but the pronunciation of "aortic stenosis" was so different from my native German—although a similar term—that I could not even picture how to spell it.

She explained the condition to me, at least the basics at this stage, which was not difficult to understand because it is technically—or morphologically rather—not a complicated condition. The main heart valve, between the left ventricle and the aorta, only had two leaflets instead of three, and these two were partly fused together. When the valve opened, the opening was considerably smaller than with a normal valve; therefore, the heart had to work harder to get oxygenated blood into the body. In time, this leads to an enlarged left ventricle and eventually to heart failure.

In Sebastian's case the left ventricle was slightly enlarged. The difference (gradient) in blood pressure before and after the aortic valve is an important measurement and can be an indication for the severity of the defect. Sebastian's pressure gradient across the valve was 98 mmHg—an indication of severe to critical stenosis. In addition to this situation, his valve was much thicker than normal, which resulted in reduced flexibility of the valve. The cardiologist suggested balloon valvuloplasty, but said that Sebastian might need open-heart surgery.

Of course I preferred the ballooning, which would take place a few days later. I was in shock! I had only taken my baby to England for a checkup, and now he was to have surgery. But this surgery was called a procedure by medical staff, since it is non-invasive. Although we had stayed in a hotel up to now, I moved into the parents' quarters in the basement of the hospital once Sebastian was admitted. No children were allowed in the parents' dormitories.

When I handed my nine-month-old, wonderful, perfect little baby over to the consultant in front of the catheter lab, it felt like betrayal, like handing him over to the enemy. I just did not want to let go of him. But, of course, they were his best friends.

Balloon valvuloplasty basically works as follows: a catheter is inserted into a blood vessel in the groin area and brought up to the heart. A ballooning device is inserted into the catheter and inflated once or twice when in the aortic valve, thereby (hopefully) opening up the fused (stenotic) part of the valve. An angiogram is also taken, and the whole procedure is carried out under X-ray control and under general anaesthesia (not with adults). I had also been worried about possible over-exposure to radiation, but these fears were quickly allayed because the paediatric cardiologist was pregnant and still participated in catheterisations several days per week without ever coming close to the maximum permitted level of radiation exposure.

The balloon dilatation was uneventful. No additional malformations were found. It had not occurred to me previously that Sebastian might have additional defects—another little shock. I realised then that "they" might not tell you everything, if you do not ask the right questions. The gradient had dropped significantly but was at 90 again the following day. We were told to go home and to come back in six months.

This had been such an overwhelming experience for me that I found it very difficult to come through the grieving period. At first I was not really aware that there was such a thing as a grieving period. After all, he was alive. He was a patient at the best hospital, but somehow I was really depressed. My concept of a healthy child had died, and that is what I mourned.

At the same time I had to accept that Sebastian has a heart condition, which, in one way or another, will remain an issue for the rest of our lives. I learnt that sudden death can occur, and, for a while, when he smiled at me, I started crying—every time. I realised that this must have a very strange effect on him, and I forced myself not to cry so much any more, at least not in front of him. I was numb and on auto-pilot for a long time. I felt very much on my own.

I was also extremely sensitive to how others responded to my baby's condition. Since he was asymptomatic, a lot of people said, "Oh, he's all right, look at him, he looks healthy." This made me feel really angry. I often thought, "Who do these people think they are! Some kind of self-styled experts who know better than cardiologists and cardiac surgeons and medical text books and myself?"

I felt pressure to get on with things; consequently, I did not talk as much about Sebastian's condition or the way I felt about it. After all I did not want to bore anyone by bringing it up again and again. I withdrew. I took stock, reassessed my life and I found that I was not where I wanted to be, not with whom I wanted to be and not doing what I wanted to do. The first thing to go was my relationship with the children's father.

Gibraltar was a country with very limited access to information: just one public library, only one book shop without any specialised books, no university. This was only a few years ago. But in 1991/92 the Internet was not a major source of information in Europe yet, and information was what I wanted above all else. I wanted to know everything I could possibly learn in order to make the best possible decision for my son.

Although the staff at GOS were helpful with answering my questions, I found I had to gain some knowledge of the subject before knowing what to ask. Since you cannot ask about something if you do not know it exists, and general questions will often only be answered in a general way, I spent many days in the medical section in the basement of Foyle's book shop in London. I read through books I could not afford to buy and took notes with Sebastian crawling and later walking amongst piles of books. I do not know if the staff minded or not, but they never said anything.

At the following appointment the gradient was at 50. Good! For the next out-patient appointment I decided to bring my six year old along so that the London visit would be more fun. We stayed in a hotel, and my parents also came to London for a few days. When we were told that Sebastian should have surgery, we were speechless.

Sebastian needed an aortic valvotomy—open-heart surgery, accessing the heart through the opened breastbone (median sternotomy). The heart is stopped and put on a bypass machine. The surgeon makes an incision in the aorta above the aortic valve, then the fused leaflets of the valve are cut open (aortic commisurotomy). The surgery takes three to five hours. My parents had to leave before the surgery took place, and with my older son there as well, it was not an ideal situation. While we were awaiting surgery, the hospital arranged for me and the children to move from our hotel to a free home-away-from-home house maintained by a charity, probably similar to a Ronald McDonald House in the States.

Both the pediatric cardiologist and the surgeon, Mr. Martin Elliott, let me have as much of their time as I wanted to discuss the options and eventualities. While Sebastian was given the anaesthetic, I apologised over and over to him that I was putting him through this. We went to a church near the hospital, and the organist was rehearsing at full volume. Any other sound was completely suffocated by the music. I kneeled down at the back where no one could hear me . . .

The staff at GOS leads parents into the Cardiac Intensive Care Unit (CICU) the day prior to surgery as a standard procedure. This is great proof of their empathy towards parents. On the tour through the units, I saw another child who had recently arrived in CICU after heart surgery, which helped to absorb some of the shock of seeing my own precious baby there the following day. Every part of his body was wired-up, and air was being pressed into his lungs by a machine. Sebastian's brother and I managed to distract ourselves from the mind-numbing, emotional impact of the surgery by concentrating on the technical details and asking staff about the function of every single device to which he was connected or being monitored. We stayed with Sebastian during almost all of his time in CICU. The surgeon said it had been a straightforward operation. He recovered very quickly but still requires regular follow-up and more surgery in the future.

When we returned to Gibraltar, I had already made up my mind that I did not want to stay there any longer. But instead of returning to my country of birth, Germany, I moved to London with my children. In Germany I have some relatives whose heart baby did not survive after being transported from one hospital to the next. Their story has sharpened my perception of the excellent hospital care we received in London, including an experienced surgical team. I am very happy with the care Sebastian receives at GOS. I have also met many German and Austrian parents who take their sick children there, or who have been referred there because some types of routine surgery at GOS may only be performed occasionally in German and Austrian hospitals. Although the move to England meant suffering initial hardships, we have not regretted the move since.

I found a job teaching in higher education and am researching medical terminology for a Ph.D. with access to all the information I want. Currently, I am discovering more about the Ross operation which will be considered as an option for Sebastian's further treatment. It is unlikely that Sebastian's valve, which is gradually fusing up again, will tolerate another valvotomy without severe leaking.

Therefore, the doctors will consider removing Sebastian's aortic valve, putting his own pulmonary valve in the aortic position, whilst inserting a donor's valve into the pulmonary position. This is a complicated procedure with a high success rate but a lack of long-term results. The cardiologist suggests another attempt at ballooning his valve before a Ross operation.

We feel very much at home in England, different from feeling like a herd of sheep or goats on a rock; however, I am extremely grateful that the Gibraltarian chief pediatrician referred Sebastian to such an excellent hospital and that the Gibraltarian National Health Service provided the means for this initially.

Now Sebastian's checkups and future operations are covered under the state plan, the National Health Service. Paediatric cardiologists here discourage parents from taking out private health insurance for their heart children. The only advantage of private insurance is that the patient can sometimes have a private room rather than sharing one with three to seven others.

In the U.K. there is little social support and very few contacts with other heart children and their parents other than via the Internet. On request, the hospital gave me a list of addresses and phone numbers of some support groups in the U.K., but none of them appears to be operational; therefore, I am considering starting a support group in the U.K.

We might not stay here forever, but my first and foremost concern will always be for Sebastian to have access to excellent specialist facilities, wherever we may move to in the future.

During our stays at the hospital, I have met some children who suffer from much more complicated heart conditions than Sebastian. For me this has been a frightening and guilt-ridden experience every time. These children and their parents are a reminder to us that we are very lucky indeed, and it has helped me put things in perspective. In general, I found that talking to other heart parents helps because they are the only ones who know what it feels like—they have been there, too.

My older son told me that when Sebastian was smaller, he used to think his brother would die at any moment, but now he knows that this is unlikely. Sometimes he thinks that I care more about his younger brother because of his heart problem. I reassure him that this is not true. He did not mind being at the hospital when Sebastian had surgery. In fact, as a budding scientist, he said he learnt a lot and felt privileged to see how things worked in Intensive Care.

Now five years post-op, I can cautiously enjoy life again, and I am enjoying it with my children. Sebastian is just over six years old now and doing well, although his gradient has slowly deteriorated from 20 post-op in 1992 to about 45 in 1997. He will require further open-heart surgery—nobody knows how many times. Presently, he is not on any medication and never has been, but, like with most heart children, antibiotic prophylaxis is required in case of injury and invasive procedure (such as dental work). Although his heart condition is not complicated, he does have a reduced life expectancy—statistically speaking. I always have an underlying fear, since every type of heart surgery carries many risks and potential complications could lead into all sorts of options. I fear that Sebastian will face difficulties or disabilities and even more complicated surgical procedures that I have not even considered up to now—or death.

In life, Sebastian is a very bright, an incredibly determined and happy little boy. None of his classmates have ever asked him about his scars. When somebody asked him once what he had on his chest, he just answered "a scar," and the person was too embarrassed to ask any further questions. Sebastian does get tired quickly; he cannot walk far without pausing, and when we go cycling on weekends, I regularly pull him more than half the way.

Luckily he also enjoys quieter pastimes, such as a game of chess. He has passed the entrance test to a private (day) school and has just started there in Year 2. I expect him to do well academically. I have taken on a second job to pay for his school fees and hobbies such as skiing and golf. Why not! He should have the best while he can. He deserves it.

Mothers in the Hospital

One of the hardest things for a mother to endure is seeing her child in the hospital. Moms of healthy children solve most "medical problems" with something handy in the medicine cabinet, with band-aids or with kisses. A mother's gentle touch, her hugs, her loving attention cures that problem, when little throats are sore, ears hurt, or tummies ache. If worse comes to worst Mom spreads Vicks on a coughing child's chest, takes a temperature with a thermometer (instead of her hand), or uses a humidifier to make breathing easier.

However, when a child is in the hospital, the mom is not the expert. Mom cannot fix what is wrong. She must depend on prayers, love and the expertise of strangers to remedy any problems. A smart doctor or nurse knows to enlist Mom as part of the healing team.

There may not be anything a mother can do to heal a child's heart defect. Wishing, praying and loving does not cure a heart abnormality. There are many things, though, that a mother can do to inspire a child to live. A mother's love can reach where no surgeon's scalpel can go. While this love cannot cure, it *can* give a child the will to survive.

In the following three essays, moms write about their hospitalization experiences due to their child's open-heart surgery. Although Julie, Holly and Patty may not have an RN or an M.D. after their names, they were part of the team of healers whose wisdom, hard work and love guided their angels back into their homes.

The Heart of a Mother

Our Love for Alex

By: Julie Schlapfer

It took two years to conceive Alex. When he finally arrived our joy was complete; however, our celebration was quickly overshadowed by a frightening visitor. A birth defect called hypoplastic left heart syndrome.

I am the type of person who gags at a runny nose or throws up if someone else gags. My husband, Kevin, was and remains the kind of person who can take anything directed his way. We both have a strong faith in God and believe that what we are given is for a purpose. We were quickly thrown into a situation in which we had no control or knowledge. We relied on our faith, each other, family and friends for support in this difficult time.

We rapidly assumed unexpected roles. It was not the typical dad-comes-home-at-the-end-of-the-day situation. Instead of a mother at home bubbling with news of baby's "firsts," we were in a hospital. From 8:00 a.m. to 11:00 p.m., we were incubator sitters. Over the course of three years and three open-heart surgeries, we became pros at living in the medical world.

In the beginning Alex was so young he did not understand what was happening. By his second and third surgery, however, he was more than well aware of his surroundings and caregivers. We tried to make Alex as comfortable as possible. Over the course of the two months we were in the hospital, Alex spent day and night hooked up to IVs, heart monitors, ventilators and chest tubes. He was bothered at all hours for tests necessary for his survival.

No child should have to endure living in an ICU. Alex did this three times. It became Kevin's and my mission to make the time Alex spent in the hospital as happy as possible. I spent the days at his bedside, leaving only briefly to go to the bathroom or get a quick bite to eat. Kevin spent the nights at Alex's bedside, sleeping in a fold-out chair, wearing eye blinders and ear plugs to diminish the monitor sounds. It was an exhausting time for both of us; however, Alex's well-being came first.

Alex had a stuffed animal named Puff which he carried constantly. In order to make Alex feel comfortable with medical procedures, we made sure that whatever was done to Alex was also done to Puff. He is the only stuffed animal I know who has endured multiple IVs, blood pressure readings, temperature checks and X-rays. Puff was at Alex's side during surgery, even returning from the operating room with bandages just like Alex. All this made Alex feel as though he was not going through the procedures alone.

We found that a very important aspect of Alex's recovery was our participation. I do not mean just changing the bed linen, feeding him or walking him around the ward. I mean being there when the IVs needed changing, giving him a reassuring kiss, letting him know he was okay. It meant lifting him from his bed with four chest tubes hanging from his body so he could be put into a little wagon and wheeled into the playroom for a change of scenery.

I even insisted on holding my son when it came time for the chest tubes to be removed. They are literally pulled out, something which might cause most people to faint. Afraid as I was, I knew Alex needed me, and I found the courage to do what I needed to encourage him.

As much as our times in the hospital were stressful and often exhausting, I cannot imagine what Alex was going through. It was this thought that kept us going in addition to the undying love we have for Alex, our precious gift from God. How could we do anything but be there to care for him?

We are truly blessed to have medical resources so close to home. The surgeries took place at Boston Children's Hospital. The doctors and nursing staff displayed impeccable care. We are grateful they allowed us to participate in most areas of Alex's care. We found at Boston Children's Hospital that a parent's voice is always heard and on many occasions accepted, which Kevin and I found to be an invaluable ingredient in the care and recuperation of our son.

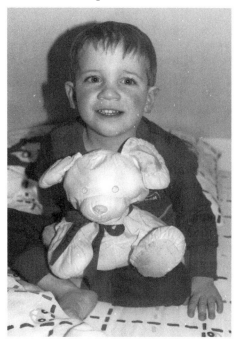

Alex and Puff

The Heart of a Mother

Supporting Sadie

By: Holly Scheyer

My daughter, Sadie, was born on May 15, 1995 with hypoplastic left heart syndrome. She has survived three open-heart surgeries, two balloon angioplasties and a surgical debredement for a staph infection after her last open-heart surgery.

We have spent over two months of her life at Children's Hospital in Seattle. Sadie does not behave like a "sick" child though; she loves life and all it has to offer. She loves to sing, laugh and play games and has a great sense of humor. Sadie is our first child, and although it has been tough, I know we have grown to be better people through this experience.

Sadie's first two open-heart surgeries occurred before she was five months old. She had relatively quick recoveries and no problem gaining weight. We were told that the surgeons like to do the third surgery (completion Fontan) about a year after the second, but she ended up waiting twenty months because her health was fine, and the doctors wanted to wait until after cold and flu season.

This period of time allowed us to establish a sense of normalcy in our lives and also gave us time to prepare for her final open-heart repair. The surgery was then scheduled for spring 1997 but had to be postponed twice due to illness. I wondered if Sadie somehow knew that surgery was approaching because she was having more colds than ever before. Fortunately, she made it through a bout of influenza and two separate colds, finally having the Fontan on June 25, 1997.

I had a lot of apprehension not only about the surgery but also about how Sadie would cope with the whole experience now that she was old enough to somewhat understand what was happening. Postponing surgery worsened my anxieties because I would prepare for the surgery then be told we must wait. Part of me was relieved that we had more time to enjoy with her before the surgery, but I think my fears increased the longer I had to wait. During this time I really felt the need to talk to others whose children had been through the Fontan and also those who were approaching it. I spent much of my free time on the Internet gathering information and emailing or chatting with other parents of children with heart defects. My motto was "knowledge is power" because I wanted to understand all the physical aspects of the surgery and be able to ask the right questions. My husband, Kurt, was dealing with his fears inwardly so I could not turn to him as much as I would have liked. This was difficult at first, but we learned to accept that we had different ways of dealing with our feelings.

Fortunately, I was able to learn a lot from a friend whose son, James, was having his Fontan before Sadie. She would keep me apprised of James' recovery and give me advice about how to deal with situations at the hospital. For instance, she recommended the primary nurse who had taken good care of James. She also put a sign above James' bed that read "Please wash your hands before touching me," which we ended up doing for Sadie. I was able to help her by sharing information that I had gathered from the Internet. James was in the hospital for about a month because of pleural effusion (fluid drainage around the lung), but he seemed to be handling his long-term stay in the hospital well, which gave me hope for Sadie's recovery. Unfortunately, another child that we knew of did not survive his Fontan operation, and although we did not know his family well, it broke my heart. I tried not to compare, but about a week before Sadie's surgery date, I had an emotional breakdown.

My grandmother was in town, and we were getting ready to go out to dinner with the whole family. I was not in the mood to be social, so I went into the bedroom and laid down. I could not stop crying which was the catalyst for a family discussion about our fears concerning Sadie's surgery. The discussion helped to relieve my heavy load a bit by learning that everyone was feeling concerned and that I did not have to be strong all the time. In addition, my family realized how much support I needed, and during Sadie's recovery they gave us an amazing amount of assistance.

I recalled from the past surgeries that the feeling of helplessness can be overwhelming during the operation and recovery period. I wanted to find out as much as I could about ways I could prepare and help Sadie deal with her surgery. I borrowed children's books from the library about going to the hospital (I recommend Mr. Rogers' booklet *Going to the Hospital*) and bought a play medical kit for her. We added some things to the kit that we had collected from other hospital stays, and she really enjoyed playing doctor. Due to Sadie's age I did not mention the operation until the day before; however, she was familiar with some of the tests that she would go through from reading the books.

Sadie's grandmother and great-grandmother helped me design and sew a cozy floral gown for her and a matching one for her dolly. Her dolly was given to her from her other grandmother who had embroidered a zipper (scar) and a heart with the words "I Love Sadie" written inside it.

Also in preparation, my family and I decided to have a meeting with two individuals whom we knew from Children's Hospital (a clinical nurse specialist and social worker) to discuss the surgery and get some ideas for helping Sadie. One of the ideas they suggested was to make a cassette tape for her to listen to with headphones while she was in the operating room. Perhaps Sadie's subconscious would absorb familiar music and encouraging voices instead of hearing the scary machinery and discussion in the OR. We thought that was a great idea especially because we believe that Sadie is terrified of sounds that remind her of being in surgery.

Luckily my brother happens to have recording equipment in his home, so he helped me with it. We recorded relaxing music (Native American flute) for background, and during part of the tape, we talked about how much we love her and how strong and healthy she is. We also told her a story about a little girl going through heart surgery. We talked about the feelings she experienced and explained her happiness upon returning home. I sang some songs Sadie likes and read some of her favorite stories, and my brother talked about all the fun things she would get to do when she got out of the hospital. We had fun putting the tape together and felt good knowing that we could do something constructive to help Sadie through surgery when we would feel most helpless.

This resulted in a very successful surgery and relatively short time on the respirator after surgery (she was extubated the first night). When she was able to talk, she rambled on all night long about all the things she wanted to do when she got out of the hospital—the same things my brother had talked about on the tape!

We went through ups and downs during Sadie's recovery, although her heart function remained fairly stable. Ten days after surgery, Sadie was able to come home, but we ended up back in the hospital the next night because she had a staph infection and pleural effusion. It was very difficult to return, especially since we had to spend most of that night in the emergency room waiting for answers.

One of the ER nurses told us we won the parents' award for being calm. When you have been through difficulty, you learn to handle other things easily! Because of her infection and other complications, Sadie ended up staying in the hospital for twenty-three more days. During this time Sadie had to endure many painful and unpleasant procedures, which were very difficult for us to watch. It was not always easy, but I held her hand and comforted her during every procedure I could. I spent every night with her and never left her side unless there was a family member there to keep her company. Fortunately, I did have my family's support because Kurt had to return to work and was unable to be with us as much as he wanted.

The longer we were in the hospital, the more outspoken I became with the nurses. Ever since Sadie's second open-heart surgery, she had not been able to sleep through the night, and sleeplessness in the hospital was even worse. I instructed the nurses not to disturb her unless absolutely necessary and that I would let them know when she would wake up at night so they could take her vitals. For the most part they followed my request, but not always.

One nurse came in to change a diaper while Sadie was sleeping, and I just about lost control. It seemed that the nurse was more concerned about her shift records than about Sadie and me getting the rest we needed. After a couple weeks of sleep deprivation, I started to go a little crazy. I always felt as if I had to have one eye open at night. Any chance I got I took a nap. I let the staff know that when we were resting we did not want to take phone calls or be disturbed.

Eventually when Sadie was more stable, I requested no nightly disturbances and vitals to be taken once per shift in the official orders. When I had a problem with something, I went directly to one of the cardiac nurses. I found them to be understanding and accommodating when it came to my concerns. At one point Sadie was having a problem with fluid retention, and I was very worried. Doctors did not have an explanation and did not seem concerned. I consulted with a cardiac nurse, who figured out the problem; Sadie's antibiotic, which was diluted with sodium chloride (salt), caused her to swell.

Another problem we encountered was inconsistency in terms of nursing care and rooming situations. I asked to have a primary nurse and more privacy (which meant a room with two beds instead of four). It was difficult for Sadie to have a different nurse everyday especially when she got to the point of being upset with anyone wearing a hospital badge.

I give Sadie a lot of credit for taking care of herself. She became very insistent about the things she did or did not want. I let her be as vocal as she wanted even though she could not always get her wish granted. Her favorite sayings were: "NO OWIES," "NO MEDICINES," "GO AWAY," "ALL DONE," "LEAVE ON" (whenever they tried to peek under her gown). I tried to keep her as comfortable as possible by requesting pain medication when needed (they did not automatically give it to her). When she needed a blood draw, I asked to be told ahead of time so that we could get EMLA cream to numb her skin.

To make Sadie's stay easier for her, we brought comfort items from home such as books, videos, music, a blanket, a pillow, dolls, toys and games. She also found comfort in wearing her new sneakers. She even wore them in her sleep because when we tried to take them off she complained! She loved playing with stickers, bubbles and things to draw on (a Magnadoodle).

Because Sadie was being very picky about what she wanted to eat, I asked people who came to visit to bring favorite foods we could not get in the hospital. She also went through a period when she did not want to drink much. I feel very fortunate that I was still able to nurse her because sometimes it was the only thing she would request. It was also very comforting for her and gave her the extra nutrition that she needed.

Sadie loved to be pushed in a wheelchair as much as possible once she was able, and we spent a lot of time in the playroom. She especially looked forward to having people come visit her; so did I. Those times gave me an opportunity to take a break and go for a walk, take a shower or get something to eat. I carried a pager with me in case I was needed.

I did not have much free time, but I tried to write in a journal once a day which helped me keep my sanity. I am really glad that I did this because the experience becomes a blur after awhile. When we got home from the hospital, I wrote a summary of our experience and sent a copy to friends and relatives. I also was excited to report our homecoming to my Internet support group. Many of them were envious because their children were awaiting the Fontan. This really helped me put things in perspective. We were over our biggest hurdle. Even though we had to endure thirty-three grueling days in the hospital, we were very fortunate to be home. Now I felt that I could be even more supportive of others whose children were going through surgery.

Sadie adjusted very quickly to being home. We had taken pictures of her at different stages of her recovery so that we will be able to explain the experience to her when she is older. We made a scrapbook for her which has items such as Sadie's hospital bracelet, get well cards, meal tickets and discharge papers. I wonder what she will remember from her hospitalization when she grows up. I know it was a traumatic experience, but we did our best to make her feel safe and loved, which is what is most important.

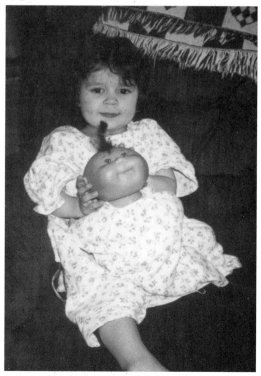

Sadie Scheyer

Finding the Good

By: Patty Roswick

When we were getting ready for the Fontan I got a bunch of stuff to make a pretend doctor's kit. We pretended to do X-rays and did the "yucky stuff" (Vaseline to pretend to do echocardiograms), and I even made coughing something really funny. I got Meghan to think coughing was funny because I knew how important—and painful—being able to cough would be post-op.

Probably the most important thing that I did was to get Meghan used to a Christian lullaby CD that I had bought. I played it for a long time before her Fontan every time she slept. We bought a jam box that had a CD player (with constant replay) and a walkman which automatically turned the tape over when it was done. When Meghan went into surgery, we requested that she listen to the walkman the whole time. The hospital staff was happy to oblige.

When Meghan woke up, we put the jam box on the head of the bed and played it constantly. Then, when she was moved to the floor, we played it whenever she slept. Not only was it great for her to have something totally familiar, but it also drowned out a lot of noises.

We packed everything we could to make her hospital surroundings more familiar. From day one she slept on her own crib sheets with her own bumper pad and even her mobile. We brought crib toys and stuffed animals. She slept in her own pajamas.

At the time, we had a Doberman pinscher, so I took a video of him playing around the house, and brought it to the hospital. Meghan totally lit up when I showed her. And of course we brought her favorite videos.

I feel that it made a big difference to her to have so many familiar things around her. Also, at that time (1991) the hospital was taking temperatures rectally or under the arm. Once Meghan's temperatures were consistent, the nurses let us take her temperature with our ear thermometer. Actually, I gave everyone in the room their own cover so even the nurses could use it!

One of the most meaningful things I did was not specifically for Meghan but for me, too. Every single day, no matter how impossible it seemed at times, I would make myself find at least one thing that was a positive step for her, and I would write it on my calendar. Sometimes it would be as little as her temperature going down a few degrees or giving a smile that looked like herself or her lungs not gaining fluid. There were nights I would rack my brain, feeling like the whole day was terrible, but I always came up with something!

I made a sticker with "I'm Going Home!" in big letters. I saved that sticker for my calendar for the day Meghan would come home. We were in the hospital for seventy-nine days for the Fontan, and at times I felt as if we would never leave, but I always looked at that sticker and thought of how happy I would be on that day. Finding something positive each day really affected my attitude.

Even though my calendar was not specifically for Meghan, I think it helped me maintain a good attitude. I am sure Meghan felt my optimism, which helped her feel reassured that she would recover. We are now many years past her last surgery, but I will never forget the day I finally got to put that sticker on my calendar!

Editor's Note: This essay first appeared as a post to the HLHS listserv.

A Mommy's Feelings

by: Tracy Adams

I am the mommy.
I am the one who is supposed to make it all better.
My arms a refuge where pain and discomfort are not allowed;
And yet, here I am unable to make the owies go away.
I see you lunge and reach out to me.
I hear your weak voice saying, "Mama, I want you."

And I can do nothing.

Only stand here in helplessness with my heart breaking.
If only I could take your place.
I would gladly bear the pain, knowing you were not.
I would eagerly take upon myself this burden placed on you.

You look at me with sorrowful eyes that do not understand.
"Why don't you help me?" I see them plead.
Perhaps this is the greatest cross a mother can bear—to see her child in need and be rendered helpless.
I am tremendously grateful to know this is temporary.
Soon you will be in my arms, and I will love the hurt away.

We will hold each other tightly, and, perhaps then, both our hearts will heal.

Teaching Others, Learning Ourselves

The great scientist and philosopher Francis Bacon said, "Nam et ipsa scientia potestas est" which translates to: "Knowledge itself is power" (from the *Oxford Dictionary of Quotations, Third Edition*). This is perhaps one of my favorite quotes. On many occasions I have discovered the power of knowledge; however, Bacon's quote became particularly poignant after researching Alex's heart defect.

Bringing home a critically ill baby, who survived open-heart surgery just two weeks prior, was overwhelming. There were so many things to learn. My life suddenly had a tremendous amount of complications which were not there just one month before. I knew taking care of a newborn was challenging, but that pales in comparison to taking care of a "sick" newborn.

After about three months, I was able to resume a semblance of a normal life. I finally felt ready to search for the information I longed to have. With every doctor's visit, I begged for information. I called the American Heart Association (AHA). I scoured the pediatric library at our local hospital. There was nothing on my son's heart defect. Nothing I wanted to read, that is. I did find an older copy of a booklet published by the AHA which covered congenital heart defects in general. It dedicated one lone sentence to HLHS, indicating that most babies with this heart defect die. I also found a book entitled *The Heart of a Child* which was written by two doctors and a nurse. I anxiously opened the book, flipping to the index. The few references to HLHS were less than comforting. I knew there had to be something better than this!

I decided to educate myself about my son's heart condition. I kissed my boys and my husband and drove the hour and a half to my alma mater, U.T. at Austin. I knew it might take some time to find the information, but I felt certain something would be available.

Hours of searching on Med-Line revealed a number of articles about HLHS. Most of the articles were about the operations created to save children with this condition. I printed everything I could find. To my disappointment almost everything written on the topic was for cardio-thoracic surgeons or pediatric cardiologists. I wondered how I would ever make sense of the diagrams, the jargon, the statistics; but I just kept searching and printing anyway.

When I finally pulled into my driveway, Frank came out to greet me. He could see I was emotionally spent. While waiting for some of the articles to print, I scanned the abstracts and overviews. These articles did not do much to comfort me. The statistics and complications they reported were frightening. Knowing my sweet baby was alive and well made me realize that no amount of statistics or old analytical data could be applied to *my* Alex.

I discovered that pediatric cardiology is a relatively new area of study. The gains in this field of study have been nothing short of miraculous. Every year surgeries are created, new materials are developed, equipment is invented and all of this has had an overwhelming impact on the medical field as a whole. I soon learned that what my own heart had told me was true! I could not use the research from the 1980s to tell me about my son's (born in 1994) future. No, it was not going to be that simple.

My husband and I soon discovered that we could not sufficiently understand everything written in the journal articles I copied because we lacked some of the background knowledge necessary. Therefore, Frank went to the medical library where he worked and borrowed pediatric cardiology books. We pored over the books gleaning as much information as we could. Since Frank was a nurse (a critical care nurse, no less!), he was able to assimilate the information faster and easier than I, yet I was determined. Sometimes it took multiple readings of passages for me to understand what was written.

By this time I began a small support group with which I communicated regularly. I discovered, to my delight, that these parents also wanted to understand more about HLHS. Many admitted to me that they just had not known what to ask or where to find the information they needed. Because some of the parents had not understood information the doctors provided, they were embarrassed or afraid to ask more questions. I felt this was wrong and decided to do my part to help, not only for myself, but also for these other struggling parents.

Originally I had intended to write a small ten-page booklet with explanations of what HLHS was, the corrective surgeries, medications used and some general information. As I began collecting and writing information for the booklet, I shared it with my support group. Before I long, I was getting phone calls and letters asking me to research other areas. The end result was a 118-page book! This might not have been a problem, except that all of the publishers I queried kindly rejected the project stating that the intended audience was too small.

Although I received one rejection after another, I knew these publishers were wrong. I could not believe that not one of them was willing to publish this book for philanthropic reasons. Perhaps one of the things that kept me going were the kind hand-written notes at the bottom of the form rejection letters where editors encouraged me to seek other publishers. Finally, Frank and I decided that we would just publish the book ourselves.

On a trip to the bookstore, I discovered *The Self-Publishing Manual* and realized that making this book available to the other parents was possible. I started working even harder on the book and talked to my son's doctors about the project. My son's surgeon, Dr. John Calhoon, was quite encouraging and even offered to write the Foreword. He also agreed to look over the final manuscript for technical errors.

Several months seemed to go by fairly quickly. I had a laptop computer which I used to write the book. It became an extension of my arm. After I put the boys to bed at night, I frequently stayed up until 2:00 a.m. working on the book. But, I was still far from done when Alex's second open-heart surgery was scheduled.

Taking the laptop computer with me, I decided that if I had to be stuck in the hospital while Alex was being operated on and convalescing, at least I could get some work done. Where else would I have nurses and doctors available around the clock? I needed to focus on this positive aspect of being in the hospital because it was difficult seeing Alex hospitalized knowing what could happen.

While Alex underwent surgery and we were in the waiting room, the seriousness of the situation struck me. Before this point I had been in denial and assured myself that everything would be fine. Afterall, the hemi-Fontan was the least risky of all of the surgeries, and Dr. Calhoon's statistics for this surgery could not be better—he had never lost an infant to this procedure. But while I sat in the waiting room typing away on my computer, a feeling of dread washed over me. Through a cloud of tears, I continued working on the medication section of the book until I could type no longer. I closed my eyes and thought, "What am I going to do if Alex doesn't make it?" I shook my head, pushing the negative thought out of my mind. I knew I had to think positively. Then I took a deep breath, looked at my computer and said to myself, "This is your legacy, Alex. Whether you make it or not, this is for you."

Hours later the nurse finally came in to talk to us. The surgery had not gone as planned. Alex did not end up having the second surgery, the hemi-Fontan. In a previous meeting Dr. Calhoon had indicated Alex might be a candidate for the fenestrated Fontan, a combination of the second *and* third surgeries, but he would not know until he looked at Alex's heart. The nurse told us that Dr. Calhoon would be out to talk to us shortly and that Alex had the fenestrated Fontan. I remember marking on my computer that Alex made history again. He was the youngest baby Dr. Calhoon had performed this procedure on and his first HLHS baby to skip the hemi-Fontan. I was so thankful I had researched this possibility and that we had met with the doctors before Alex's surgery, but I was scared, too.

Knowledge is empowering, but knowing what can happen is terrifying. I knew all too well how complicated and unusual this was. Once again I had to rely on my faith in my son's doctors and on the medical field overall. I also had to trust my heart that everything would work out. I was not disappointed.

Finding Support

Over the last four years I have been impressed by the parents, grandparents, aunts, uncles, friends and professionals wanting to understand congenital heart defects (CHDs) better because of children they know. Most of the time I communicate with parents or grandparents. I am always happy to share whatever knowledge I have with them and to learn from them, too. It has been heart warming to see how generous and caring people can be with the information they have. Had it not been for mothers caring about others, this book would not have been written.

Surfing the Internet for CHD information can yield an enormous amount of data. Some of the information one comes across are parents' stories of hope. Some information comes from professionals or people educated in the area of congenital heart defects. Unfortunately, some websites are written by people who do not understand their situation, thus containing erroneous information. There are also tragic personal stories which can actually misinform others or cause incredible despair. The problem is that there is no regulation whatsoever regarding the information available online. While this censor-free world has invited a great deal of creativity and freedom of expression, it could also cause irreparable consequences.

Mona Barmash saw the need for accurate information regarding congenital heart defects online. After doing book reviews for another online publisher, Mona decided that a different kind of site was called for. She envisioned a site where all of the information would be reviewed by a board of certified professionals first so that nothing inaccurate or misleading would be presented to the readers. She wanted a user-friendly site where parents could meet other parents and chat with them about important issues. Mona noticed many personal sites about babies but little information was available about older children, teenagers or adults with CHDs, so she created the Children's Health Information

Network and found volunteers to create the Congenital Heart Disease Information and Resources website.

Since the beginning, this website has maintained an integrity other websites devoted to medical issues should emulate. The information presented is always clear, accurate and current, probably because of the multidisciplinary board of physicians and nurses who review everything before it is published. The site is updated on a regular basis, and Mona sends out email messages to let patrons know that new information is available. It has grown tremendously since Mona started it in 1996 and now even includes PDHeart, a website and listserv started by Canadian father, Peter Littlefield.

From the work station in her laundry room, Mona volunteers countless hours to her website which is a 501(c)3 non-profit organization. She has a number of listservs she maintains, the newest being one for parents of teens with congenital heart defects. The HLHS listserv has almost 200 people registered. Responding to the needs of the person with congenital heart defects as they grow up, Mona also has a listserv for adults with congenital heart defects (ACHD).

One of the unique aspects of Mona's site is The Memorial Garden. Even though C.H.I.N. was close to financial bankruptcy, Mona agreed to give bereaved parents a listserv and a portion of her website. The Memorial Garden is a place for pictures and stories about the children who have passed away due to congenital heart defects and the CHD-L is the loss listserv.

What keeps a woman writing grants, pleading for money from the AHA, going to meetings and helping others? Mona is the mother of a child with tetralogy of Fallot, and she sees the need to educate others. She knows how much information we can share amongst ourselves. Her site features articles from doctors and other professionals answering many common questions about heart defects and the consequences of having a heart defect. She knows how badly this information is needed, and something inside of her will not give up.

Considering how much *mis*information is available online, we are fortunate to have someone like Mona Barmash devoting her time, veracity and loyalty to the CHD cause. Because of her devotion, people around the world are learning about congenital heart defects. Because of her dogged determination, her site continues to be a shining example of how one woman can lead the world to the truth.

The majority of people worldwide do not have Internet access. Many people still search for information the good old-fashioned way. They visit their local library. Some library patrons are fortunate enough to meet librarians who care about helping them find the information they need. Some librarians have a passion for helping others to become strong advocates for their children.

When reference librarian **Alysanne Crymes'** son, Brendan, was born in 1993 with complete congenital heart block, an ASD and tricuspid regurgitation, she decided to learn as much as she could to help her son. Because of Brendan's condition, Alysanne has become knowledgeable about congenital heart defects and knows where to look for answers to the many questions we all have.

Alysanne is in the unique position of being able to help library patrons with specific CHD questions. She takes each individual's questions to heart and searches the stacks, the reference section and the Internet until she has satisfied that person's desire for knowledge. Alysanne knows what it feels like to search for information with a lump in one's throat; she's been there. Her mission has become that of helping others with children's health issues.

Brendan and Alysanne

Being a strong advocate for our children is important to Alysanne. She says, "Armed with knowledge, you are able to make informed decisions and can discuss intelligently any options or treatment decisions with the doctor. The library is a great place to start . . . A good doctor will welcome your input and understands that you know your child better than anyone. He or she will talk to you respectfully and as a partner in your child's care. They will welcome questions and answer them completely and in a way that you can understand."

Another mom, **Michelle Rintamaki**, assists others in understanding the complexity of their children's heart defects. From the basement of her Wisconsin home, she puts together packets of information for parents of children with CHDs. The support group

Michelle works with is known as Kids With Heart, and she has shown that she is a mom with heart, too.

Although the American Heart Association spends a scant amount of money on resources for congenital heart defects, Michelle determined to educate her local chapter on the necessities for such funding. She became a member of her local AHA and educated her community about the need for someone to do something. Still a volunteer, Michelle was given money for long distance phone calls, business supplies, copying and mailing. Unfortunately, the AHA in Green Bay, Wisconsin stopped its funding to Kids with Heart in January 1, 1998.

Undaunted, Michelle puts together hundreds of information packets for parents. People from the community at large, and the Internet community have helped Michelle in her quest to provide information to parents. This information helps many parents understand their children's complex diagnoses, surgeries and complications.

Michelle, increasingly concerned about issues important to adults with CHDs, joined the ACHD listserv. John, Michelle's son, has tetralogy of Fallot and is ten years old. John's future, whether it be college, trade school or finding a job, made Michelle aware of the plight of today's adults with congenital heart defects. She has begun an online campaign to spread awareness of the many problems which exist today. Most of our young adults with congenital heart defects have difficulty getting health insurance, life insurance and equal employment opportunities. Michelle can only speculate what the future holds for John. She hopes her efforts will make the future brighter for her son and for all our children.

Becoming an Advocate

The following essay is written by a mother who has a mission to educate people in her region of the United States about CHDs. She has talked to reporters in order to spread awareness of hypoplastic left heart syndrome (HLHS).

Lenore Cameron distributes books throughout the community hoping that doctors and medical institutions will be informed of the options available to parents of children with HLHS. Based on her own experience, Lenore has written a passionate essay about understanding her child's heart defect and being his advocate. You will soon discover why Lenore feels strongly about the value of a second opinion.

Saving Our Children Through Educating Ourselves

By: Lenore M. Cameron

On June 6, 1996 Jeffrey Thomas Cameron was born. At forty years of age I finally had what I had always dreamed of, two beautiful sons. My husband and I were so proud. My three-year-old son, Matthew, was beaming as he held his new baby brother.

The day he was born, Jeffrey only nursed a couple minutes at a time and then fell back to sleep. I mentioned to the nurses how much Jeffrey slept; they helped me wake my "sleepy baby" but seemed unconcerned. My gut feeling was that something was wrong, but I didn't say or do anything about it. Eager to go home, we were both discharged the day after he was born.

For the next several days Jeffrey slept most of the time. He nursed very little and his breathing appeared to be faster. Concerned friends mentioned this to us, but we reassured them that Jeffrey was fine.

When Jeffrey was six days old, I took him to the pediatrician for a weight check and mentioned his rapid breathing. The doctor said that was "newborn breathing" and seemed unconcerned (since Jeffrey had gained two ounces), until he heard a heart murmur. Then he explained that murmurs were common and usually went away on their own. When we returned three days later to check his murmur, it was gone. What a relief!

That evening, though, Jeffrey woke up crying every three hours to feed, but then would simply lay in my arms. I knew something was wrong. The next day Jeffrey's breathing was so labored his stomach caved in with every breath. He appeared gray in color. Little did we know, Jeffrey was in respiratory distress! Because I was so upset, my husband, Timothy, took Jeffrey to the hospital. An hour later he phoned me to say Jeffrey was being transported by air ambulance from our local hospital to a children's medical center.

That was when we learned that Jeffrey had hypoplastic left heart syndrome. We were told we had three options and none of them were very good. All I could think of, when I heard those words, was that my baby was dying.

Our options were 1) the Norwood procedure (a set of three open-heart surgeries), 2) a heart transplant or 3) compassionate care. We were told that most parents chose the third option. A dismal picture was painted of the Norwood procedure, and we were never really given the second option as a choice. We were told that it was almost impossible to get a newborn's heart.

Initially I chose the Norwood procedure, but my husband was concerned about Jeffrey's quality of life. Needing to know answers to our questions, we turned to a nearby ICU doctor who was even more pessimistic than the pediatric cardiologist. He told us that if the baby survived the three surgeries, he would probably be in and out of hospitals and need medication for the rest of his life. He stressed to us that this option was a " lifelong commitment." Wasn't having Jeffrey a lifelong commitment?

Unfortunately, after this, both my husband and I agreed to take Jeffrey home to die. We felt this was Jeffrey's only option. Within thirty minutes, we were out the door with Jeffrey in my arms and two pages of diagrams of the heart in my hand.

Based on what we were told, Jeffrey was not supposed to make it through the night. When I awoke the next morning, Jeffrey was still asleep by my side. Millions of questions went through my head. What is my son dying from? What was the diagnosis? All I knew was that it had something to do with his heart.

I phoned and spoke with the same ICU doctor getting the diagnosis again. HLHS. Isn't it odd that all we had on Jeffrey's condition were two pieces of paper? Wasn't there any literature for us to read?

The next day (Sunday) I sat on the couch with Jeffrey by my side or in my arms. I barely moved. I remember drinking water and looking at Jeffrey's lips. They were dry. My God! What kind of mother am I? My child must be starving for he hadn't nursed since Friday evening! Just because he was dying didn't mean he had to starve as well.

I started expressing milk and feeding it to him with a medicine dropper. As the day went on, I got better at it and got more milk in him. Within two days a La Leche Leader was in my home. Aware of my situation, she brought an electric breast pump to help me.

While I stayed home with Jeffrey, I had several friends ask me about his birth defect. They couldn't believe nothing could be done. I realized from trying to answer their questions that I had been so overwhelmed at the hospital that I couldn't remember what I had been told. I called the pediatric cardiologist and made an appointment for the next day (Thursday).

This time when Jeffrey and I saw the doctor there seemed to be some hope. The facts didn't sound as frightening. Why was this? Because we weren't in the ICU? Was it because Jeffrey wasn't in respiratory distress now?

I asked the doctor for some information on HLHS assuming he had something to give parents. He said he had nothing. I couldn't believe this and was very upset.

Regardless, next I had to convince my husband to go with the Norwood procedure. But how? I started by asking Timothy what his fears were. Realizing he came to false conclusions based on what he heard on Saturday, I convinced him to speak with a doctor who actually did the Norwood procedure.

On Friday, Dr. Freed, a pediatric cardiologist from Children's Hospital in Boston, phoned and spoke with both of us. With me on the kitchen phone and Tim on the bedroom phone, we listened as he explained the staged surgical procedures and asked us if we had any questions. I kept quiet knowing that Tim had to ask his own questions. After about thirty seconds of silence, Tim started asking questions. I looked up at the sky and said, "Thank you, Lord."

Unfortunately, Tim still wasn't convinced. He wanted to talk to a surgeon who actually performed the procedure. Tim went to work while we waited for the surgeon's call. The wait made for a very long day. Finally at 6:00 p.m. the surgeon called to my husband at work. After a half hour conversation with the doctor, Tim called me and said, "Call Hartford. We're taking him in." As soon as he came home he hugged me and said, "Sorry it took me so long."

Meanwhile I phoned the pediatric cardiologist and was told an on-call doctor would return my call. When I answered, he said to me, "You're picking an odd time of the day." I'll always remember that ridiculous statement. I didn't have a flat tire that needed fixing. This was my son's life!

While the doctor called Boston to make arrangements, I got the rest of the family ready. Tim walked in the door, and I was packed. *We were driving Jeffrey to Boston.* I didn't realize how stupid that was until I heard the doctors and nurses in Boston say, "A hypoplastic baby came up by car?" Why hadn't the pediatric cardiologist arranged for Jeffrey to go by ambulance?

Eighteen days after birth, on June 24, 1996, Jeffrey had the Norwood procedure. He was discharged two weeks later. We call him the "miracle baby" but we know, from having talked with other parents of HLHS children, that we all have miracle babies.

I believe that Jeffrey has a guardian angel. For him to live for six days after being diagnosed with HLHS without any medication is a miracle. He held on until we got him the help he needed. We feel so lucky we were given a second chance.

I also believe things happen for a reason. Why did this happen to Jeffrey? Why us? What about future HLHS babies and their parents? I don't want them to go through what we did. What could I do to help other parents?

When we returned to Boston in January of 1997 for the second surgery, social worker, Sarah Lualdi, was passing out *Hypoplastic Left Heart Syndrome: A Handbook for Parents* to parents in the ICU. That's when I learned of this great guide. I was jealous. I would have loved to have had it seven months before when Jeffrey was first identified.

When we got home I ordered one for myself. Recently I have supplied copies of this handbook to six pediatric cardiologists in Connecticut. Wouldn't this help other parents of an HLHS child? I hope it saves a life.

Why don't the doctors help us more? Don't they feel helpless when they tell parents they have no written information? Have they become too complacent? Aren't they parents themselves? How would they like it if they were told their child was dying of a rare birth defect, and there was no information, just the words of a doctor?

How many babies have they seen? Haven't those parents asked for information? Maybe they were like us, in shock when they heard the news. I didn't think of asking for information then. Maybe other parents chose to go with the third option.

If Jeffrey had died, I don't think I'd be doing what I am now. Had he died, I don't think I would have questioned anything. I've learned so much since his surgery, especially since meeting other parents of HLHS children.

Maybe there are few families in Connecticut with a surviving HLHS child. If they were presented with the facts like we were, that's very possible. Another group of pediatric cardiologists in Connecticut told me that most of their HLHS patients are identified in utero and parents are advised to terminate the pregnancy. They, too, had no written information for me.

Is it right for doctors to advise parents to terminate pregnancies or to give parents such doom and gloom information? Where is the hope? Where is the written information so that parents can make an informed decision instead of a decision based on one doctor's opinion?

This isn't right. We don't live in the 1960s, 1970s or even early 1980s where there was no hope. Since the development of the Norwood procedure in the 1980s, we now have hope. Jeffrey is living proof.

I have felt a great need to inform others of the hope now available for children like Jeffrey. Just recently I decided to unite as many HLHS children as I could find, take their picture and send it to local pediatric cardiologists. Jeffrey was only one face of hope, and I wanted more.

On December 7, 1997, I organized a get-together at Chuck E. Cheese in Worcester, Massachusetts. I only knew of a few people initially, but ten families showed up! They came from New Hampshire, Massachusetts, Rhode Island and Connecticut. Now I have my Picture Of Hope.

We had another reunion on May 24, 1998 with seventeen families joining us! Parents came from six neighboring states just to meet other families and to have their child be in the picture of HOPE.

One local newspaper printed our story, except they neglected to describe the options we were given. I felt it took away from the message I had hoped to send. The article also neglected to mention that had we not gone for a second opinion, Jeffrey would have died. This is the message I would like others to know. Other reporters have also done stories on Jeffrey.

I am hopeful that through my reunions and quest to disseminate information about congenital heart defects to my local community that I can help other parents. I know that my efforts have made a difference already. I have received phone calls from people who have lost children to this defect years ago and from mothers whose children are awaiting surgery.

It was important for me to find out as much information as I could. I had to educate myself. I'm so thankful I got a second opinion. If I hadn't, Jeffrey would have died. Because I have my son, because of this gift, I feel privileged to help educate others. I only hope I can spare other parents from feeling the same way I did. I trust that, when parents realize that our children are afforded the same quality of life as any other child, they will do everything in their power to save their children, too.

Matthew, Jeffrey and Lenore

Mothers As Advocates

I was shocked when I stopped at a convenience store for gas and saw a copy of our local newspaper, the Gatesville Messenger, with a picture of my sons and me on the cover. I expected to see an article after meeting with a reporter but not on the front page! The article was well-written and divulged a good deal of information. For the most part, everything the reporter, Larry Kennedy, wrote came from me, except one sentence which took my breath away. ". . . Meanwhile, Anna has become an activist in informing parents about the heart defect that almost claimed her youngest son's life . . ." An activist? Me?!?

When I decided to do this book I knew of some really wonderful "activists" who had done even more than I had. Some of these women had been at it for years; others had just begun, but I could see they were passionate and knew where they were headed. I asked a few of these women to write for this chapter. To my surprise each one in turn was shocked I asked her to write for the "Advocacy" chapter. Like me, they had been so busy doing what they did, they had not taken a breath to stop and realize how many people they helped. Like me, they only knew there were so many other families who needed our assistance, our support, maybe even a little of our strength. Unlike me they had not had the jolt of seeing in print that they actually were advocates or activists in the realm of congenital heart defects.

So, what exactly is an "advocate"? If you look in the dictionary an advocate is someone who comes to the aid of another. I have several advocates in my support mission, and through our goals of educating and supporting families of children with congenital heart defects, I have become especially close to these inspirational women.

I feel fortunate to be the one to tell some of their stories, share some of their loving works and give recognition to a group of women willing to volunteer because, like me, they feel they must. Something in their hearts and souls will not let them rest unless they do something. These women are doers and have become more than mothers to their "heart" children. They have become role models for us all.

How To Be An Advocate

By: Tricia Christensen

When we welcome a child into our lives, we accept certain responsibilities for the child's financial, emotional, physical and spiritual well-being. We soon learn how to diaper, feed and comfort. We know what to do when baby falls and we know how to make baby laugh and smile. These amazing skills we acquire can easily be taken for granted. Yet an objective look reveals that just as our children are growing and learning at a stunning rate, so are we.

As our children age we learn about daycare, reading, math. We might suddenly know all the rules of softball or the five positions of ballet. Of course, we do these things because we want to take an interest in our children's lives. Our growing knowledge connects us intimately with our growing children. We would feel left out if we didn't understand a child's fascination with airplanes or couldn't name all his or her dolls or stuffed animals. With all this expertise we acquire, and with our children's expanding knowledge, it is often hard to understand how easily our confidence can be shaken by "expert" opinions.

Experts can come in the form of other parents, teachers, writers of parenting books and, of course, physicians. We are often the most daunted by the opinions of our children's doctors and teachers. We accept that our teachers know how to teach and our doctors know how to practice medicine. They are, afterall, trained professionals, and we are "only the parents."

If one has a healthy, reasonably well-adjusted, developmentally on-track child, probably the role of "only the parent," will be sufficient. But should a serious problem arise such as the chronic illness of a child, this role will not be enough. Suddenly the very thing that will be at the center of our children's lives is the one area we will not understand. We will get lost among the experts working on and for our children. And if we act as "only the parent," all that we know and all that we have learned about our children will be lost too.

It is precisely at this point that confidence in ourselves as parents must be very high. No expert can know our children as intimately as we do. We must abandon our role as "only the parents" and instead become advocates for our children. When parent and professionals work together, the child will receive optimum, individualized care.

But what exactly is advocacy? I have heard parents ask me this many times. "I don't like my doctor, but I don't know. I guess he knows best." "They won't let me stay with my child for more than fifteen minutes." "Nobody is telling me the whole story about my child's condition." Parents express not only frustration with the limited role as the parent, but also a sense that it's us against the vague "they, nobody, he, them." That is not advocacy but an adversarial relationship, where "they" are these unknown, shadowy figures who have all the power. True advocacy dismisses this relationship and instead proposes that parents and medical practicners belong to the same team. Both have equally important jobs.

The more knowledge the parent acquires, the more equitable the relationship. Perhaps a better term is awareness; the more awareness parents have of their child's defects, doctors, hospital policies, medical staff, and of their child as a whole, the more parents participate as part of the team.

Most of us fear conflict and avoid it if we can. Sometimes conflict is necessary to produce change. And in those moments where a dispute arises, it is essential to remember that the judgment of the professional is not really the issue. The issue is providing optimum care for the child. Advocacy is not a personality contest! This doesn't mean having a knock-down, drag out fight with a nurse or doctor. It means asserting our position and feeling justified that we are acting in the best interests of our children. An action on behalf of a child usually does not require "telling someone off." It can be soft-spoken and gentle, coming from a sense of security that the advocate is "in the right" about an unacceptable situation. My own personal experience has led me to believe that the more reasonably I present my point of view, the more I accomplish.

My "heart" child, Gerard, was diagnosed in utero, thus I had a fair amount of time to prepare for the birth of my son. I worried and sweated about everything I could think of during the twenty-two weeks between my child's first fetal echo and his birth. But this preparation was incredibly advantageous. It gave me a chance to learn to deal with the many doctors and nurses I would meet in the upcoming months. Even that first day at the radiologist was a lesson in how to state my needs clearly and effectively.

My obstetrician scheduled a routine sonogram for me at sixteen weeks, just to make sure the baby was growing properly and doing well. I had no worries that they would find anything problematic, so I decided to go to the appointment alone while my husband and son went to a nearby park to play. Aside from secretly wishing for a girl, the only other thought I had about the sonogram was that I hoped they would get me in quickly so I wouldn't have to hold water in my bladder forever.

At first the sonogram seemed to go as planned, the miracle of tiny fingers and toes, arms, legs and a rounded head displayed themselves on the screen. The technician pointed out each little part, including the fact that my baby was a boy. By then it simply didn't matter as I looked at that adorable, defenseless child swimming around so happily inside me. The technician's manner seemed to change abruptly.

Suddenly she was no longer talking, and instead began taking slide after slide of my child's heart. "What is going on?" I asked, terrified to hear the answer. She told me that she could not tell me but that she would be back with the radiologist on staff in a moment. I waited there as my irritation and fear rose exponentially.

When the radiologist arrived and he and the technician looked at the screen in perfect silence, I felt completely tongue-tied. I knew I had to act, to ask something and finally I got the courage to say, "If you don't tell me what the problem is, then I am not going to leave this room." The radiologist replied that he would call my obstetrician and ask for permission to disclose his findings directly to me. He obtained permission and was back in a few moments, telling me to follow him to a room where we could talk. My husband had fortunately returned from the park, so he and my son traipsed into a tiny room where pictures of my unborn child's heart were displayed on several lighted screens.

"What we basically are seeing is that your child's heart is on the wrong side of his chest. We can't really tell you what this means. Some people have their heart on the wrong side of their chest and have no problems. But you need to see a pediatric cardiologist for a more conclusive exam."

I was given instructions to call UCSF and make an appointment for a fetal echocardiogram. At that point I didn't even know what a fetal echocardiogram was, only that it sounded incredibly frightening. Numbly, my husband, son and I filed out of the office. I don't know how I made my feet work, or how I got to the car. Total shock and disbelief consumed me. This was not what I had planned. How could this happen to me? Even worse was not knowing exactly what was going on. I got home and made the appointment, which the office wanted to schedule for several weeks later. I begged them to see me sooner, as soon as they could. I told them, "You have to understand that I'm in Hell here!"

I will never forget how much compassion the echo office showed me by making an appointment for an echo just two days later. Both at the radiologist's and in talking to the technician at the echo lab, I made it clear—without hysteria— that I had certain needs. Thinking back on it, if I had waited for my doctor to phone with the results, I might have waited for a day or two before I knew what the next step would be. Then if I had not expressed my sense of urgency to the echo lab, it would have been several weeks before I knew my son's diagnosis.

The uncertainty of what was wrong was difficult to bear even for two days. If I had not made my needs clear, that awful waiting time could have gone on for weeks. It was clear to me that I had a right to demand information from the radiologist and to inform the echo office of the urgency of my appointment. Parents would do well to remember that they and their children have rights in a medical setting. Knowing these rights can do much to eliminate the intrinsic fear we all seem to possess, that we'll be considered "pushy," "bitchy" or "unreasonable."

My next step into the role of "advocate" seemed a logical one; I needed to get as much information as I could, and quickly! In the two days prior to my first fetal echo, I feverishly combed the Internet, found a wonderful book on CHDs and contacted a number of families who had children with CHDs. I found everything I could possibly find in that short period on dextrocardia and its related defects. I made myself fully acquainted with the basic circulatory system and the various components of the heart. I was driven by my need to feel connected to what was happening, rather than feel alienated by terms I couldn't understand.

Even with all the research I had done, I still knew comparatively little. But at least this frantic search had somewhat leveled the "playing field" between doctor and patient. I contend that these two days of searching were the best thing I could have done with my time. Faced with a situation where I was basically powerless to change the outcome, I was at least able to use my energy and my restless need to do something, to empower myself by becoming as knowledgeable as I could. By the time I walked into the echo lab, I already knew the worst case scenario and had prayed for the best case scenario. I was prepared to ask questions and find out what I might reasonably expect for my child's future.

As it turned out my son's defects were the worst case scenario. He had dextrocardia, pulmonary stenosis, complicated transposition of the great arteries and a huge VSD. This meant that Gerard's heart was definitely on the wrong side of his chest (dextrocardia) and a huge hole existed between the two ventricles (VSD). The two major arteries arising from the heart were switched in a complicated manner. He would require several surgeries to palliate this condition. There was also some doubt as to whether my son had a spleen. Fortunately, the diagnosis was mostly accurate but slightly off. Gerard does have a fully functioning spleen, and what was originally diagnosed as right atrial isomerism was changed after he was born to dextrocardia with abnormal heart. The questions that I was able to ask on that first day were, I guess, fairly knowledgeable because the echocardiologist asked me if I was a physician. I answered him, "Not yet, but give me a couple of months, and I will be if it helps." Being a man with a sense of humor, he teased me for months afterwards about how I was going to hang out my shingle and put him out of business. Yet I detected a slight amount of tension on the doctor's part that I had acquired so much information. He told me quite pointedly that he didn't want me to "get in over my head," or "misinterpret the material I read." There certainly was a bit of the "leave the doctoring to me" attitude.

This caution on the echocardiologist's part prompted me to reply that I was a pretty intelligent person, and a very good researcher. Furthermore, if I came back from my research with questions about what to expect, wouldn't it be his job to clear up any misconceptions I might have? By stating my position so clearly, I was able to convince the doctor that I could be responsible for gathering medical information. I would certainly be guided first by his opinion, yet for my own sake I needed to feel included and a part of the "medical world" my son would be involved in. To do less just did not seem like good parenting to me.

My next step was to familiarize myself not only with my son's defects but also with the hospital where he would be treated. I enlisted the help of a wonderful social worker from my hospital's nursery. She made herself available to me on a frequent basis, answering my questions about what would happen after my son was born. With her, I toured the PICU and the ICN. These were difficult tours, but they did help ease some of the shock that I might feel when I first beheld my child in an ICN or PICU.

I knew the first time I would see my son he would be covered in tubes and wires, that monitors would beep, and that he would be intubated. I worried about how much involvement I could have with Gerard in those early days. Would I get to see him when I wanted to? Would I be able to nurse him? Could I hold him? The social worker answered these and many other questions with the patience of an angel. Her work on my behalf taught me something extremely important: I could and should enlist others to help me. Advocacy does not mean picking fights with everyone involved. It means finding those who are best equipped to help us care for our child in the most appropriate manner.

Through my social worker, I learned that I was going to have to make some compromises. My definition of "mothering" my child in his infancy was going to be sorely challenged by his medical restrictions. A part of me resented this intensely. But I always tried to stay calm and remind myself that some of the restrictions placed on visiting, holding and feeding were for Gerard's ultimate good. The most important incident I had during my son's first hospitalization, which proved the power of advocacy, took place several weeks after Gerard's first surgery. Gerard was having extreme difficulty with feeding. He was jaundiced, dehydrated and his surgical wound was not healing properly. At the time, I found myself in contact with about eight different doctors and nurses all arguing about what should be done for Gerard.

The varied opinions overwhelmed me, and I felt that some type of plan on how to treat all these difficulties had to be made quickly before

Gerard lost more ground. With the social worker's help, I was able to arrange a meeting between all the principals of each group of doctors. Together we came to a consensus and a treatment plan was made.

During the meeting, we appointed one "contact" person who would relay information between all the doctors and back to me so that I was aware of Gerard's treatments and any changes in his condition. Had I not proven myself as competent to take part in the discussion, I might have had the additional stress of listening to a variety of opinions and being even more confused than before. I felt that I had a right to be in on the decisions being made about my son's care. My medical knowledge, my knowledge of the staff, and my confidence as a parent all contributed to the feeling that someone needed to take the reins and coordinate a plan. This meeting resulted in a much smoother treatment plan for Gerard and a much less confusing method for me to get all the information I wanted about his condition.

Equally important to learning the "medical ropes" was for me to get to know Gerard. Whereas I had time during my pregnancy to become familiar with the medical aspects of Gerard's condition, it would take time after his birth for me to determine exactly who Gerard was and what he would need. One thing I learned very quickly about my son was that he was very comforted by holding a soft, little hospital-issue hat. Clenching that hat in his tiny fingers was a sure way to keep him more comfortable when he had blood draws or when he was scared, and we couldn't hold him. With each new nurse that we had, I made sure to tell him or her that my child was very attached to his hat. Even a short, quick statement like that is an example of advocacy. Stating my child's needs helped me provide the best care I could for him. Every nurse knew about Gerard's hat, and I can't recall how many times it was lovingly placed back in his hands even for something as simple as a diaper change.

I soon learned that the hospital was not the only place for me to be Gerard's advocate. Every time I took Gerard to a doctor I found opportunities to be his voice. It was during doctor's visits that I was able to share my concerns. I made it a point to explain as clearly as I could how Gerard was developing or what I felt his problems were. By providing information as objectively as possible, I continued to assist Gerard in getting the personalized care he needed.

Advocacy must also include an intelligent choice of doctors. We are, after all, the consumers and we need not merely accept whichever doctor is assigned to our care. I found it important to find a doctor whose personality fits with Gerard"s and my needs. If I feared my son's doctor, I know I would be less effective as an advocate.

I know that I felt a tremendous respect and reverence for the doctors and nurses who worked so diligently to save Gerard's life. These feelings are natural, but we should not allow them to impinge on the advocacy process. I still felt comfortable asking a caregiver to wash his or her hands before touching Gerard, or if necessary presenting viewpoints in variance with the caregiver. Doctor-parent relationships should be ones of mutual respect, where parents and doctors work together as equal parts of the team and where opposing viewpoints are respected and discussed.

Our role in the care of our special children should never be as "only the parent." For me, becoming deeply involved in Gerard's care has led me to become a better advocate for my child. And in response to the request of others, I have also begun a Northern California support network for families with CHD children, Hearts for Hearts' Sake. Both personally and professionally, I strive to support parental involvement and partnership in our children's medical care. In this way, I hope that Gerard and all children with CHDs will be helped to live as normal and healthy a life as possible.

I hope that essay empowered you. It did me. The following vignettes describe a variety of methods used by mothers to be advocates for their children. Although each of these women are extraordinary women, their actions could easily be replicated by any other person seeking to be an advocate for the CHD cause.

Working with the Media: Jane Hunt

Jane Hunt is the mother of a child with a severe, complex heart defect. Marcus' heart defect, summed up in the label " single ventricle," has been reconstructed through a number of operations culminating in the Fontan procedure. Ever since Marcus' heart defect was identified, Jane has been his strongest advocate and shortly thereafter became a public advocate for all children born with congenital heart defects.

While thinking about what advocacy is and who seemed to personify advocacy, Jane's name popped into my head first. Jane, a well-educated, articulate woman, clearly states her concerns and needs to others. She impressed the doctors treating her son enough that they referred reporters to her on a number of occasions.

The cardio-thoracic surgeon who treated Marcus chose Jane and her family to participate with him in a television spotlight sponsored by the American Heart Association regarding congenital heart defects. In this spotlight Dr. Steven Dewan and Jane Hunt explained what it is like to have a child with a congenital heart defect, as well as the specifics surrounding Marcus' complex heart. Using a model of the heart, the reporter even explained to the audience how the heart is "replumbed" after the Fontan operation.

Jane was also interviewed for a hospital publication to share information about Milagros, a support group, she helped start. She advocated the need for parents to talk to others as well as an opportunity to continue educating themselves about life-long effects of congenital heart defects. Patrick Finnigan, M.D., Marcus' pediatric cardiologist, was also interviewed for the article. He emphasized the importance of parents supporting each other by recognizing that families of chronically ill children tend to have a high incidence of emotional problems and divorce. He felt that support groups could benefit families which in turn would benefit the afflicted children.

Perhaps the most exciting activity Jane took part in came after Marcus was selected to be the pediatric cardiology "miracle child" for the Children's Miracle Network (CMN) for the central Texas region. Marcus' story was told by Jane and his doctors, and the CMN team put together an incredible presentation on him. When viewing the presentation for the first time, Jane found herself crying and marveling at the strength of her baby. Because Marcus was videotaped after his Fontan, Jane was struck with how far he had come, and how strong he looked. The story of Marcus' life reported by an unbiased stranger took Jane down memory lane and left her inspired.

Lucas, Jane, CMN Interviewer, Bill and Marcus

Jane's fervent desire has been to inspire, educate and support other parents as well as the community at large. With the help of her child's doctors, the nurses who run Milagros, the Children's Miracle Network and the reporters who have spread the news, Marcus inspires others. He is living proof of the miracles of modern medicine. His mother is proof that the power of a mother's love can change the world.

Seeing Myself as an Advocate: Anna Jaworski

When you find out your child has a congenital heart defect, you immediately feel vulnerable and helpless. After the shock wears off, you feel exhausted and perhaps even despondent. There is something that you can do, though, that helps. Perhaps more than anything else you need to talk to someone who has been there. You need to talk to another mother who has felt the same horrible feelings you've felt, imagined the terrible things you've imagined and understands the fears you are afraid to voice. But, how do you find these mothers?

Before Alexander's heart defect was diagnosed I never knew there were so many children born with heart defects. When I thought of birth defects, I thought about deafness, blindness, cerebral palsy, cleft palate, spina bifida, and Down syndrome. I never really thought about the heart except as associated with certain other syndromes. Imagine my surprise when I discovered that heart defects are the number one birth defect in the United States! One in a hundred children will be born with a heart defect. That is why, when you begin talking to others about your child having a heart defect, you will find that almost everybody knows of, or is related to, someone who has a heart defect.

When Alex was in the hospital having his first open-heart surgery, there were three other families in the hospital at the same time because their children had the same heart defect. I collected their names, addresses and phone numbers, and these people became my first support group. We shared information, tears, hugs and many hours on the phone with each other. After a while I wrote a newsletter to keep everyone updated. As the word spread that I had started this support group, I began hearing of more parents to add to the list. By the time I had finished writing my first book, we had a nice section listing all of the parents, their children and important information. Thus some parents felt free to call others, and there was a ripple effect of support filtering throughout communities all over the United States.

After meeting with a local reporter, I wondered how much effect a newspaper article from a small town, such as Gatesville, would have. Little did I know others would spread the news to those who really needed it. A few days after the story broke, I received two phone calls from two different women in Odessa. Odessa is about eight to ten hours away from Gatesville. One of the women had a friend who lived in Gatesville and knew of her child's heart defect. As soon as her friend saw the newspaper article, she ran to the post office, bought an envelope and a stamp and immediately sent the story to her! This mother was desperately looking for another mother to talk to and to help her start a support group. The other mother who called me had a relative in Gatesville who did the same thing.

Not long after I was on the Internet, I began "meeting" parents from all over the world with children with congenital heart defects. Mark Levinson, M.D., a cardio-thoracic surgeon, created a wonderful site known as The Heart Surgery Forum. When I told John Calhoon, M.D., my son's surgeon, that I had decided to get Internet service he told me I should check out The Heart Surgery Forum. I was quite impressed when I saw the site. Even though the site was developed for surgeons, Dr. Levinson had included a section especially for parents or heart patients to ask questions (The Scrub Sink) and a place for others to learn about heart defects (The Learning Center).

I corresponded with Dr. Levinson for a while via email and then sent him a copy of my book, *Hypoplastic Left Heart Syndrome: A Handbook for Parents*. He was quite enthused about the book and did an online review of it, including a direct link to my email address. It was because of this publicity that I began to meet even more parents than ever before.

Helping a Friend: Sheri Berger

Getting on the Internet changed my life because my support group began growing at an astonishing rate. After searching for information on the Internet, I found a wonderful site, The Congenital Heart Disease Resource Page, developed and maintained by Sheri Berger. This woman is the friend of a mother who had a child with tetralogy of Fallot. In an effort to provide support to her friend she began searching the Internet for resources. She gathered so much information about congenital heart defects and Down syndrome that by 1995 she decided to create a web site (http://www.csun.edu/~hcmth011/heart). This site includes book reviews, links to personal and professional web sites, as well as links to a clearinghouse of associations and organizations designed to help or support parents and professionals working with children with congenital heart defects.

Over time Sheri's website has changed in appearance, but never in the helpful information she provides to the public. I was amazed the first time I corresponded with this generous woman, and discovered that she did not have a child with a heart defect. She told me that she created her website due to the tremendous amount of information she had gathered for her friend. When I asked her why she continued to maintain and update her website, she told me that she did it because of the thank you letters she received from parents. In spite of the enormity of the undertaking, she finds that she cannot abandon the site because she knows how many people are helped by her efforts.

HLHS Resource: Laura Ulaszek

Within a short period of time, I began corresponding with a good deal of parents via the Internet. I began to meet parents of children who had passed away, but the parents were wanting more information on the birth defect which claimed their children's lives. I began meeting other parents of children who had just been identified. Many parents wrote to me because their children or grandchildren had been through one surgery but had others to go through, and they were finally ready to learn as much as they could. Perhaps one of the largest-growing groups of people are men and women who have just found out they are expecting a child with a heart defect. These intelligent parents have worked through their grief enough already to seek out as much information as they can.

As I began corresponding with so many parents, I noticed some parents' names come up over and over. I could see that these parents, like me, were doing their part to help others. Some of us became close friends, even though we have never met in person.

I'm not exactly sure when I "met" Laura, but I believe it was shortly after her son, Brian, had his Norwood operation. Brian has hypoplastic left heart syndrome. Laura also has two daughters, but she always made the time to help other parents. I saw her often posting notes of encouragement to parents. I noticed she genuinely seemed to care about the welfare of other parents, and she guided them to get second opinions or to try and find additional information. She shared the names of articles she had found helpful and told parents where they could find the articles and how to do online searches.

Laura and I noticed that we were meeting more and more parents of children with hypoplastic left heart syndrome. Since this heart defect is complex and requires a number of surgeries (or a heart transplant), we found that there was a group of people on the Internet who had similar questions and experiences. Laura finally realized that these parents' needs were different from some of the parents of children with other heart defects, and she decided to do something to help this homogeneous group.

Realizing that many parents wanted more frequent contact than just an occasional note, she felt that they warranted their own listserv. A listserv is maintained by a person (usually, but not always, someone who has a web site) who forwards messages that members write to all of the others who have joined the list. Laura asked Mona Barmash who ran The Congenital Heart Disease Information and Resource Network website, if she would be willing to sponsor a listserv specifically for parents of HLHS children. Mona agreed. Laura communicated with parents from all over the world and started keeping track of everyone's email address. She let everyone know about the listserv. Now, there are over two hundred families and health care professionals on the listserv. We post notes about our children's progress, pray for each other when our children are hospitalized, ask each other questions and advice, pray for each other when a child doesn't make it and inform each other of activities we can participate in for the betterment of all our children.

Laura also started a weekly chat on America Online (AOL) so that parents could "meet" to discuss issues of importance to them. Sometimes when the parents are chatting you would not even realize that they all have children with heart defects because topic of conversation is that which any parents discuss when all together—potty training, allergies, the normal bumps and bruises of life. The one thing that keeps parents returning to the chat is the feeling of security they have from talking with other parents who really understand why they are concerned about what medications can be given, the scare they felt when a certain event occurs or just the frustration of trying to potty train a toddler who takes a diuretic like Lasix.

Laura's children—Kristine, Brian and Jennifer

CHD Leader: Sally Pearson

As much as we have seen the need for parents to have other parents to lean on and learn from, there needs to be someone willing to assume a position of leadership. If nobody is willing to volunteer the time and effort needed to organize and publicize the facilities and support available, then support groups end up disintegrating. Somebody with unending and unwavering enthusiasm and faith needs to be in charge. After years of always being that someone, many people experience burnout. But I know of a woman who has continued to give everything she has to keep her support group alive despite the apathy she may have encountered—Sally Pearson.

Sometime after I came home from San Antonio with Alex, I called the home office of the American Heart Association in Dallas. I asked where their support group meetings for parents of children with congenital heart defects were held. I was told, to my great surprise, that the American Heart Association had no such thing. The AHA was really geared more toward adults with acquired heart disease.

Although the AHA did not have anything for parents, I found out that there was a mother in Dallas devoted to helping other parents, Sally Pearson. I soon discovered she was the mother of an older child with a complex heart defect. I called Sally and we talked for a long time. I found out that she had belonged to a support group run by some parents and that she had held almost every office in that group at one time or another. She put me on her mailing list for the support groups' newsletters which enabled me to keep up with her and the other parents and children served.

To my surprise, two summers ago I got a letter from this very support group asking if they wanted to disband. I was sad to see what had once been such a big and helpful group, perhaps lacked enough interest to continue. I was not surprised, though, when I received a newsletter some months later with Sally's name listed as one of the officers. Obviously, enough parents felt there was a need for the support group to continue, and Sally once again had volunteered.

(back) Patrick, Sally, Shannon
(front) John and Emily

I could write about many more such mothers—mothers who saw a need and did what they could to fill it. Most of the support groups I know about are run by mothers. Most of these positions are totally voluntary, and the mothers are not paid but instead give generously of their time and resources to keep the groups going.

All of these mothers have children who are inspirational and special. Our children make us appreciate every day we have with them. They have brought many of us together so that we know people we never would have had occasion to meet otherwise. As inspirational as our children can be, what often goes without saying is the way so many mothers inspire others. Their attention to their children and to children with congenital heart defects everywhere has made them advocates of people all over the world. The activist movement they have started for children born with congenital heart defects will be felt for generations to come in every corner of the world.

The following is a list of some support groups for the CHD community. This is not a complete listing of support groups. There are some national support/advocacy groups, such as Parent-to-Parent, which have branches in many states. The hospital social worker should be able to guide you to local support groups; however, be aware that support group information is constantly changing. If any of the following information is not correct, you may be able to find the information you need in your local phone book or on the Internet.

Support/Advocacy Groups

United States

Arizona
Arizona Children's Heart Foundation
P.O. Box 32116
Phoenix, AZ 85064
(602) 841-4451
(602) 535-8922 (fax)
Email: AZCHIHeart@aol.com
http://www.achf.org

Families with Heart
Sutter Memorial Hospital
5151 F St.
Sacramento, CA 95819
Contact: Andrea Robertson
(916) 733-1025

Hearts for Hearts' Sake
4050 Princeton Drive
Santa Rosa, CA 95405
Contact : Tricia Christensen
(707) 525-1558
Email: triciac@heartsforhearts.org
http://www.heartsforhearts.org

Pilot Parent Partnerships
4750 N. Black Canyon, Ste. 101
Phoenix, AZ 85017
(602) 242-4366 (V/TTY)
(602) 242-4306 (fax)
(800) 237-3007 (AZ only)

Family Support Network
1850 E. 17th St., Ste. 104
Santa Ana, CA 92705
(714) 543-7600
(714) 543-2766 (fax)
Email: fsn4u@juno.com

Parents Helping Parents
The Family Resource Center
3041 Olcott St.
Santa Clara, CA 95054-3222
(408) 727-5775
(408) 727-0182 (fax)
Email: info@php.com
http://www.php.com

California
Families Caring for Families
Family Resource Center
113 W. Pillsbury St., Ste. A1
Lancaster, CA 93534
(661) 949-1746
(661) 948-7266 (fax)
(877) 824-8400

The Heart Connection
Adult Congenital Heart Disease
c/o Berkley Cardiovascular
Alta Bates 2450 Ashby Ave.
Berkeley, CA 94705
Contact: Zoe
(510) 204-8272
Email: J.M. Steinlauf at joyce@lmi.net
http://users.lanminds.com/joyce

Colorado
Effective Parents Project, Inc.
115 N. 5th St., Ste. 540
Grand Junction, CO 81501
(970) 241-4068
(970) 241-3725
Email: epp@gj.net

Connecticut

Little Hearts
1 Springdale Road
Cromwell, CT 06416
Contact: Lenore Cameron
(860) 635-3222
Email: Lenore1231@aol.com

The National Organization
of Rare Diseases (NORD)
100 Rt. 37
P.O. Box 8923
New Fairfield,CT 06812-8923
(800) 999-6673

Parent to Parent Network of CT
The Family Center
Dept. of CT Children's Medical Ctr.
282 Washington
Hartford, CT 06106
(860) 545-9021
(860) 545-9002 (TTY)
(860) 545-9201 (fax)
(877) 743-5516
Email: mameade@ccmckids.org
http://www.ccmc.org

Delaware

Parents Available to Help (PATH)
222 Mountain Rd.
Whilton, CT 06897
(203) 834-0852
Toll-free: (800) 399-PATH (CT only)

Parent Information Ctr. of DE, Inc.
700 Barksdale Rd., Ste. 16
Newark, DE 19711
(302) 366-0152
(302) 366-0276 (fax)
Email: PEP700@aol.com
http://members.aol.com/picofDEL

Florida

Arnold Palmer Hospital for
Children and Women
92 West Miller St.
Orlando, FL 32806
Contact: Julie Harper (social work)
(407) 649-9111 ext. 5924
Grandparent Contact: Carol Self
(407) 299-5224

Family Network on Disabilities
2735 Whitney Rd.
Clearwater, FL 33760
(727) 523-1130
(727) 523-8687 (fax)
(800) 825-5736 (FL only)
Email: fnd@gate.net
http://www.fndfl.org

H.O.P.E.—Heart Organization
for Parents & Education
Cardiac Care Center
3100 SW 62nd Avenue
Miami, FL 33155
Contact Kim Weindrop
(800) 666-HART

Pediatric Heart Foundation
P.O. Box 540354
Lake Worth, FL 33454-0354
Contact : Laurie Bernat
(561) 738-4554
(561) 738-4553 (fax)
Email: LBernat@aol.com

Georgia

Heart to Heart
6322 Millbranch Road
Columbus, GA 31907
(800) 207-9411

Kids at Heart
1405 Clifton Rd. NE
Atlanta, GA 30322
Contact: Social Work Dept.
(404) 325-6250

Medical College of Georgia
Children's Heart Program
Volunteer Council
BAA 800W
1120 15th Street
Augusta, GA 30912
Contact: Pat Harrell
(706) 721-2336
(706) 721- 3838 (fax)

Idaho

Parent-to-Parent of GA
2872 Woodcock Blvd., Ste. 230
Atlanta, GA 30341
(770) 451-5484
(770) 458-4091 (fax)
(800) 229-2038 (GA only)
Email: info@parenttoparentofGA.org
http://www.parenttoparentofGA.org

Palouse Area Parent to Parent
2714 8th Ave.
Lewiston, ID 83501
(208) 746-8599 (phone/fax)
Email: irel102w@wonder.em.cdc.gov

Illinois

Bereaved Parents of the USA
P.O. Box 95
Park Forest, IL 60466
(708) 748-7672
(708) 748-9184 (fax)

Children's Heart Services
P.O. Box 8275
Bartlett, IL 60103-8275
Contact: Laura Ulaszek
(630) 415-0282
Email: CHLDHRTSVC@aol.com
http://www.childrensheartservices.org

The Compassionate Friends
P.O. Box 3696
Oak Brook, IL 60522-3696
(630) 990-0010
(630) 990-0246 (fax)
Email: tcf_national@prodigy.com
http://www.compassionatefriends.org
(This is the national office for The
Compassionate Friends; check your
phone book for a local chapter.)

The Heart of the Matter
20128 Westport Drive
Frankfort, IL 60423
Contact: Cindy Tishka
(815) 469-9146
Email: CT875@aol.com

Next Steps--
Parents Reaching Parents
100 W. Randolph, Ste. 8-100
Chicago, IL 60601
(312) 814-4042 (V/TTY)
(312) 814-5849 (fax)
(800) 275-3677

Parents With Heart
702 N. 4th St.
P.O. Box 576
Ashton, IL 61006
Contact: Monetta Young
(815) 453-2377

Treasured Hearts
Pediatric Cardiology
Loyola Medical Center
Maywood, IL 60153
Coordinator: Lynn Graham, RN
(708) 327-9102
(708) 327-9107 (fax)
http://www.lumc.edu/services/
clindept/cardio.htm

Indiana
Our Hearts
1738 N Shortridge Rd
Indianapolis In 46219
Contact: Susie DeLoach
(317) 322-1017
Email: ourhearts@liquidgravity.com
http://www.geocities.com/
heartland/village/9266

Massachusetts
Adult Congenital Heart Assoc. (ACHA)
273 Perham Street
W. Roxbury, MA 02132
Contact: Karen Klein
(617) 325-1191
Email: Coatlique2@aol.com
http://www.adultcongenitalheart.org

Massachusetts Federation for
Children with Special Needs
95 Berkeley St., Ste. 104
Boston, MA 01226
(800) 331-0688

Missouri
Positive Parenting Partners
United Services
4140 Old Mill Parkway
St. Peters, MO 63376
(636) 926-2700
(636) 447-4919 (fax)

Nebraska
Parents Encouraging Parents
NE Dept. of Ed.
301 Centennial Mall S.
P.O. Box 94987
Lincoln, NE 68509-4987
Contact: Ginny Wright
(402) 471-2471 (V/TTY)
(402) 471-5022 (fax)
Email: ginny_w@nde4.nde.state.ne.us

New Jersey
The Heartline Group, Inc.
c/o Harold & Cindy Flockton
5 Teal Court
Sewell, NJ 080808
Contact: Harold or Cindy Flockton
(609) 218-9030 (phone/fax)
Email: cflocktn@aol.com

New Mexico
Parents Reaching out (PRO)
1000 A Main St.
Los Lunas, NM 87031
(505) 865-3700 (V/TTY)
(505) 865-3737 (fax)
(800) 524-5176 (V/TTY/NM only)
Email: proth@swcp.com
http://wwwparentsreachingout.org

Kansas
Families Together/Parent to
Parent of Kansas
501 Jackson, Ste. 400
Topeka, KS 66603
(785) 233-4777 (V/TTY)
(765) 233-4787 (fax)
Email: family@inlandnet.net
http://www.kansas.net/~family

Boston Adults with Congenital Heart
Disease Support Group
Children's Hospital Medical Center
300 Longwood Ave.
Boston, MA 02115
Contact: Dr. Julie Newman
(617) 332-6028

Parents and Cardiac Children
Together (PACCT)
55 Lake Avenue North
Worcester, MA 01655
Contact: Nancy Hagberg, RN
(508) 856-4154

SHARE (Pregnancy and Infant
Loss Support, Inc.)
St. Joseph Health Center
300 First Capital Drive
St. Charles, MO 63301-2893
(314) 947-6164
(314) 947-4786 (fax)
(800) 821-6819
Email: share@nationalshareoffice.com
http://www.nationalshareoffice.com
(This is SHARE's national office; check
your phone book for a local chapter.)

Nevada
Nevada Parent Network
University of Nevada—Reno
COE, REPC/285
Reno, NV 89557
(775) 784-4921
(775) 784-4997 (fax)
(800) 216-7988

Pediatric Family Support Group
Deborah Heart and Lung Center
200 Trenton Road
Browns Mills, NJ 08015
(609) 735-2923
(609) 893-6611, ext. 4351
(609) 735-1680 (fax)
Email: andrewsl@deborah.org
http://www.deborah.org

New York
Big Hearts for Little Hearts
34 Sintsink Drive West
Port Washington, NY 11050
Contact : Ruth Maszrik
(516) 883-4080

Maine
York County Parent
Awareness, Inc.
160 Main St., Midtown Mall
Sanford, ME 04073
(207) 324-2337
(207) 324-5621 (fax)
(800) 564-9696 (ME only)
Email: ycpa@smpa.org

Family-to-Family
Children's Hospital
Center for Families
300 Longwood Ave.
Boston, MA 02115
(617) 355-6279
(617) 734-6251 (fax)
Email: ctrfam@a1.tch.harvard.edu

Michigan
lil Heart to lil Heart
850 Crawford St
Flint, MI 48507
Contact: Laura Marshall
(810) 232-2055
Email: marshall2@ameritech.net

Montana
Parents, Lets Unite for Kids
516 N. 32nd St.
Billings, MT 59101
(406) 255-0540
(406) 255-0523 (fax)
(800) 222-7585 (MT only)
Email: plukmt@wtp.net
http://www.pluk.org

New Hampshire
Parent to Parent of NH
P.O. Box 622
Hanover, NH 03755
(603) 448-6393 (phone/fax)
(800) 698-5465 (NH only)

Young Hearts
791 Frederick Court
Wyckoff, NJ 07481
Contact: Barbara McFadden
(201) 848-9608
(201) 848-9492
Email: bjmcfadden@att.com

Hope for Hearts, Inc.
Children's Medical Center
S.U.N.Y. at Stony Brook
Stony Brook, NY 11794-8111
Contact: Rose Weiss
(516) 499-4476

209

North Carolina
Families with Heart
Pediatric Cardiovascular Program
DUMC Box 3090
Durham, NC 27710
Contact: Mary O'Brien
(919) 681-3057
(919) 681-8927 (fax)
Email: myrick001@mc.duke.edu
http://www2.mc.duke.edu/depts/
peds/card/pcphmpage.html

The Carolina Parents' Network
108 Burnett-Womack Bldg.
CB #7065
Chapel Hill, NC 27599-7065
Contact : Margaret Morris
(919) 966-3381
(919) 966-3475 (fax)
Email: mamorris@med.unc.edu
http://apollo.med.unc.edu/
surgery/cardioth/general/cpn.htm

Ohio
Healing Hearts
95 Spruce Drive NW
North Canton, OH 44720
Contact : Cardiology Department
(330) 258-3222
(800) -358-KIDS
Email: TBickimer@aol.com
http://hometown.aol.com/TBickimer/
healinghearts.index.html

Oregon
Caring Hearts
Legacy Emanuel Children's Hospital
2801 N. Gantenbein
Portland, OR 97227
(503) 413-4636

Pennsylvania
Hershey Hearts
P.O. Box 163
Hershey, PA 17033-0163
(800) 864-2349 mailbox #3388
Email: bigyimmer@aol.com
http://www.hersheyhearts.org

Rhode Island
The Rhode Island Association
for Cardiac Children
P.O. Box 3904
North Providence, RI 02911
Contact: Lina Lonardo
(401) 353-3966

South Carolina
Family Connection of SC, Inc.
2712 Middleburg Dr., Suite 103-B
Columbia, SC 29205
(803) 252-0914
(803) 799-8017 (fax)
(800) 578-8750
Email: famconn@mindspring.com
http://www.mindspring.com/~famconn/

South Dakota
SD Parent Connection
3701 W. 49th St., Ste. 200B
Sioux Falls, SD 57106
(605) 361-3171
(605) 361-2928 (fax)
(800) 640-4553 (SD only)
Email: Bschreck@dakota.net
http://www.sdparent.org

Tennessee
Parents Encouraging Parents (PEP)
Cordell Hull Bldg., 5th Fl.
425 5th Ave. N.
Nashville, TN 37247-4750
Contact: Suzanne Rothacker
(615) 741-0353
(615) 741-1063 (fax)
Email: srothacker@mail.state.tn.us

Texas
Central Texas--Adult CHD
Support Group
1004 Bell Springs Rd.
Dripping Springs, TX 78620
Contact: Laura Wright
(512) 264-3204
(512) 264-0938 (fax)
E-mail: buck@prismnet.com

Congenital Hearts
P.O. Box 167
Mound, TX 76558-0167
Contact: Anna Jaworski
Email: Ajaworski@aol.com

Hearts and Souls
Cook Children's Medical Center
801 7th Avenue
Fort Worth, Texas 76104
Contact: Melinda Harty, RN or
Teresa Land, RN
(817) 885-4124
(817) 885-4251 (fax)
Email: heartsandsouls@geocities.com
http://www.geocities.com/
Springs/Villa/1217

Jacob's Heart
3622 Indian Forest
Spring, TX 77373
Contact : Jamie Gartner
(281) 350-1635
Email: TGart65885@aol.com

Milagros
Children's Hospital of Austin
601 E. 15th St.
Austin, TX 78701
(512) 324-7642
http://www.goodhealth.com/gh-mag/
janfeb97/milagros.html

Thumpers
P.O. Box 760086
San Antonio, TX 78245
Contact: Shiloh Anne Hanshew
Email: hanshew@Texas.net

Utah
Primary Children's Medical Center
Graduate Parents
100 N. Medical Dr.
Salt Lake City, UT 84113
(801) 588-3899
(801) 588-3869 (fax)
Email: PCSWAR2@ihc.com

Vermont
Heart to Heart
108 Cherry St.
Burlington, VT 05401
Social Work Contact: Betsy Lawrence
(802) 863-7338
(800) 660-4427

Heart to Heart
60 Maple Ridge Road
Underhill, VT 05489
Parent Contact : Julianne Nickerson
(802) 899-3798
Email: LamaDaiz@aol.com

Parent-to-Parent of Vermont
1 Maine Street
#69 Champlain Mill
Winooski, VT 05404
Contact: Jo or Marion
(802) 655-5290
(800) 800-4005
Email: p2pvt@together.net

Virginia
Hearts United Give Strength & Support
Children's Hospital of The King's Daughters
601 Children's Lane
Norfolk, VA 23507
Contact: Fran Bright
(757) 484-4593
http://members.aol.com/Hurlbutk/
precioushearts/index.htm

Precious Hearts
P.O. Box 3013
Sterling, VA 20167
Contact: Kim Hurlbut
(703) 421-3767
Email: HurlbutK@aol.com

Washington
Heart-to-Heart
Children's Heart Center
Children's Hospital
P.O. Box 5371
Seattle, WA 98105
Contact: Social Work Department
(206) 526-2053
(206) 527-3839 (fax)

Kids With Heart
1578 Careful Drive
Green Bay, WI 54304
Contact: Michelle Rintamaki
(800) 538-5390
Email: gbkds4hrt@aol.com
http://www.execpc.com/
~kdswhrt/kwh.home

Wisconsin
Growing Hearts
1010 High Avenue
Sheboygan, WI 53081
Contact : Peggy Annus
(920) 458-5542

MUMS National Parent-to-Parent Network
150 Custer Court
Green Bay, WI 54301-1243
Contact: Julie Gordon
(877) 336-5333
Email: mums@netnet.net
http://www.waisman.wisc.edu/
~rowley/mums/index.htmlx

Helping Little Hearts
2625 Taylor Avenue
Racine, WI 53403
Contact : Leanne Evans
(414) 632-5540
Email: Evans@wi.net

Wyoming
Parent and Information
5 N. Lobban
Buffalo, WY 82834
(307) 684-2277
(307) 684-5314 (fax)
(800) 660-9742 (WY only)
Email: tdawsonpic@vcn.com
http://www.wpic.org

Other Countries (in alphabetical order)

Australia
Heart Kids Family Support Group
PO Box 2277
Carlingford Court 2117
Sydney, Australia
Contact: Lisa
Phone: 61-2-9871 4196

Heart Kids WA
1186 Hay Street, West Perth
Telephone: 08 9481 4883
Fax: 08 9481 4899
Email: heartkids@inf.net.au
http://www.heartkids.asn.au/
main.htm

Canada
CHAIN
1688 Boul Lorrain Gatineau
Quebec, Canada J8R-3G1
Phone: (819) 643-9663

Children's Heart Society
Box 52088, Garneau Postal Outlet
Edmonton, Alberta
T6G 2T5
Phone: (403) 454-7665 or
Toll-free: (888) 247-9404
Email: ch@childrensheart.org
http://www.childrensheart.org

Little Hearts
7 Dolphin Cresent
Glace Bay, Nova Scotia
Canada, B1A 3T1
Contact: Joanne Shepard
Phone: (902) 842-0217

Heart Kids of SA Inc.
155 Hutt Street
Adelaide, 5000
Email: heartkids@geocities.com
http://www.geocities.com/
Heartland/Acres/4787

Heart Kids Vic. Inc.
21 Kalonga Road
North Balwyn 3104
Contact: Margaret
Phone: (03) 857 8748
http://www.vicnet.net.au/vicnet/
HeartKids.html

CHASE
c/o Cardiac Clinic
The Hospital for Sick Children
555 University Ave.
Toronto, Ontario
M5G 1X8
Phone: (416) 813-5848 or
(416) 813-5582

Heart Beats (Children's Society of
Calgary)
Box 30233, Chinook Postal Outlet
Calgary, Alberta T2H 2V9
Contact: Lavene Morin
Phone: 279-9502

Pacific Children's Heart Network
300 30 East 6th Avenue
Vancouver, BC V5T 4P4
Contact: Colleen Corder
Phone: (604) 874-2799
Fax: (604) 875-6744
Email: ccorder@dowco.com

Heart to Heart Cardiac
Support Group, Inc.
P.O. Box 3017
Norman Park
Brisbane, Queensland. 4170
Contact: Veronica
Phone: (07) 33769557
http://www.geocities.com/
HotSprings/Spa/5652

Sensitive Hearts
Contact: Juley Foley
Email: the foleys@vds.net.au
http://lqt.vds.com.au

Children's Heart Association of
Newfoundland and Labrador (CHANAL)
147 Elizabeth Drive
Gander, Newfoundland
Canada A1V 1H2
Phone: (709) 256-8530
Email: chanal@thezone.net

Helping Other Parents Endure (HOPE)
c/o 4833 Straume Avenue
Terrace, B.C. V8G 2C8
Contact: Pauline Montague

Special Hearts
182 Natchez Rd.
Kitchener, Ontario, Canada
N2B 3L2
Phone: (519) 699-4727
http://granite.sentex/~s_hearts/

France

Association Nationale Des
Cardiaques Congenitaux (ANCC)
Nord/Pas-de-Calais delegation
55, Avenue du Cimetière
59110 la Madeleine France
Contact:Sophie Desmyter-Lesquebault
Phone/Fax: 03 20 55 71 67
Email: sdesmyter@nordnet.fr

E.U.R.O.R.D.I.S. (European
Association for Rare Disorders)
9, Rue du Serre Bois
les Loges d&nsquo; Orvault
44700 Orvault France
Contact: Bernadette Gauteir
Email: sdesmyter@nordnet.fr
http://www.infobiogen.fr/agora/
associations/ANCC

Iceland

Neistinn
Pósthólf 830
121 Reykjavík
Iceland
Phone: 354 507 3110
http://www.islandia.is/~neistinn

Nordic Assoc. for Sick Children in
the Hospital (NOBAB)
Reyniberg 3
IS 220 Hafnarfjör>ur
Contact: Esther Sigur>ardóttir
Phone: (354) 565 2632
Office Phone: (354) 563 1188
Fax: (354) 562 4440
http://www.centrum.is/nobab/

Umhyggja
Laugarvegur 7
IS-101 Reykjavík
Iceland
Phone: (354) 552 4242
Fax: (354) 552 2721
Email: umhyggja@itn.is
http://www.itn.is/umhyggja/
Umhyggja_eng.htm

Netherlands

Hartstichting
Prof. Bronkhorstlaan 2
3723 MB BILTHOVEN
The Netherlands
31-30-2290244
Contact : Karin Bus
E-mail: hartark@euronet.nl
http://www.hartstichting.nl/
sub_index_0.html

New Zealand

Heart Children NZ Inc.
P.O. Box 26473
Epsom
Auckland, NZ
Contact: Angela Wadham
Phone: 09 631 5644
http://www.heartchildren.org.nz/
index.htm

Scotland

Bravehearts
26 Fernbank
Ladywell, Livingston
Scotland
EH54 6DT
Contact: Alan Kennedy
01506 496628 in UK
+44 1506 496628 outside UK
Email: braveheart@cableinet.co.uk
http://wkweb1.cableinet.co.uk/braveheart/

Shared Care Scotland
109/111 Duncan Crescent
Dunfermline
Fife
KY11 4DA
Phone: 01383 622462
Fax: 01383-622813

Singapore

Heartkids Support Group
Club Rainbow
P.O. Box 447
Orchard Road Post Office
Singapore 912315
Contact: Helen Ng
Email: helenng@pacific.net.sg

United Kingdom

Down's Heart Group
17 Cantilupe Close
Eaton Bray
Dunstable
Beds
LU6 2EA
U.K.
Phone: + 44-1525-220379
Email: Downs_Heart_Group@msn.com

Grown Up Congenital Heart (GUCH)
Beech Cottage, 26A Quarry Road
Winchester, SO23 OJG
U.K.
Contact: Judy Shedden
Phone: (UK) 0800 854759
Email: judy@guch.demon.co.uk
http://www.guch.demon.co.uk

Heart Link
18 Briar Walk
Fishponds, Bristol
BS16 4JJ. England
Email: rwall@heartlink.org.uk
http://www.heartlink.org.uk

Heartlink House
351 Fishponds Road
Eastville, Bristol BS5 6RD
England
Phone: 017-939-5512
Fax: 017-939-5513

Shooting Stars

When I found out about Alexander's heart defect the threat of losing him loomed ominously over me everyday. The words of the surgeon and the pediatric cardiologist, "If he dies before the next surgery, it's not your fault" brought me no comfort and instead caused me many sleepless nights. Every thirty minutes or so, I ran into Alex's room to see if he was still breathing, if he was still with me. When I did sleep, nightmares filled my nights, and I would awake in a cold sweat and run into Alex's room. If I could not hear him breathing or see his chest move, I would pull myself closer and closer to him until the sound of my beating heart drowned out any other sound in the room, and I became concerned lest my beating heart should wake him. Finally I would put my finger on his upper lip to feel the warm air exhaled through his nose, and then I would straighten his blankets, place a kiss on my finger, touch his head and retire to my room.

Once a doctor identifies your child's heart defect, you must face a situation which few others realize—that your child could die before you. Each and every day is a gift. You face Mortality. You embrace Life. Many of us pray like never before. We see the beauty of every day, every act, every being and are filled with an overwhelming sense of awe and admiration for what living in this world is all about.

Luckily many of us have been able to elude the inevitable, if even for only a little while longer. Some of us live in denial that it could ever happen to us. Some of us live in fear knowing it could happen to us. Some of us have chosen to rejoice in the blessing of each day. Some of us have taken our child's state of being as a mission to help others. Some choose to let their love of their child be the catalyst to grow as a more compassionate person.

The following essays are from mothers whose children have died due to their heart defects. These women could have wallowed in self-pity. They could have turned their back on the world. They could have let indifference and apathy harden their heart. Instead they chose to honor their child's life and keep their child's memory alive by compassionate acts of kindness, which linger on as continual reminders of what Love really is.

What kinds of things help a mother to cope with her child's illness or death? Deb Gilmore found strength and courage in writing to other parents of children with congenital heart defects. Her support group was comprised of parents from all over the world. They form a unique subset of parents—parents online. Parents with computers and a modem can hook up (for a nominal charge) to the World Wide Web or the Internet where there is a cyber-world of friends and family. In remembrance, Deb wrote the following letter to the friends who prayed for her and her family.

My Candle in the Wind

by: Deb Gilmore

Gosh, how do you start a letter like this? The last couple of weeks have been far more of a roller coaster ride than I ever want to endure again. Had it not been for Dr. Norwood, Dr. Murphy, Dr. Pizarrio and a wonderful staff, I feel as if this would have had a much different outcome on our emotions.

Matthew is not doing well at all. He had come through the surgery with flying colors, and we were excited. We talked about having Matthew in our room the next day. His heart was fixed to perfection, and he looked great. At 10:00 p.m. they extubated him; at midnight he had his first bottle, and he even smiled at us. At 2:00 a.m. he went into cardiac arrest!

This was a great shock to all of us because he was doing so well. Dr. Pizarrio and the staff maintained CPR for forty minutes while they got Matthew onto the ECMO (Extra-Corporeal Membrane Oxygenation) machine. Matthew remained on ECMO for four days and was finally taken off of it. He seemed to be stable and doing better. The doctors did a baseline CAT scan, and it did not show anything unusual; so we waited.

Matthew then went into kidney failure and had to be put on peritoneal dialysis. After a few days it looked as though his kidneys were starting to work again—just a little, but at least something. After a few more days though, it became evident that his kidneys were in true failure. Another CAT scan was done. This one showed severe damage to the brain—the only part not affected was the brain stem.

We continued with his maintenance hoping for some sign of life to be there, and slowly his eyes opened, and he moved just a little. We were not sure, however, if his movements were controlled or just an involuntary reaction.

On Friday Dr. Murphy had to bring us the worst news of our lives. He said that Matthew most likely would never get any better than his current status. He wondered how we wanted to proceed. He said it much nicer but that was the bottom line. We asked to have a neurologist come and look at Matthew, which was arranged for us.

At this point, we had been told by several doctors that when there is severe brain damage and kidney failure, there is not much hope for recovery. You have basically two choices: 1) do maintenance and keep the body alive or 2) stop life-support and let nature take its course.

These are not easy decisions to make. Do you take your child off life-support and let him die? Or, do you maintain life-support for months or years with your child institutionalized, being supported by machines, risking infection, losing muscle mass, and finally the failure of all organs? There is maybe a 1% chance that anything will ever change, and even if it did, there would be no guarantee as to what the quality of life would be. Then, too, is the possibility that other heart problems might arise from having so much other trauma. Please understand we have not been given the option of having a handicapped child; we have been given the option of having a child who cannot see, hear, move, or eat. There is basically *no life* present at all.

We have decided on the second option. It has taken us three weeks of going back and forth emotionally and weighing all the options to finally make this decision. It has been the hardest decision we have ever had to make. Matthew was wanted so much and loved even more than that! He was such a special child with lots of laughter and sunshine in his spirit. We do not know how we will live without him. Just going to a McDonald's without him will be terribly hard to do. We have to believe, though, that it is in his best interest to let him go.

Sorry, but I had to stop for a while, and it is now Monday, the 15th of September. The neurologist came in today and confirmed what the other five doctors had said. There was *no hope* of Matthew ever getting any better. We immediately called my husband's parents and family and asked them to come to be with us. We asked to keep Matthew on life-support until they arrived, and the doctors agreed.

When Matthew is taken off all life-support machines, the doctors expect him to survive for three to five days before finally passing on. Matthew's lungs, however, were filling with secretions, and he was already getting worse even before he was taken off life-support. In a way this gave us a sort of sign that we were making the right decision.

The hospital at this time gave us many options on how we wanted to deal with this: we could leave Matthew in the Intensive Care Unit and visit him, or we could take him to our room to hold and love and maybe even take him outside in a stroller for a walk. This is something I never thought the doctors would agree to. Dr. Pizarrio said, "What better way to go to sleep than to be outside in the sunshine?" They assured us that Matthew would not be in any pain. The toxins would just build up and put him into a deep sleep from which he would never awaken.

That afternoon my husband's family arrived, and Matthew was taken off life-support and brought into our room. Matthew was held by each family member as they said their final good-byes. Before we went to bed that night, we asked to have Matthew monitored with a pulse-oximeter so we would wake up if something should happen.

We wanted desperately to be with him when he left, and we did not know just when it would happen. The nurse put Matthew's bed between our beds and raised our beds to be the same level. Then she left us saying that she would check every two hours to make sure that Matthew was doing okay. We held and loved Matthew through the night, sleeping in bits and pieces here and there. Around 2:00 a.m. the pulse-oximeter sounded the alarm the first time. His heart rate had dropped below 80!

His heart immediately recovered and went to 110 beats per minute. This happened a few times more and gave us the impression that he was floating slowly back and forth. My husband then set the alarm to go off below 60, and we went back to sleep. At 6:00 a.m. the alarm went off again, and we realized that it was happening.

We turned the alarm off but left the monitor on so we could tell how Matthew was doing at all times. His heart rate continued slowly dropping 60 - 55 - 50 - 45. And then at 6:30, on the morning of September 17th, his heart rate dropped abruptly to 0. Matthew had left us and gone to Heaven in a quiet and dignified way! His passing-on was so calm and peaceful.

We called the nurse in. She came and removed the rest of the IV lines. My husband and I then gave Matthew his final bath, changed his diaper one last time, and dressed him in a darling outfit that his sister had brought him. All the staff that was working came in to grieve with us. I feel as if they loved Matthew, too.

All I can say is that we are so thankful for the peace we feel with this. We hurt so badly inside, and this morning was the hardest because we could not touch him and kiss his lips. But he is in a far better place— no more surgery, no more pain!

My husband and I have a hard road ahead of us. I am sure that when Brandon gets here around the 21st of December, we will have less time to grieve. Matthew will never be forgotten, but Brandon will see that we have laughter and joy in our lives again. I am so glad that I am already pregnant because I feel that it would have been a lot harder to "want" to be pregnant again. We have suffered a great loss and never planned to go through something like this, but I believe that God makes things happen for a reason. We feel blessed that we had a wonderful and happy fifteen months with Matthew and that we were given a chance to say good-bye.

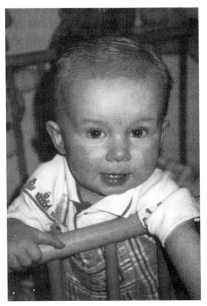

Matthew Gilmore

Editor's Note: This essay first appeared as a post to the HLHS and PDHeart listserv.

Perhaps the most difficult part of losing a child is the fear that your life is not worth living anymore. Many mothers wonder if they will be able to get out of bed in the morning. Some wonder if they will ever feel joy in their heart again. Read on to see what helped Aleta know she still had a purpose for living.

387 Pictures

by: Aleta P. Riesberg

"IT'S A BOY! Here's your beautiful baby boy!! Looks like we have a solid citizen here!" the doctor said while I waited to behold our baby for the first time. As I was craning my neck to see him, all around me was a sea of people in blue-green scrubs. The room bustled with activity as they cleaned him off and calculated the APGAR score. "9!" a nurse announced. I thought to myself, "That's okay, after twenty-two hours of labor, four hours of pushing and a C-section, a 9 is not bad." A minute later, I heard another figure, "8.5!" Hm, I didn't think it went down. Usually, the score goes up.

My husband, Brian, was taking pictures. I heard someone ask, "Does this baby have a name yet?"

"Yes," we said in unison, "Sullivan. Sullivan McLean Riesberg." Suddenly, the nurse mumbled something about having to get him to the nursery right away. She brought him over to me while the surgeon stitched me up and said, "Say hello, Mom."

"Hello, sweetheart," I said, as I kissed him on the forehead. She started to take him away, and I asked to kiss him again. In one swift motion, she passed him by my lips and said, "We need to go. We've got a problem here." I looked at Brian and asked him what was going on. He said they had to put Sullivan on oxygen quickly. He wasn't breathing right. I told him that it was okay; lots of babies need oxygen at birth, simply routine.

An hour passed in the recovery room. Brian kept me up-to-date on Sullivan's progress. He said there were a few doctors looking at him. They had taken some X-rays and were calling in some neonatologists from the Medical University of South Carolina (in Charleston). I was confused. I didn't understand all the fuss. Brian said that the baby's heart was enlarged, and they were going to run some tests to see why. Now I started worrying. My elation was replaced by an overwhelming feeling of concern. I just wanted to see Sullivan again and hold him for the first time. I couldn't wait any longer!

The Recovery Room nurses wheeled me into a private room. With constant trips back and forth to the nursery, Brian was running on nervous energy. We wanted some information. Why weren't they bringing Sullivan into the room? Where was he? What could possibly be wrong? Brian returned and said a doctor would be in to explain everything in just a few minutes.

That's when our world turned completely upside down. The neonatologist informed us that Sullivan was diagnosed with an enlarged heart and even worse, hypoplastic left heart syndrome. He went on to say that this condition is very serious in nature and that we had three options. They were "a heart transplant, which is risky because the waiting list is quite long, and he would probably die while waiting for a new heart; surgery, which hasn't been proven to be all that effective with only a 50%-80% survival rate; or do nothing, and take him home." My first thought was that we'd take him home and get out of this depressing place. If he needed surgery, why then, we'd arrange that at a later date, perhaps in a few years when we knew what the outcome would be. I was in total denial. This just couldn't be happening. The doctor then explained that if we took him home, death was inevitable, probably within a few days, if not hours. He left the room as fast as he had entered. Meanwhile Sullivan was being prepared for transport to MUSC.

Brian and I sat in the silence. Then we burst into tears, feeling overwhelmed by the words just spoken. Minutes later my mom and sister walked into the room and saw us crying. They knew by looking at us that things were not good. I asked my sister to call the rest of the family and ask them to come to the hospital as soon as possible. Within an hour, our parents and siblings were in the room with us. We all prayed for Sullivan to be blessed by God and survive this ordeal. We decided that surgery was the best option for Sullivan. After notifying the doctors and staff, we made arrangements for me to be transported to MUSC, too, so I could be close to Sullivan. I was still recovering from surgery; Sullivan was only hours old.

Six days passed before Sullivan's surgery, during which time Brian and I became what we call "armchair surgeons." We learned everything there was to know about the series of operations from the Norwood to the completion Fontan, thanks mostly to the information my father-in-law gathered off the Internet. The surgeon and cardiologists were thorough with their explanations, but we knew their time was valuable. In my father-in-law's search, he happened upon one of the best pieces of information a parent in our situation could have had: *Hypoplastic Left Heart Syndrome: A Handbook for Parents* by Anna Jaworski. Through Anna, Bill was able to obtain a world of information not available to us through the hospital. We carried the diagrams the cardiologists had given us around for those six days.

We must have explained the procedure twenty or thirty times to friends, family, even the nursing staff on the post-partum floor. Brian was asked a few times if he had a medical background. We'd just laugh and say, "no." We explained that we were in sales and marketing. We were confident that all would go well. How could anything go wrong? We knew this procedure inside and out, and besides, we had all the confidence in the world in our surgeon, Dr. Scott Bradley. He's one of the best in the country, in the world for that matter. Plus the team of cardiologists were top-notch. We knew our son was in good hands.

Most of our fears dissolved. We saw "Sully Mac" whenever we wanted in NICU. We could touch him occasionally. We took hundreds of pictures. Two days had passed when I heard the words I longed for. His nurse, Tracey said, "Would you like to hold him?" I thought, "Would I? Lady, are you crazy? Of course I would!" My heart was pounding. I was so excited. I told Brian to get the camera, fast! Oh, I couldn't wait. Do I sit or stand? With all the IV's, I wasn't sure what to do. How do I hold him? Am I going to hurt him? What about the nitrogen levels? Doesn't he need to stay under the "cake topper"? Tracey just laughed at all my questions. She offered me a rocking chair and a pillow. "Here," she said, "Get comfortable. I'll place him in your arms. I'm sure you'll do just fine." I immediately talked to Sullivan, rocking him gently. Brian took pictures, anxiously awaiting his turn. I knew I only had a few minutes, so I wanted to savor every last second looking at his beautiful face, rubbing his soft cheeks against mine, smelling, kissing, cuddling and cooing like only a mother knows how. I didn't want to be selfish; I knew Brian was patiently waiting. Sully's heart rate changed quite a bit while I was holding him, a natural reaction to a mother's touch and voice.

Brian and I traded seats, and I helped him handle all the tubes and IVs. Then it was my turn to take pictures. A love I had never known before blanketed my soul. Minutes later we had to put Sullivan back in his tiny bassinet, safe and sound under the nitrogen mix. We sat beside him for hours, reading *The Rainbow Fish*, talking and comforting him. This had become our daily routine all the way through day six, the day before surgery.

At midnight we went home to rest before returning to the hospital. At 5:00 a.m. we walked Sullivan to the Operating Room. I sang "You Are My Sunshine," as I did every night before I left and every morning when I first saw him. I sang it softly just outside of the hole in the "cake topper" as close to his ear as I could get. And this time, I added at the end, the strongest prayer I'd ever prayed in the few short words, "And, please, God, don't take my sunshine away."

The surgery went well, and we took him home fourteen days later on December 30th. He was in the hospital twenty days. I got on the Internet during nap times to "talk" to Anna and other mothers in the same situation. This helped tremendously for I was not alone. After two weeks at home, we were ready to settle into a daily routine. Brian decided to attend the Regional Sales Meeting in Florida. His flight left early Tuesday morning, January 14th. That afternoon I dressed up Sullivan, finished a roll of film, took it to be developed and stopped by the grocery store for some milk. It was a little before 7:00 p.m.

Sullivan got a little fussy when we first walked into the store, so I picked him up and held him. We walked back to the milk section, and a woman commented on my beautiful baby. I went to move him from my shoulder to a cradle position, and when I did, he just laid there, lifeless. I called his name. I called his name again and again—no response. I ran to the front of the store screaming for help. I needed an ambulance, NOW! A physician happened to be standing at the customer service desk getting a refund. He jumped into action immediately, helping me do CPR. I still do not know who this wonderful man was. I wish I could thank him.

Sullivan's heart rate stayed around 60 beats per minute. He was ashy grey in color and gasping for breath every three to five seconds. The hospital knew we were on our way. Sullivan's cardiologists were waiting for him to arrive. Once there, they worked on him for about another forty-five minutes before pronouncing him dead at 7:58 p.m. Dr. Waller said his heart rate never got above 40 beats per minute. They tried, and, I'm sure, did the best they could. Dr. Waller came in the little waiting area where my mom and Brian's dad were waiting with me to tell us that he didn't make it.

His compassion softened the blow. I was completely numb. I felt like a rag doll. I couldn't move. My ears were ringing, and my gut wrenched. They prepped Sullivan, and I held him for a while. We needed to contact Brian. A neighbor went into our house to get the number for Brian in Florida. Within minutes we had him on the phone. He couldn't get a flight out that night but booked one for 6:00 a.m. He was back in Charleston by 9:00 a.m. the next morning.

We took Brian to the hospital to see Sullivan and hold him. Sullivan, wrapped in a baby blanket, was wheeled into the chapel in a little red wagon. He was still ashy grey, but this time he was freezing cold from the morgue. A natural instinct made me hold him close to warm him. I began to rock instinctively, as well, until Brian caught my eye and motioned me to stop. We held him as long as we could. We came to some sort of peace about the whole ordeal. There was a certain element of serenity about the room that was comforting.

The next few days were chaotic, as we planned the funeral. It was beautiful. The children in attendance released white helium balloons. It was a day to be remembered. Like my father said in his eulogy, "Sullivan, you deeply touched the hearts and lives of everyone who knew you, and we will never forget you." Dad suffered a fatal heart attack himself the following weekend.

The next few months were rough. I cried everyday. I experienced that strange phenomenon of aching arms. It is so real and painful! I went through all the stages of grief bouncing back and forth between anger, depression and bargaining. Every time I thought I was getting close to acceptance, something would happen, and I'd hit rock bottom again. To make things worse, Brian and I were never in the same stage of grief together. Of course, maybe that's a good thing, but at the time it was frustrating.

One day I'd be so angry at the world, and he would pipe in with some cheery bargaining statement "Yeah, Hun, but look at it this way: he's in a better place now." Oh, boy! Would I go on a rampage about how "the best place would be back in my arms, ALIVE!" And then on another day, he would be feeling sad and depressed, and I would chime in with my bargaining statements. The most volitile combination was when one of us was angry, and one was depressed. Can you imagine what that day was like? I'd be depressed, and he would get frustrated and angry about the whole ordeal, and then when I saw him angry, I would feel guilty and become even sadder. Within an hour, I'd be mad at the world and angry with God, and then that would depress him. The emotions of those days put the highest, fastest, meanest roller coaster ride to shame!

A close friend of ours is a therapist, and we accepted her offer to help. At our house one day, she explained all the stages of grief and gave us an idea of what to expect in the days and weeks to come. By the end of her visit, we were laughing at the textbook behavior we had displayed. It was comforting to know we were "normal." We were not crazy; we were not heading for d-i-v-o-r-c-e. We were, in fact, g-r-i-e-v-i-n-g. She left knowing that we would take care of each other and watch out for tell-tale signs. Brian and I got to the point where we recognized that the other was in a particular stage and could talk the other one through it. This felt like a healthy road to recovery.

We attended Compassionate Friends meetings. After a few meetings, I realized how differently men and women grieve the loss of a child, especially when it comes to acceptance. We made some great friends there and eventually the guys were going to the local minor league baseball games the nights we mothers attended meetings. That was good for them, and this was good for us. It was mutually understood and respected.

On the outside, I was hanging tough. People thought I was doing so well. But what they didn't know was that on my bad days, I hid. I still do. It's easier for me to withdraw for a few days at a time. For a while, though, friends and family kept me occupied. I needed that.

Overall, I sunk about as deep as a mother could go. The pain was unbearable. Every morning my eyes opened to another day. I dreaded it. How could I survive another day? My heart ached; my arms ached (they still do sometimes, and it has been almost two years); I was weak in the knees and numb all over. Then a few months passed. The pain didn't lessen; it just got easier to deal with. Then finally one day I gave myself permission to start letting go. Don't get me wrong. I'll never forget, nor will I ever "get over it." I just knew I needed to start living again, to salvage something of my life and my marriage.

We tried to get pregnant again and move on with our lives. Having always wanted children, we felt we needed to follow our dreams of having a family. We conceived two months after Sullivan's death. I was reassured by the doctors that although the chances of this happening again were rare, there were tests available to diagnose this or any other defect. I never felt I wanted to get pregnant to replace Sullivan, rather we wanted a second child, a brother or a sister to Sullivan. I underwent a battery of tests to prepare us if there were a defect of some sort in this baby.

The second pregnancy was easier in a lot of ways. I knew what to expect. Unfortunately, I knew too much of what could go wrong. "Ignorance was bliss," we'd say. Grieving the loss of Sullivan was even more difficult now. I had so many pregnancy-induced emotions flowing around my body it was hard to decipher which were O.K. and which were a little overboard. Our situation was skewed by our move from South Carolina to Rhode Island in May. That was difficult in itself, leaving home, family, friends, and especially Sullivan, but the promotion from a statewide sales rep to a Global Product Manager for Stanley-Bostitch was just too good to pass up. I rolled with the punches by this point in my life, sort of took a "what next" attitude. Bring it on. Let's see just how much we can handle. I slowly realized how good things really were becoming, thankful for what we had. Afterall, we had each other and another baby on the way.

The move, in a way, was a blessing. It was becoming harder, not easier, to see the familiar surroundings. To get off the island we lived on, I had to drive past the grocery store where Sullivan went into cardiac arrest. Just across the bridge was the hospital Sullivan was born in (and me, too!), and across the street from that was the Medical University where Sullivan had his surgery. I was surrounded by traumatic memories. I needed to get away, and I guess God answered that prayer.

We had already asked ourselves if we wouldn't be better off emotionally to move across town. Our neighbors were wonderful, some of our best friends. I'm sure they would have understood, but we felt a strong sense of community there. We loved our house. We had picked out a lake lot with a century old oak tree in front. I had the nursery decorated in the Rainbow Fish theme. I had painted a Rainbow Fish mural border on two walls, glitter puff paint and all. I couldn't go in Sullivan's room without getting weak in the knees and achy all over. For months everything sat just where it was the last day he was home with us. I choose not to disclose how long diapers stayed in the Genie. (Just for the record, there was no odor!)

I couldn't throw anything away. I couldn't even wash the sheets he napped on his last afternoon. I finally washed the crib sheets the day before the movers came in July, but not before I sat on the floor with them and had a good long cry. I had repainted every room of the house back to neutral colors before putting it on the market, except for the mural. I couldn't do it. Even if it meant losing a contract, I just was not going to do it. Fortunately, the house sold in four days, and the new owner apparently liked it. That made me feel good.

I could hardly bare the thought of leaving Sullivan. We had originally planned on cremation but were talked into burial when planning his funeral. Of course, we never thought we would leave Charleston, and when the time came, the thought crossed my mind to exhume and cremate. The only thing that kept me from doing it was that we buried him in the most beautiful spot in Charleston—he's on a beautiful grassy green hill about fifteen yards from a tidal creek with huge oaks and draping moss, dogwoods, azaleas, and camelias and a huge magnolia tree close by. It's just gorgeous—so typical of southern "low country" setting. We joked that Sullivan got waterfront property before WE did! I DO love to visit with him there. It's so peaceful.

On November 17, 1997, God blessed us with another beautiful baby boy, Adam McLean Riesberg. I truly had a reason to live again. I didn't understand why the post-partum blues got to me so bad this time. Everything was fine. Adam was healthy. But still, something was not quite right. It seemed like nobody was mentioning Sullivan's name anymore. His first birthday was rapidly approaching, and I didn't have time to sort my feelings about the one year anniversary mark of the day our lives turned upside down. My mom and sister were here for Adam's birth and through Thanksgiving. I loved having them here. My sister kept calling Adam "Sullivan." She would correct herself and apologize, but it actually let me know that his name was on the tip of her tongue, so she was thinking about him.

My family had put a lot of thought into how I was going to handle "The Big Day." I knew I had a newborn to nurse and care for. Mom left on December 9th, and Brian's mother was due to fly in on the 11th, so I was all alone on Sullivan's birthday. I must admit, the anticipation of the day was worse than the day itself. Brian and I decided he would go to work, and if I needed him I would call. I woke up a few times in the middle of the night to nurse Adam, at midnight, 2:00 a.m. and again about 4:45 a.m. That was a bittersweet moment for me. There I was rocking and nursing Adam in our dark bedroom. I watched the big red numbers on a digital clock counting down the minutes for me. I spent the whole feeding reminiscing about the minutes before my C-section exactly one year before. I relived the whole experience. The clock changed to 5:06, and I thought, "One minute to go; here it is." Then 5:07 appeared. I sat in the silence of the early morning hours. Adam had fallen asleep again. At 5:08, I said to myself, "Now, there! You made it through that minute. Now you just have to ride out the rest of the day." I eventually fell back asleep before dawn broke.

I spent most of the day staring at the walls. Each of my family members called me throughout the day. We'd talk a little, cry a little, laugh a little. I knew they were trying to cheer me up. Their intentions were sincere. A few of my close friends called. I was so deeply touched that they remembered. The weather outside took a turn for the worse. The impending snowfall and subsequent closings were being covered on television and radio. It got my mind off things for a while. In the late afternoon, the first snow of the season began to fall. It was beautiful. I looked at it as a "gift" from my little angel above. I smiled.

I took a little different approach to the anniversary of his death. It took careful planning. In the days leading up to January 14th, I decided that I would try to carry on a normal day, just as any other, until the seventh hour. I made sure Brian would be home a little early from work. We ate dinner early. I fed Adam, changed him and gave him to Brian. I had forewarned Brian that he would be on duty from 7:00-8:00 p.m. Afterall, it was just another day to him.

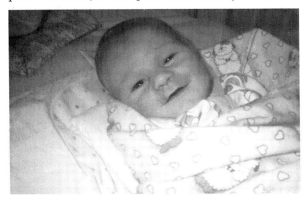

Sullivan McLean Riesberg

I had made a date with myself. At about 7:00, I sat down with Sullivan's photo album which contains 387 pictures of him. I went through page by page. That took about forty minutes. I sat contemplating once again the meaning behind all of this and the purpose of Sullivan's life here on earth. He accomplished small miracles. He brought distant family members together again. His well-being, and then eventually his death, was the topic of many conversations.

We all slowed down long enough to put life itself into perspective. And even, in a way, I feel as though he was an angel sent here by God to tell my dad it was okay to die. His congestive heart failure had been diagnosed for about six months, and he was in pain. Looking into Sullivan's eyes, we all saw the eyes of a sage. Sullivan's life definitely had a purpose, and he served it well. I'm so proud of what he accomplished in his short life. By 7:58 I was sobbing. I missed him terribly. Why did this have to happen? Why! That lasted about fifteen minutes and my date with myself to grieve was over. It was time to get back to my responsibilities. Adam needed me.

Adam McLean Riesberg

Deirdre Bronchick turned her own tragedy into a vehicle for helping other parents. With intelligence and insight, Deirdre shares her story.

An Angel's Cause

by: Deirdre Bronchick

I should preface my daughter's story with the following facts. Around the twenty-fifth week of my pregnancy, I was diagnosed with IUGR (intrauterine growth retardation), but there were no apparent causes of my condition. From this point on I was under the care of a high-risk perinatalogist. During one of the earlier ultrasounds the doctor also determined that there was an artery missing from the baby's umbilical cord. The doctor said this is often indicative of a birth defect, yet after numerous ultrasounds he could not find one. I was subjected to semi-weekly non-stress tests during which my baby's heart was very slow to respond to stimulation and was often non-responsive. However, the chambers of her little heart appeared normal, and despite her lack of in utero growth, everything else seemed to be in order.

It was decided that our baby, who by that time we had decided to name Paige, would be better off outside the womb, and a C-section was scheduled at the end of my thirty-sixth week. Paige was born on May 18, 1996 and weighed three pounds, thirteen ounces.

During the first forty-eight hours of Paige's life, my husband, Jeff, and I were probably as happy as we will ever be capable of being. I will never forget the sound of Paige's first cry as she was lifted out of my belly. I do not know who cried more, me or the baby. I was so relieved when I saw my husband's happy face. I felt an overwhelming sense of relief that I assume every parent feels when they are told everything looks great and that their child, in addition to having ten fingers and toes, appears to be very healthy. Within minutes Paige was ushered over to me so I could introduce myself and give her a big welcome kiss. She was then quickly delivered to the NICU because of her low birth weight, but everything appeared fine at this point.

On day two of her life, I felt well enough to go to the NICU and give breast-feeding a try. One of Paige's doctors mentioned that he detected a heart murmur while examining Paige but that we should not worry since they are relatively common in newborns; however, a consultation with a pediatric cardiologist was scheduled for the following morning to rule out any problems. We had a great day experimenting with diaper changes and feedings. We were all pretty exhausted, so I sent Jeff home that night so that he could get a good night's sleep.

Late the next morning, one of the cardiologists came to see me after examining Paige. We will never forget that day because it changed our lives. Just by looking at the doctor's face, I knew something was wrong. He said we had a very serious problem and that her defects were complex. He showed me diagrams explaining the architecture of Paige's heart as compared to a normal heart. At the time, I was alone waiting for my husband to arrive, and I just started to panic. Nothing he was saying was sinking in, other than the fact that on a scale of one to ten and ten being the worst case scenario, Paige's situation was at least an eight. I was utterly devastated and heartbroken. We had tried to conceive for twenty months and were both ecstatic when I became pregnant. Like everyone else, we never thought this would happen to our little angel.

Paige was diagnosed with the following heart defects: subpulmonary ventricular septal defect, atrial septal defect, stenotic pulmonary and aortic valves, stenotic pulmonary arteries and a large aortopulmonary window. After my husband arrived, we sat down with Paige's team of doctors, and they explained her case in detail to both of us. Neither of us are doctors, so needless to say it was initially very difficult trying to comprehend her situation. What made the situation even more troubling was the fact that the doctors at this point were dumbfounded. Paige's combination of defects were very uncommon, and they had not seen many cases like hers.

We walked out of that meeting, and both fell to pieces. Some of our family and friends were just arriving at the hospital; it was going to be so hard to see them, as they rushed up to us with big smiles on their faces. We had not seen the baby yet that morning and were momentarily scared to even walk into NICU to visit her. I did not want to cry on her; I did not want her to know how crushed her mommy and daddy were. The fear of becoming so attached to Paige and then losing her scared us so much. At that point, the terrible pain I was still feeling from the C-section seemed so insignificant. Somehow we managed to muster up enough energy to walk in the NICU. All we needed was to hold her, and I know at that point we somehow found the strength that was going to get us all through the next six months.

Paige's case was too complex for the hospital where she was born, and the doctors decided to transfer her to a hospital with a pediatric cardiac unit. The following morning she was transported to UCLA Medical Center and was immediately retested. The UCLA cardiology team concurred that the original diagnosis was correct. Her condition remained stable, and it was decided that she was not a candidate for immediate surgery due to her small size. Her doctors felt that she would not survive the extensive amount of time required on the heart-lung machine, given her low weight. All they could do for her now was try to fatten her up, so she could go home.

Finally, when Paige was three weeks old, they sent her home with us. She had finally started to put on weight, albeit at a slow pace, but the doctors were pleased. She was being fed half from a bottle and the remainder through an NG tube. Over the next few weeks, Paige's weekly weight checks continued to indicate a slow but steady increase; however, at approximately seven weeks of age, she was too fatigued to take the bottle and starting having digestive problems causing her to vomit frequently.

Paige's catheterization, which had been put off while the doctors waited for her to gain weight, was performed at eleven weeks of age. The results were not too promising and showed remarkable thickening of the ventricles among other things. Before we knew it, we were having preliminary discussions with the cardiac transplant team. Paige stayed in the hospital for six days, while we resolved her feeding problems. She was finally sent home with a continuous feed pump, more medications and a supply of NG tubes for me to use at home. Still, no surgical decision was made, and we continued to wait. At least we would have Paige back home with us.

She had a good month cardiac-wise, and the feeding pump was working well. Paige was putting on weight at a reasonable pace; however, within weeks her digestive problems began again, and she started having some very scary choking episodes at home. During these episodes she would become cyanotic. What followed was a series of frustrating visits with the GI team. They determined after another twelve day hospital stay and extensive testing that there was nothing wrong with Paige other than her defective heart. Her little heart was simply failing her. We were so upset at this point. Every day she was in the hospital was taking away from time she should have been spending with us at home.

The next few weeks, all we did was wait to see what the inevitable surgical decision would be. We were certainly, by this point, well-equipped to care for Paige at home, given all the training we had received at the hospital. I hated having to place NG tubes in her. She always cried, but I was the one who would give her the proper amount of hugs and love that was required after such an ordeal. By five months of age, Paige grew to be over eight pounds, very close to her desired weight for surgery.

At our next visit with the cardiologist, in late October, we were told that the surgeon decided after discussing her case at their last conference that Paige was not a good candidate for reparative surgery, and he suggested a heart transplant. The concept of a transplant had not come up in two months, and we just were not prepared to go that route. We had a few consultations with the transplant team and sincerely felt that we did not want to put our child through the pain, heartache and the rigmarole associated with transplants. We sat on this idea for several days while conducting our own research. We were beginning to become resigned to the idea but still with many reservations. While we were happy with our doctors, we certainly would at the very least require a second opinion.

The following week was an emotional roller coaster. We next met with Paige's surgeon. He again outlined all the risks of either operation, and after he had answered all our questions he said we should think about it some more and let him know what route we wanted to take. I could not believe that he was leaving this decision up to us. I felt so ill-prepared to make such a monumental choice. I told him I could not make the decision; we talked a little more and moments later he decided that he would do the repair and not the transplant. Although Paige's chance for survival was approximately 60%, or at least that is what they thought going into the surgery. We both felt so incredibly relieved.

This decision was reaffirmed for us days later when we went for a second opinion. The other surgeon with whom we consulted concurred that Paige's heart should be repaired and not replaced. Paige's surgery was scheduled for the following week on November 11, 1997.

On Sunday, November 10th, we took Paige for a long walk on the beach. We dressed her up in her cutest outfit and took numerous pictures. We laughed; we cried; we gave her what was to be her last bath. Later that day we took her to the hospital, admitted her and then sat around trying not to think about what might happen the next day.

Very early the next morning, November 11, 1996, I carried Paige to the operating room and handed her to one of the nurses. I will never forget that horrible walk; Paige luckily had no idea what was happening. My husband and I just stood in the hallway and cried for so long. We received hourly updates from one of the nurses that really did not reveal much about Paige's status. It was not until eleven hours later that I actually talked to the surgeon. After outlining what they had done during surgery, he said her chances for survival were slim due to her ventricles being so severely hypertrophied; they just could not get her little heart to start-up again. I do not think the numbness that sank in at that point has left me yet. Luckily, I did get to hold my little angel briefly for one last time before she left us.

I can be happy with the fact that Paige was a happy little baby; once she learned how to smile, she never stopped. She never suffered or was in pain and was just loved so dearly that her short time here was at least very happy. We miss her immensely and want another baby so badly. It is such a terrible, lonely feeling losing a child. So few people know what to say. Some friends with children do not want to include you in their plans, for fear of what, I am not quite sure, and the worst part is that no one wants me to talk about Paige.

Paige was the best thing to happen to me besides marrying my husband. Hopefully we'll make a brother or sister for Paige soon. I conceived again, four months after Paige passed away, but I unfortunately miscarried. It was not easy for me emotionally to be pregnant again; I missed Paige so badly that being pregnant just reminded me of her even more.

In the mean time, we will focus our energy on the Paige Bronchick Foundation (PBF), which we founded shortly after Paige passed away. The mission of the foundation is to further research causes of congenital heart defects and to improve clinical and surgical techniques enabling children born with heart defects to survive and lead healthy and meaningful lives. The foundation will help fund research efforts, fellowships and other programs designed to attract talented and dedicated doctors and researchers. Pediatric cardiology needs experts to further study congenital heart defects to make advancements in pediatric cardiology and pediatric cardiovascular surgery.

While there are a number of fine organizations, such as the American Heart Association, which sponsor research into cardiovascular diseases, the majority of their efforts and research dollars are focused on "middle-age" heart diseases. Sadly, pediatric research and applications of treatments for pediatric use often lack sponsors. This is partly due to the lower incidence of congenital heart defects versus middle-aged cardiovascular diseases, and well-to-do donors contribute to causes closer to one's heart (so to speak). Also, most pediatric doctors have a strong desire to work with children. It is more difficult to get these doctors interested, in what some consider, a less people-intensive career field such as research.

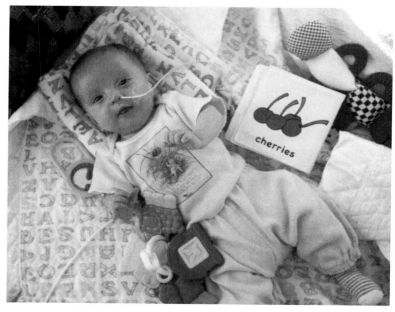

Paige Bronchick

Paige's doctors were exceptional, talented, dedicated and caring. Pediatric cardiology has come a long way over the last twenty years. It is our hope that through the Paige Bronchick Foundation, we will be able to contribute the funds needed to increase the chance of survival for other infants born with congenital heart defects.

Claire and Kylie Bronchick

Editor's Note: On July 17, 1998 Deirdre gave birth to twin girls, Claire and Kylie. In 1999 the Paige Bronchick Foundation will be renamed The Paige Foundation.

I think one thing these brave women thought about is how in the world they could survive without their child. I, too, wondered what I would do if anything ever happened to Alex. What's worse is that I found myself worrying about Joseph (my healthy child) even more, too. What would I do if I lost either of my precious sons? How would I survive?

I had the good fortune of being put in touch with a gentle soul who would teach me much about dealing with death. Jan Heckman is the mother of a child who died of a heart defect. Perhaps what has cemented our friendship more than anything is Jan's willingness to share her story. When I told Jan about this book, I asked her if she would share her story of how she came to a sense of peace after losing Adam. Her story is one of the hope and tranquility that comes from truly loving and letting go.

My Shooting Star

by: Jan Heckman

How do you come to a sense of peace when the child you love is gone? How do you find the will to keep going when your heart aches so much you wonder how it keeps pumping? When is it okay to let go, knowing your baby is "safe"?

Adam's story begins in 1989. We discovered his heart condition during a routine exam at thirty-four weeks gestation. Like so many others, we were given a dismal report at best. Looking back, I realize just what a miracle his life was and still is. I will say from the start that not everyone is chosen to be a parent of a special child.

When I think of Adam, I think of a shooting star—a bright, brief, brilliant light that comes into view unexpectedly and leaves even as your heart is thrilling at the sight. He was always giving away smiles to everyone, and he melted hearts wherever he went. In my own heart, I feared the worst and hoped for the best, all the time taking my cues from parents who we saw going before us through the maze of tests, counseling, surgeries, trips out to Philadelphia and leaps of faith I did not know I possessed.

Adam thrived. I can honestly say that other than being small, he developed normally in every other way, but just slightly delayed. We tried to live life as normally as possible and keep the fear at bay by enjoying him "while we have him." At times I fought hard to suppress my "mother's intuition" that the worst of our fears would indeed come to pass.

In June of 1990 we went to Philly for what was supposed to be the last of Adam's surgeries (the completion Fontan). Everything seemed wrong. I wanted to scream, to come back to Texas, to have it over with, to have him well, to have a "normal" life again. Every emotion under the sun ran through my head and my heart, and I was scared.

The surgery went "fine," although the recovery seemed slow, and Adam did not "snap back" as he had with the other two surgeries. Complications, small ones, seemed to pile one on top of the other: effusions, partially paralyzed diaphragm, poor eating, too many "taps" and a team who seemed much too stressed and stretched to really listened when we said, "Something's wrong."

Six weeks after his surgery on a clear Sunday morning, Adam's heart arrested. It was one of the very few times that neither his dad nor I were with him, as we had stayed in shifts for that six weeks. Despite immediate attempts, Adam had severe hypoxia during that event. He had several other arrests over the next several days, and he became irreparably brain damaged. After a week back in the ICU, he did stabilize, and we transported him home to Texas where we could once again have a say in his care. After a week at home in the ICU, he died quietly on a Saturday afternoon.

How could this happen? We had done everything we knew, and we still lost him. My heart was broken. I did not want to live. I did not want to die. I could not think clearly for months. It always amazed me during those first days, weeks, months, even years—when I needed my energy the most for "grief work," it was not to be found. I knew I had to get to a place where I could live again—to come to some kind of resolution about Adam's life *and* his death.

I sought help through The Compassionate Friends, family, friends and my faith. I cried without shame (still do) and tried to address my fears as they arose. The lessons I learned along the way during Adam's life became so important to me during the days following his death. Taking life one day at a time, putting trust in a Higher Power, taking leaps of faith about what to do and what *not* to do. I felt Adam's presence all around me, but, oh, how I longed to hold my baby. That ache persists without overpowering me now.

For a time I was sure the pain and heartache of losing him would overpower all the good memories. My biggest fear was that his life would be forgotten all together. I knew if that happened, it would be like losing him over and over again.

Somehow with the passage of time, rivers of tears, therapy and prayers, I found that I was able to speak his name, to think of him without crying and to pass his favorite foods in the grocery store without becoming ill. I knew that I was coming to a place of peace, but I constantly wondered—what about Adam?

In my mind I knew he was resting in God's arms, but I missed having him in *my* arms. I prayed for resolution. It came to me one night in a dream.

In this dream I saw Adam—dressed only in a diaper, no chest scars, a healthy weight. He was laughing aloud, as he was being thrown into the air and caught by loving arms. It was the one thing I had longed to do but never could because of his heart and the surgeries he had endured. I knew he had arrived at a place he needed to be—I knew I had, too. It was as if I had permission to live again and not just exist.

Adam Heckman

Face Of A Child

by: Dolly Lee

What a joy it is to see a little one smile,
It warms even the coldest hearts - the happy face of a child.
Sometimes we seem to forget the importance of our children,
A gift that God loaned us borrowed straight from Heaven.
We are to be their teachers, the most important job on earth
To raise a child, surrounded by love, from the moment of their birth.

Sometimes parents forget them, there's too much on their minds
They go about their busy lives and the children are left behind.
Life is far too short to worry about possessions,
God could call them home in just a matter of seconds.
We need to know we've given them all we're capable of,
Not in money or possessions, but in knowledge, time and love.

We must slow down and cherish the time with them we have
So there are no regrets if God should call them back.
We are never guaranteed how long we get to keep them,
Their time upon this earth is only known to Him.
Cherish each day together, not a moment should you waste,
Share your time, share your love and put a smile on a child's face.

ope

The essays in this section are what every mother of a special child needs to hold close to her heart. When a mother is told her child could die in infancy all she really wants to hear is that there is hope—someone else's child made it or someone just created a new procedure or that medical technology has made a breakthrough. We have to hold onto a thread of hope, for to lose hope is to lose everything.

Can a daughter with a congenital heart defect ever become a mother herself? Will my son live to see his bar mitzvah? Will I ever be able to let my child out of my sight long enough to enjoy summer camp? Will the time ever come when my life is not totally consumed by thoughts about my child's health? The answers to those questions are in this chapter.

When a pregnant woman discovers her child has a heart defect, she wonders if her life will ever be the same. It will not. But there is hope. There is hope in tomorrow. There is hope in all of our children's tomorrows. With every day that passes, doctors and scientists learn more about the human body and how it works. With every day that passes more mysteries are solved, more life-saving procedures are created, new drugs are developed and answers to questions are discovered.

The one hope that all of the mothers in this book share is for a day to come when no child has to endure heart surgery, no parent has to hear that their child could die and that no family suffers the loss of a life too soon. Until that day comes, rejoice in the hope that these stories provide. There is always hope. All we have to do is search deep within our souls to find it—or look in the eyes of a child.

"If you can dream it, you can do it."

-Walt Disney

Life After Surgery

For many of us the worst part of having a child with a congenital heart defect is the waiting—waiting for a heart, waiting for surgery, waiting for another surgery, waiting for the end of the surgeries. We want it to be over, behind us, so that we can get on with our lives, our "normal" lives.

Once the surgeries are over, most of us dare not take a deep breath of relief, at least for a little while; however, time goes on, and before long many of us find that we do not think about the heart defect like we used to. It stops consuming our every waking moment. It becomes part of our child and part of our life, but it does not *rule* our lives.

Life gets easier; it gets better. Life with a CHD child, although challenging, can be quite wonderful. The day may even come when the CHD does not define your life or your child's. It just becomes the gentle reminder that makes your heart happy for every day.

The following essays illustrate how life can be after open-heart surgeries become a distant memory. What is the quality of life for these mothers and children? A child's CHD need not overshadow every waking moment. No, indeed. Listen closely, for the mothers in the next three stories have finally taken their deep breaths.

A Birthday Reminiscence

By: Deanna Brennan

Today is June 20, 1997, Tyler's third birthday. This morning as I watched him run and play with his sister, I saw what anyone would see: a beautiful, blond boy about two years old, happy and healthy with a bit of a belly.

I thought back to when Tyler was born. He was a healthy size with a few minor problems, a clubbed foot, undescended testicles, wet lungs and a heart murmur. No one seemed too worried. Then came his second day of life.

Tyler was in an incubator in the ICU at Omaha Children's Hospital. He would not eat, and when the nurses got something into him, he could not keep it down. The doctors diagnosed his heart defect as pulmonary stenosis; "Just a narrowing of the pulmonary valve, nothing to worry about. He may need to have a heart cath done when he is much older . . . five years maybe," was really all that was said. The attention went, of course, to the feeding refusal.

My husband and I wondered if the heart and the appetite were somehow linked. We even got a second opinion. Everyone agreed that Tyler's heart was fine and had nothing to do with his anorexia. Oh yes, that is what they called it. My son was anorexic from two days of age. He still is. A year passed, and Tyler was still fed for the most part with a nasal gastric tube. He was eating a little baby food by the time he was a year old, but he hated to eat. And everyone knows that you cannot make a toddler do anything he does not want to do. Still we tried.

In July of 1995, when Tyler was thirteen months old, I took him to the Mayo clinic. I thought the doctors were the best and would tell me what I could do to help him. We stayed a week while doctors performed tests, and technicians drew blood. We had seven specialists see Tyler. We just knew there was an answer somewhere.

Finally we were told there was indeed a link. It was not all caused by his heart, although the heart was involved. Dr. Micheals, the geneticist, told me after an elaborate family history and exam that my son had a genetic syndrome. It was one which had no test, but we were given a working diagnosis. Tyler was diagnosed with Noonan's syndrome, and in ten years when a test is available, we can be sure. Meanwhile the specialists recommended that he have a G-tube placed for feeding.

So we followed the doctors' orders, although we wondered "why?" We heard all kinds of theories: his brain connectors were messed up; he did not digest right; allergies, and so forth. Each one had a little truth to it I am sure. The true test came in November 1995, when we moved to Illinois. We were referred to Rush Presbyterian St. Luke's Medical Center. We met with our new doctors, and although we had Tyler's heart checked two months prior, they arranged for the new cardiologist to see him.

Dr. Cutilletta, the pediatric cardiologist, perused the records we brought with us and listened to Tyler. He looked at me with a funny expression then looked at the records again and ordered a echocardiogram and X-rays. I have never been so scared. They said we had to have that cath done right away and set it up for the next day.

Tyler's heart pressure was up on one side, and his murmur was upgraded (louder).

The cath was done and four hours later I found out that Tyler not only had severe stenosis but also a very large ASD that had been unseen in over a dozen previous echocardiograms, including theirs. The doctors were unable to do anything without open-heart surgery. Those were the scariest words I had ever heard. The surgery was scheduled for two days later.

Tyler came through like a trouper. He was moved to intermediate care within two days and then the doctors discovered he had pneumothorax and chylothorax. We were told that his condition was very serious. His lung collapsed four times, and he got very sick. I was then told that I may not ever get to take Tyler home. The doctors gave him about a 50% chance of survival. He pulled through day by day, and most of the time he was happy and awake. You would not know he was anything but tired had it not been for the machines and chest tubes.

From November 1995 to February 1996, we were in and out of the hospital. Some good days, some bad days. He had central lines everywhere at some point. He was on TPN (total parenteral nutrition) for two months with no oral feeds. And that was when he started to act hungry. It was the very first time he finished a bottle of formula. I had always thought that the heart defect had something to do with Tyler's eating problem. Tyler still never ate his daily allowance of vitamins and calories, but he did eat. Sometimes when he was off tube feeds for awhile, we would even see a little gain.

It was during this period that I felt I needed to learn more about Noonan's syndrome, at least more than the doctors were telling me. I purchased a computer and went online. I found the Noonan's Syndrome Support Group and more information than I would ever have hoped to find.

I am told that kids with Noonan's syndrome do not eat or grow very well. Tyler never did, and we came to accept that. Sometimes he goes two months off his tube feedings and gains weight. He has ups and downs like any special child. We have come to love that roller coaster ride and hate it at the same time. Tyler was delayed in speech and motor skills. He walked and talked late, and we spent a lot of time with him. His hospital stays were time for us to have a lot of one-on-one attention.

He never really had much energy before the surgery. Watching him now at age three running around the table and laughing just about brings tears to my eyes. We are very close and have connected on a level no one else can really understand.

Of course this has affected my family. It has caused our family to fight, cry, support and love. I have a five year old who had to be shipped from family member to family member during the worst of it, and everyday she would ask if Tyler's heart was fixed enough for us to come home. I cannot describe how that affected me.

It is hard not to treat Tyler a little differently. My daughter sees me do it everyday. She tells me that I love him more than her. It hurts my heart to know what she has been through. She was too young to be overly involved or able to understand everything going on with Tyler; all she knew was that her life was changed forever after Tyler was born. She is old enough now, at five, to understand that I love her and her brother, but since they are different, they are loved differently. Today she accepts that I hope she always knows how special she is to me.

One thing we plan is a special Mommy/Daughter day. Occasionally, when we have not spent much quality time together, we let Daddy take over "Tyler duty." Ashley sets the itinerary, and it is just the two of us. While she loves Tyler, she is also jealous of him, but I know the love will win out over time.

I struggle each day to show my children the special love I have for them in my heart. It is so easy for me to identify my short-comings, but in spite of that, I must gather my strength and courage to continue forward. Deep down I am hopeful they know how very special and unique each of them is to me.

It is on a day like today, Tyler's third birthday, that I realize how very lucky we have been. We have had to deal with behaviors that most people take for granted—mostly eating and growing. We have had to learn how to be strong advocates for our children. We have endured open-heart surgeries, separations, fear and grief.

It has not been an easy road to travel; however, regardless of the difficulties each and every moment has been precious. I appreciate each of my children in a different way now that I have Tyler. Ashley and Tyler have made me take notice of life in a new way. Now I realize just how blessed I am to be a mother, and I would not have it any other way.

Having a Healthy Baby

By: Deb Chapman

Wanting another baby after the birth of a heart baby is something that some families can only dream of. I have been fortunate to live it. I did not just want a baby after having a heart baby. I wanted to know how it felt to actually experience the birth of a healthy baby, be able to see and hold a new baby, nurse it and have it come live in my room.

On December 4, 1985, I gave birth by C-section to our second son. Our oldest son, Michael, had already named him Paul because God was going to give him a little brother. During my pregnancy with Paul, mother's intuition told me there was something wrong. Several times I asked my obstetrician if there was something wrong with the baby's heart . . . it sounded funny. The answer was always the same, "Why do you say that?" I longed through this pregnancy to know what it was like to not have my baby whisked away to the NICU, which happened after the emergency C-section I needed with Michael. Because of fetal distress and the inhaling of meconium, Michael, too, is an NICU graduate. Once again I was to be denied.

I was awakened to the words, "Your baby has a loud heart murmur and fluid on his lungs. We need to send him to University Hospital to see a cardiologist. Do not worry; the cardiologist assigned to your son is young, a fairly new graduate and possibly one of the best in Canada. If anyone can help he should be able to."

Was I surprised? No. Devastated? Yes. Paul is not the first with congenital heart disease in my family. There are, or thought to have been, several. I was briefly able to see Paul before he was transported to the other hospital. I was transferred the next day, but by then Paul had already undergone a cardiac catheterisation and was awaiting a second. His diagnosis was not good at anytime but certainly not in late 1985: double outlet right ventricle, transposition of the great arteries, hypoplastic left/right ventricles, superior/inferior ventricles, VSD, pulmonary stenosis, hypoplastic mitral valve and the list goes on. As you can see anything that could have been upside down, small or backwards, was. He was put on prostaglandin to keep his PDA open, but it was not working.

On Day 2—the second time I saw him, his 02 SATs were 35. They had his head in a plastic bag, and his little chest was heaving up and down gasping to breathe. His cardiologist, Dr. Yashu Coe, was taking him back to the cath lab to do an atrial septostomy. If this failed, all we could do was pray. Transplant was not an option because the first one had only been done in Loma Linda a few days before and the Norwood was too new as well.

Paul came back from the cath lab pink and settled. It was amazing. Six days after his birth, we were discharged home. All his defects and his new ASD all seemed to be working together. For two and a half months, we were home and thriving. At his next check-up his SATs had once again dropped to the 40s and sometimes reached the low 60s. He now needed a B-T shunt. After his shunt, for the first time in his short life, he had really pink feet and hands. He grew like crazy and was a happy and content baby. I did not know what the future brought for us, but for the moment I had my baby.

Because Paul was not the first heart baby in my family, plus he had features of a possible syndrome, we decided to see a geneticist. My family tree of heart children was somewhat extensive.

My grandmother had a brother who died at a very young age of "something wrong with his heart" since birth. My grandmother's sister had a son who died at the age of fourteen on his way to heart surgery. He, too, had something wrong since birth. This same sister had a great-granddaughter born with CHD. My mom's brother has a daughter (who has since had a healthy baby and is pregnant again) and a granddaughter with congenital heart disease, and we have Paul. We were told our chances of having another CHD baby increased from 2%-5% if we chose to have another baby. At the time we were content with our two boys.

As Paul got bigger my maternal clock once again started ticking. When he was nearing three, I desperately wanted another baby and not for the reasons I mentioned at the beginning of the story. My family did not feel complete. Something was missing. I was very confident that I would have no trouble conceiving again. Afterall I did not even have to think about it the first two times. Why should this time be different? Month after month went by without any success. After one year of trying, I decided it was time to seek medical advice.

After undergoing several tests—some not so pleasant—there was no real explanation as to why I could not conceive. I switched doctors and underwent more testing. Same results, same answer, only this time worse. He felt I would never conceive and that I should start accepting this fact. In my heart I already knew this, and once again I was devastated. I could still hear Paul telling me one day he wanted me to have another baby so that if something happened to him when he was getting his heart fixed, Michael would not be lonely. Never mind Michael being lonely! I do not think he realised how lonely we would all be without him, his wit and charm. He didn't realise that he could never be replaced. But to a five year old, it really was that simple. Just have another baby.

In late 1991 Paul started to get sick—lots of chest infections, shortness of breath and wheezing, possible heart failure. When it first happened, I blamed it on the real Christmas tree. We had never had one because of my asthma, but this Christmas Paul wished for a real tree. We spent a small fortune on the most perfect real Christmas tree money could buy. I think each of us who has a child with a chronic or life-threatening illness has done some of the very same things. We are willing to give or do anything so that our children experience things in life they might not have time for.

That beautiful tree lasted about two weeks (two days after Christmas), and down it came. But the wheezing and shortness of breath did not stop. By this time I had accepted the fact that I would not have another baby. I was involved with helping at school nearly everyday. The Children's Heart Society had become a great passion, and I did not have time for another baby. Besides Paul was six; Michael was nine; Eric (my husband) was nearing thirty-six, and I was nearing thirty-three. In my mind I was getting too old anyway. During Christmas break I wanted Eric to do something permanent about birth control just in case. He would not. I guess it would be up to me.

Michael was born on New Year's Eve, and since his birth we had never been out. Friends of ours talked us into going out with them, and another set of friends agreed to babysit the boys and celebrate Mike's birthday. The dad was an obstetrician and on-call, so they also were not going anywhere. I felt comfortable leaving Paul and his medications with them. We went out, and I did not enjoy the evening one bit. I worried about the boys, especially Paul, the whole time.

January came and went, and I had not been feeling all that great. I just thought it was the winter blahs, but we were going away for a family weekend to Jasper on February 14. Just the pick-me-up I needed. One of my very good friends had given birth to an unexpected baby in the middle of January, and I think I can say I was thankful it was her and not me. On February 7th I had gone to visit Cindy and my new godson when it dawned on me.

My period was late. This never happened. I was consumed with the reason why this might be. I got up and said I had to leave. I know she thought I had gone off the deep end. I had to go to the doctor to see if I was *pregnant*. I could not be. I was ready for this three years ago, not now. I went to the office and had a pregnancy test. I was sitting in the waiting room when the doctor came down the hall with a big smile on his face and this little white thing in his hand that had a plus sign in it. I looked at him and said, "What is that thing and what does that plus sign mean?" Happily he informed me I was pregnant.

I became hysterical. I do not know why; I just did. I think the big thing was fear of the unknown. Would I be able to carry this baby to term? Would there be something wrong? All the past fears I had with the birth of Michael and Paul resurfaced.

Paul seemed to be a little healthier and definitely happy that he was going to be a big brother. He said he was getting a sister, and he would call her Taralyn Marie.

In June of 1992 his health started to get a little shaky, but summer was coming, and he would be away from the school germs giving his body the rest it needed. At this point in time, Paul had still only had the B-T shunt, but there was some talk of the Fontan. I personally felt, after the advice of our cardiologist, research and reading that if we had to go for the big one, I preferred transplant. I knew we would have to always deal with rejection, side effects of medication, but I also knew Paul always wanted to have pink lips, play hockey and run as fast as his brother. Could a Fontan give him this? A transplant could. Paul had already enjoyed playing hockey, baseball and being as normal as his heart and oxygen SATs of around 65 would allow. I am proud we were able to let him do all of these things and believe me there were times I was terrified something would happen, but I put my fears aside to let him live. The first time he played baseball, I coached the team. The first time he played hockey, his dad helped coach the team. Little concessions to let him be normal.

June 29, 1992, I went in for my first fetal echo. My mom came up from Calgary to be with me. I, at this point, had put all fears of having another child with a CHD to the back of my mind. Not so this day. I could barely lay on the table. In my mind I was rehearsing how calm I was going to remain when the cardiologist told me that this child has . . . Afterall, I had never given birth to a healthy baby. I would have my breakdown in the car with only my mom present.

During my echo the tech kept me abreast of everything that she was able to see, and according to her, the heart was normal. It was of proper size, and the only thing that she would not be able to see were small holes. I would need to return four weeks before my delivery date to ensure that the heart and its chambers had continued to grow. Wow! The possibility of having a normal C-section delivery was almost within my reach. I also knew what sex I was carrying. But that was only for me to know. Everyone else had to wait until my scheduled delivery date of September 29.

Time came and went very quickly. Paul had taken ill again: RSV, asthma, pneumonia, heart failure. We did not know it, but he did respond to all treatments and was doing well again. In the middle of August, I felt compelled to take our family on a holiday to Yellowstone Park; something was nagging me to go there. I remember visiting the park as a child and being in such awe. I wanted my boys to have these memories as well. We went and had a wonderful time, and we were able to add another picture to our book of memories.

August 29th I went back for my final echo. I prepared myself for bad news. I had rehearsed, once again, staying calm until I got to the the car and then freaking out without anyone seeing me. Everything was still normal with the baby's heart. I was also able to see the baby very clearly. Same nose, eyes and head shape as the boys. It is truly amazing I knew what it was going to look like before birth.

Paul started grade two and Michael started grade five. On September 28, I had to have an amniocentesis to ensure the baby's lungs were fully developed before having the planned C-section. My OB/GYN called late that evening and said everything was ready, and I was to be at the hospital at 8:00 a.m.

Until this time, other than brief moments, I had put all my fears of having another child with CHD or any birth defect in the back of my mind. I believe it was self-preservation. Now the fear of having another child with a CHD frightened me, and I found I could not control myself. I was absolutely beside myself, and I did not care who was witness to it.

I know this sounds selfish, but I desperately needed my mother in the OR with me, although I kept this to myself. I had also chosen to have an epidural so that my husband and I could experience the birth of one of our children. I had developed several avenues of support throughout University Hospital, and each of them came by to check on us at one point or another. There was a pediatric resident who Paul had developed a trusting relationship with, as had I. Dr. Christine came and sat with me for a long time and helped me get through this mental breakdown.

By the time I needed to go to the OR, I was shaking so violently the table was vibrating. Every thirty seconds I thought I was going to vomit, and I was freezing cold. The anesthetist (I learned later he was the same one that does all the heart kids) was very reassuring and even funny. The worst thing about the whole C-section is when the doctor literally pushes the baby out of that little incision. It does not hurt, but I thought my eyes were going to pop right out of my head.

I knew the baby was out because they stopped pushing, but I could not hear a noise. Why? Is there something wrong?

The doctor informed us that we had a very beautiful seven pound baby girl. He asked if we would like to hold her. I could not believe this was actually happening to me. I really had a healthy baby whom I could hold, feed and have room-in with me.

I did not know what to do. This was all new to me. I did not know if I was happy, scared or indifferent to this whole situation. When I think back, I was too scared to be happy. I was afraid of having a little girl whom I could take home after sixty hours. I was afraid of the unknown. No regular doctors appointments? Breast-feeding without tiring or worry about gaining weight? Could it really be true? It was.

What about Paul? In February 1993, his health started to deteriorate very quickly. In May he was admitted to the hospital with pneumonia and in severe heart failure. He was put on dopamine, as well as high doses of diuretics. After this the doctors would do another cath to see where Paul stood in terms of surgery or possible transplant.

The cath was done in the middle of July. Very shortly after, he was listed for transplant, and three weeks to the day of listing, we received the call that there was a heart for him. When I told Paul he smiled and said, "I am finally going to have pink lips."

All did not go well. On the fourth day post-transplant, Paul's right ventricle was failing, and he was in big trouble. I felt as if I were chasing the pot of gold at the end of the rainbow. I would almost get there, and it would be snatched away. Only a miracle could turn things around.

We got the miracle. One rejection and three weeks post-transplant, Paul was out of the hospital and back at school. The heart was not the greatest, but it did get him back playing hockey, having pink lips and being able to almost outrun his brother. He told the transplant coordinator one day that when he gets back all his energy to look out!

Once a month for the first few months, Paul had a rejection. Things went well for about seven months, and he had another one. On May 13, 1994 while seeing Dr. Coe (cardiologist), Paul had a cardiac arrest. Why? We did not know, but we soon discovered he had developed coronary artery disease and third degree heart block. A pacemaker was first priority and being relisted for transplant was a close second.

One year to the day of discharge from the first transplant, Paul received his second. He was out of the hospital in nine days, and other than a few very minor problems, he has not looked back. In September he will celebrate three years with this heart, and his little sister Taralyn will be five. Her birth was a blessing in disguise. Taralyn, Paul and Michael have all taught me about the uniqueness of each person. They have helped me understand the fragility of life, all the while appreciating their zest for living.

Each of my children's lives is a miracle. Each heart is special and unique. Michael, Paul and Taralyn are all heroes to me.

Back Row: Deb and Eric
Front Row: Paul, Taralyn and Michael

Editor's Note: Paul continues to do well, and Deb now has another heart hero in her family—Kimberly, a beautiful, Inuit, foster child.

An Anniversary

By: Anna Jaworski

As I was taking a shower today it hit me. I had already written some checks and written the date on some schoolwork my older son had done, but it was not until my mind was free to wander that I realized that today was October 17th. OCTOBER 17TH!!!

It is not a religious holiday, anybody's birthday or a day of historical significance, to anyone but me perhaps. Even my husband did not realize why this day was important. But I remember.

Exactly three years ago my baby was operated on because he had HLHS. His surgeon was doing an operation I had never heard of—the Norwood procedure. The odds my two-month-old baby would survive were slim. I remember the doctors saying a 20% chance for survival. My father, who was in the same meeting with me, remembers them saying less than a 5% chance for survival. How is that for being in denial?

I have shared my son's story in a book I wrote, but there were some things that were too painful to share that came rushing back to my mind today. I remembered the doctor at Scott & White Hospital telling me that the cause of my son's Failure to Thrive was a severe heart defect. They could not tell me *what* or *if* anything could be done. They did not know who could operate on him, just that it couldn't be done at that hospital. With that scant information, they asked me to which town I wanted my son transferred. God held Alex and me in the palm of His hand when we blindly chose San Antonio.

I remembered Alex's pediatrician coming to see us off. She took me aside in the hallway, and I could see she was fighting to hold back the tears. I touched her arm and said, "Don't worry. Everything will be fine now. At least we know what's wrong. Alex will be fine." She burst into tears and told me he probably would not be coming back.

I remember the ambulance team rushing my baby into the PICU and hooking him up to machines and exchanging information with the admitting team. I remember feeling odd watching all of this happening. I also remember feeling held at arm's length by the nurse on staff. It was seven months later, I was to discover, that the only information the staff had been given about Alex was that he was "Failure to Thrive," and he was two months old. They did not know he had a heart problem. They thought I was an abusive mother. They had not even met me.

I remember the doctors telling my parents and me about the Norwood and what they would do to Alex. When explaining the Blalock-Taussig shunt they described how it had been done years before when an artery from the arm was used as the shunt. I can still see my mother raising her hand and asking the doctor if that meant that Alex would not be able to use his arm. She was scared, but brave and trying so hard to understand . . .

Then October 17th came. The fateful day for Alex's surgery. We had waited all weekend, and I worried constantly that Alex would die before his chance for surgery. The doctors had told us that most HLHS children died before surgery and that the second highest mortality rate was the twenty-four hours after surgery. The day of the surgery, I bathed Alex and a nurse let me hold him. I cried when I wrote about that in my book. I am crying about it just thinking about it now. (Thank goodness I can touch type!) I remember kissing Alex and wondering if it would be the last time I held him. Bless that nurse who let me hold him. He gave my aching arms and heart something to hold onto during that long, long surgery.

As my husband and I walked to the elevator on the way to the waiting room, I wondered how I could live without Alex. I told my husband I did not think I could. I remember he looked at me with disbelief. At that moment my own heart hurt. It really hurt. It felt bloated and heavy, as if it could burst right through my chest with the least provocation. I told my husband I really thought I would die of a broken heart if Alex did not make it. He got angry at me and told me that he and Joey (my older son) needed me, but I wondered who would take care of Alex.

I begged God not to take Alex. How could I explain it to Joey if Alex did not make it? How could I explain it to myself? How would I ever come to grips with it?

Realizing I was allowing myself to despair, I put on the mental brakes. I had to be strong, and I had to believe. I set my mind to believing in Alex. Surely he had not fought this long just to go to surgery and never come out. God had a plan for him. I felt there must have been a reason for Alex to have been born the way he was. I just had to open my heart and my mind, and God would help me with this burden.

In the waiting room, my parents and my sister sat and made small talk. I wrote in my diary and held onto my Bible. Every three hours I went and pumped my milk. When they started calling from the OR with good news, I felt the heaviness lifting from my heart. When they told us he was on his way up to his room, I practically jumped for joy. Frank and I hugged each other, and for the first time that day, I knew everything was really going to be okay.

I will never forget what Alex looked like—he was beautiful. The most beautiful baby in the world.

Three years have passed, and it still feels like yesterday—and yet it almost feels like it happened to someone else. Could that really have happened to my Alexander? The little guy who today picked out his very first package of "big boy" underwear? The little boy who is doing great with potty training, made a knock knock joke which sent us all into peels of laughter and who plucked off my nose, hair and chin and ate them?

You mean this kid wearing his brother's hand-me-downs from last year (they are three years apart in age)—the one with his grandfather's belly—he was my "Failure to Thrive" baby? He grew an inch in a month this summer. He outgrew all of his shoes, and now he wants to pick out his own shoes himself. It had to be Dalmations or Batman. What was I thinking when I suggested Ernie and Bert?

Alexander, my three-year-old miracle—did he really set up his brother's chess board from memory just a month ago? Can he really zoom around on the computer like an old pro? Where has the time gone? Now he is counting to twenty, playing backgammon and Manchala, building towers, creating stories, talking to his imaginary friends, playing board games and UNO, singing the ABC song and all of the other songs we love; he is funny and delightful; he is thoughtful and compassionate—he is my sunshine . . .

When babies receive a new heart, they have a new "Lifeday" to celebrate. I feel that October 17th is really Alexander's Lifeday, because without the Norwood, I would not have my angel with me today.

So I'll cry a few tears for the memories, and I laughed and loved him maybe a little more because today is October 17th. I put him to bed, and we said our prayers, but I will say some more tonight. I will pray for all of the other angels out there yet to have their Norwood or their transplant, yet to have a new "Lifeday," and I will pray for all of the parents, too, that they will be granted some of the precious memories I have been blessed with. And I will say another "Thank You" for each and every new friend I've made just because Alex is the way he is. I know a special group of people now—infants, children and adults who are one step closer to Heaven just for knowing how precious life is—just for having Love in their hearts. Some of us are lucky enough to have our angels on earth, and some have angels in Heaven, but all of us are richer just for knowing that special kind of Love.

It gets better; it gets easier with time. You never forget, but the memories get pushed farther back in your mind. For those of you who have not had your October 17th yet, believe. Please, believe. Someday you will wonder where the time has gone. You will watch your little miracle, and you will take a deep, deep breath and let it out and smile. And then, like me, you will go to bed and awaken to just-another-day tomorrow. Another day. Another gift. And you will be the luckiest person you know.

Joey and Alex Jaworski (1997)

Editor's Note: This essay first appeared as a post to the HLHS listserv on October 17, 1997.

Mothers With Congenital Heart Defects

Nothing transforms a woman so much as when she becomes a mother. Taking care of babies, seeing to their every whim and loving them unconditionally is the most difficult and satisfying job a woman will ever have. This entire book is a tribute to motherhood. Throughout this book are essays and poems by mothers and grandmothers of children with heart defects; this chapter differs from the rest.

This chapter provides hope because it is written by the survivors. Michelle, Carolyn, Allison and Becky share success stories of life and motherhood. These women were born with congenital heart defects, but lived to become mothers themselves.

Mind Over Matter

By: Michelle Veschi

I was born on May 5, 1960. I have a congenital heart defect consisting of a single ventricle, transposition of the great arteries (TGA), and an enlarged pulmonary artery. Shortly after I was born, my parents noticed that I was not gaining weight and "breathed funny." A pediatrician told them it was probably asthma and sent them on their way.

Luckily my parents sought the second opinion of the man who probably saved my life. This pediatrician detected a heart murmur and sprung into action. After contacting a cardiologist several catheterizations were performed. Back then the artery in the arm/groin had to literally be cut into for the catheter to be inserted and was then stitched up.

The doctors discovered the enlarged pulmonary artery and the transposition. They were not sure about the ventricle thinking I might just have a VSD. When I was six months old surgery was performed to band the pulmonary artery, so I would not drown in my own blood. Heart surgery was in its infancy.

My parents were told that I had a 50/50 chance of surviving until age five. When I was seven years old, my cardiologist performed another cath to see the condition of the VSD. The cath proved that I had no left ventricle. The doctor told my already devastated parents that there was nothing that could be done to correct it.

The next year I contracted bacterial endocarditis from an abscessed tooth. I was hospitalized and put on IV penicillin, but my parents were given absolutely no hope that I would live. I came home on Christmas Eve and watched man orbit the earth for the first time on television!

My activities were restricted: no running, no ballet classes, no sports. My parents allowed me to do the usual stuff like ride my bike and roller skate always with the philosophy that I had the common sense to stop when I was tired.

I started to go into congestive heart failure when I was twelve. I developed intravascular hemolysis which is an entire break down of the bloodstream. I was urinating pure blood. My cardiologist in New Orleans recommended that my parents take me to Texas Children's Hospital in Houston. I was in complete renal failure when we got there. They discovered, with the use of this newfangled piece of medical technology called an echocardiogram, that I had subaortic stenosis.

We also discovered that they had a new and improved way of doing catheterizations—they just inserted a needle into your groin and put the catheter in that way! Although this was not great, it was better than what I had gone through before.

Dr. Denton Cooley did the open-heart surgery and removed the stenosis. His prognosis was that single ventricle kids never live to graduate from high school. I think by now my parents had stopped listening. They depended on the one and only thing that I have been taught to depend on, my faith in God and His son, Jesus, and the fact that mind can always overcome matter!

We were transferred to Maryland the next year. Since then I have been treated by Dr. Kuehl at Children's Hospital National Medical Center. I led a normal teenage life, graduated from high school and studied both art and early childhood education in college. I got a job shortly after college teaching preschool, but in my mid-twenties, my health started to decline.

It was recommended that I be sent to the Mayo Clinic for a Fontan. February of 1987, I had my Fontan. The man who is now my husband asked for my hand in marriage in the Intensive Care Unit after the surgery. Talk about a reason to get well! I had a wedding to plan!

The operation without a doubt was one of the roughest things I had ever gone through. I had to have tetracycline injected into my lung because it was not draining properly, and I went into renal failure. I was in the hospital about one month.

I was married on April 16, 1988 and had a huge Catholic wedding. In 1989 I developed arrhythmias—a side-effect of the Fontan. My husband and I were also very disappointed to learn that it would put me in terrible danger to conceive. Both of us wanted children very badly and were told at Mayo that this could be possible, but with the repeated arrhythmias, the cardioversions and all the new medications, pregnancy would risk my life and my unborn child's.

I was very angry about the thought of never having a child of my own. It was hard for me to accept because this was just another reminder that I was not like everyone else. I even refused to go to my friends' baby showers.

After seeing many high-risk OB/GYNs, we came to the conclusion that I certainly could never terminate a pregnancy, and my husband said it was not worth the risk of losing me. Even though we could not have a family the traditional way, we knew we wanted a baby. In 1992 we adopted a baby girl from Ukraine!

Amber is now five and a half years old and the best thing that has ever happened to me. I cannot imagine having any other child—she even looks like me. I consider her a gift from God.

Now that I am a parent, I must say for the first time that I can only imagine the utter agony my parents must have gone through all those years with me. I was an emotional wreck when Amber had tubes put in her ears!

Since 1989 I have gone through three pacemakers, numerous encounters with arrhythmias, various arrhythmia medications, and cardioversions. Just last January, I contracted a kidney infection which developed into pneumonia and landed me in the hospital for two weeks. I drew my strength and courage from my parents who fought so hard to keep my outlook positive and my life normal. I look up to all parents of children with CHDs and feel very blessed to be alive and a mother of my own child.

Leading the Troops

By: Carolyn Wise

My name is Carolyn, and I was born in Toronto, Ontario, Canada on April 23, 1948. I was diagnosed with a ventricular septal defect when I was about nine months of age. Dr. John Keith performed a catheterization at the Hospital for Sick Children in Toronto when I was about ten years of age. My parents were told that I had developed Eisenmenger's syndrome when my heart defect caused damage to my lungs. Although surgery could correct the heart defect, the pressure in my lungs had caused irreparable damage, thus heart surgery would actually endanger my life. I did not have surgery and was left to try to lead a normal life.

This was difficult because I was never able to keep up with the other kids. They did not understand how much it hurt me to be left behind. I was never able to take part in sports, and I always felt like a fifth wheel sitting on the sidelines. Even when there was a sport that I could participate in, I was always the last one chosen because I was never good enough. I was not allowed to go outside at recess during the cold Canadian winters; although some children envied that, I was still left feeling different. One teacher even made fun of me! When asked what things we need to do to keep healthy, I put up my hand with the answer, "Get lots of fresh air and exercise." The man muttered under his breath, but loud enough for me and the rest of the class, to hear "Why don't you practice what you preach?" What an insensitive man!

As a youth, I always felt rather homely, being tall and awkward and having "four eyes" and mousy brown hair. But, in the eleventh grade, I blossomed. I got contact lenses and coloured my hair blonde. What a change—there was no holding me back! Lots of boyfriends, dances, and fun! But, I always had this deep dark secret that many did not know. Because of my congenital heart defect, it was quite likely I would not be able to give birth to a baby—something I had always wanted very much. How do you tell a potential mate that you have a congenital heart defect and may not be able to bear children?

When I was twenty, I met a wonderful man. When I told him of my circumstances, he was not discouraged by it at all. He explained to me that he had some medical problems as a child and was told that he may not be able to father children. So he was very understanding. Before we got married, I went to the doctor to confirm my suspicions. And, the recommendation was for me to avoid becoming pregnant. After testing my fiance's sperm count, it was confirmed that he could indeed father a child, and it was decided that a permanent means of birth control would be best for me, as I would not be able to take the pill. A month before our marriage, I had a tubal ligation.

After about a year of marriage, I called our local Children's Aid Society, explained the situation to them, and asked how we should go about adopting a child. The social worker, of course, asked how long we had married, and when I said, "Just a year," she said that a year was too short a time to try to get pregnant. But, when I told her the circumstances of our situation, she set up an appointment for us to go in for an interview. The first interview was with several other prospective adoptive couples, and it was just to give us an overview of the adoption process and to allow us to ask questions. We then went through an office interview and two home interviews. One of the requirements was for us to have a medical examination. I explained to our social worker that I was afraid my heart condition would prevent them from allowing us to adopt. This was a very real fear! She relieved my mind when she explained that there had been others with medical conditions who were approved and did not think this would be a deterrent. So, following our medical exams, we were accepted as adoptive parents.

Our first child, a son, arrived on December 17, 1970 at the age of five weeks. Our second child, a daughter, arrived on July 31, 1973 at the age of twelve weeks. What beautiful children they were! I like to tell people that the first day we had our babies, it felt as if we were just babysitting, but, by the second day, they were ours! I was in love! The affection for a tiny, helpless baby grows very fast! For myself, I cannot fathom loving a child I had given birth to any more than I love these two children.

This little poem has touched my heart, as it explains the depth of my feelings:

Not flesh of my flesh,
Nor bone of my bone,
But still, miraculously my own.
Never forget for a single minute,
That you didn't grow under my heart,
But in it.

I was very fortunate to have been able to be a stay-at-home mom. I know that I would not have had the physical stamina to work full-time and raise a family. I feel very fortunate in that my CHD did not have a profound effect on the way I was able to raise my children, nor did it adversely affect the lives of my children. Luckily, my children were very well-behaved, and did not wear me out physically. But, I was not able to do some of the things other parents were able to do with their children. Winter sports were probably the most difficult. As a teenager, I had given skating a try but never learned to skate; however; when they had free skating for preschoolers, I got myself a pair of skates and did the best I could skating with my children. It was like we were all beginners. And, in time, when they learned to skate, off they went by themselves. I would have loved to have taken my kids tobogganing or skiing but was not able to take part in this type of winter sport. Summer was not so difficult. Every summer we would head off to the provincial parks with our camper. We did some hiking, but I avoided the big hills. As long as I had my husband by my side, I was not afraid of getting into a situation with the children that I could not handle.

I became a Brownie leader but was always careful about the kinds of activities chosen. The winter season has always been difficult for me; I tire much more quickly when exerting myself in cold weather. I remember when the Brownies would have a winter activity day, I just would not go because I could not take part in some activities, and I did not want to explain to anyone why I could not. I was always afraid of getting myself into a situation that I could not handle. The most memorable of those for me was when we took the girls on a cookout at the beach. We had to go down a big incline to get to the beach—which was fine. But, the return trip was terrible for me. I had to keep stopping to rest—I was so out of breath. Another time we took the Brownies and Beavers (five-year-old boys) up to Ottawa and walked the cold, windy streets. But, I trudged onward because I would not give in to this! I continued being a Brownie leader for seven years.

I was always the first parent to volunteer on class trips but again, fearful that I would get myself into a difficult situation; however, that never happened! I was a parent volunteer in the special education classroom of our school for two years, working two mornings a week with children with learning and behaviour problems.

Back: Jennifer
Front: Carolyn and Jeff

Miraculously, at age thirty-seven, unbeknownst to me, I became pregnant. I am still amazed by the fact that my body repaired itself. Unfortunately, the pregnancy ended with a miscarriage. I realize that was best because I know that the doctors would have advised me to abort the pregnancy. That would have been a very difficult decision to make. God, in His mercy, knew what was best for me.

Sadly, in 1988, my marriage of nineteen years ended, leaving me to raise my two teenagers on my own. These were difficult and stressful years, but I am proud to say that we made it! I have two wonderful, adult children who have both chosen loving individuals to be their life partners. My son and his wife have blessed me with a beautiful grandson who is now twenty-two months of age. Being a grandmother is a little more difficult for me physically than being a mom was. Along with having to work full-time now and feeling more fatigued, I find that over the years my physical stamina has decreased and that I suffer from a lot of joint pain due to my heart condition.

I am truly thankful that I have been able to lead a fairly normal and active life. Although my CHD has caused me to miss out on a few things in life, I have not missed out on any of the really important things. I am so happy that I was able to experience motherhood and all of the joys that go with it.

So, I will continue to push on—to refuse to let my CHD bring me down. If anything, my CHD has taught me to appreciate everyday and to enjoy life to its fullest. My heart may not be perfect, but the love I have inside it helps me to achieve more than I ever thought possible.

A Baby for Allison

By: *Allison Matthews

I was born in 1970 in Brooklyn New York at 1:58 a.m. Later that morning, as I was crying, an alert nurse noticed I was turning blue and had a PC called in to assess me. I was found to have single ventricle, transposition of the great vessels, and pulmonary atresia. Although I am not aware of all the details, I believe I had a cath that led my doctor to recommend that my parents wait until I was two years old to have surgery. Unfortunately, I did not progress as well as expected, so a Potts shunt was done when I was six weeks old.

Although I did well following that surgery, I was very susceptible to catching colds; however, in time I outgrew the colds and was an active child. I played just like any other child my age, but I rested more.

When I was five years old, I was hospitalized for SBE (subacute bacterial endocarditis). I had an IVP (intravenous pyelogram) done because I had frequent kidney infections. At the time of the IVP, I was on antibiotics for strep throat, but the doctors said we could proceed with the IVP. Well, the procedure caused the SBE and put me in the hospital for thirty-two days on IV antibiotics.

From what I remember of that hospital stay, it was mostly a positive experience. I remember the nurses pulling me in the wagon when I became upset, and my father spent most nights at my side. I know that was rough on him because he would come straight from work, drive my mother home, come back, wake up in the morning and go to work. Then he would do it all over again. My mother would get a ride to the hospital after my brother was in school and stay until my dad arrived. I can only imagine how hard it was for them, but I am thankful for their efforts.

Following that hospital stay everything went well. I went back to being my normal, active self. As I got older, I began climbing trees, playing touch football with the guys. I even went bowling with my dad and joined a bowling league. I continued bowling into my teens and twenties.

When I was ten years old, a cath was done. That hospital stay, although overnight, was hard on me. I was older and things were not explained to me as well as they could have been. What was explained, I did not understand and was afraid to ask for clarification. The results of the cath revealed that they could wait a little longer before operating on me again. The doctors were waiting for the Fontan procedure to have better success rates.

As time went on, I still did the things any normal kid would do. I even took gymnastics classes. As I got older I started doing all the things "normal" teenagers do (if you can call teenagers normal!).

When I was seventeen years old, my activity level began to decline. So I had a cath, and it was decided to go ahead with the Fontan. The surgery did not go as well as expected because there were problems with scar tissue from the surgery in 1970. By the time they got the Potts shunt closed, I was having seizures. The surgeon put in a modified Waterston shunt instead.

I was in a drug induced coma for three days following the surgery. Even though nobody told me things did not go well, I knew. This was partly because when I started to awaken, I saw my pastor and a deacon praying at my bedside. I thought they thought I was dead and tried to talk, but I do not think they even noticed. When I woke up fully, I asked a nurse (by writing since I was on a ventilator) what time it was. She said 10:00 a.m., *Saturday*. My surgery had been on a Tuesday.

According to my mother, as soon as I woke up and was ventilator free, I asked for the phone and my lungs cleared rather quickly! About four days after I woke up, I was moved from the ICU to the floor. My PC, who was my PC since birth, spoke to me regarding the surgery and how it went. He wanted to be the first to tell me in case I became upset. He expected me to take the news badly because, until I had surgery again, I would be worse than when I entered the hospital seven days earlier.

The doctors planned to do the Fontan in six months to allow my strength to return. However, five months post-op, my right lung collapsed. I was in the hospital for twenty-eight days before my lung healed. In that time I lost a lot of weight; I went from one hundred six to eighty-five pounds, and I was seventeen years old! I was unable to return to school but earned my GED within a year of the surgery.

Over time I improved. I went out, dated, was on a volleyball team and still acted like a "normal" teenager, much to my mothers chagrin; however, it was four years before I was strong enough for surgery. Somewhere in between the collapsed lung and the next surgery, the Waterston shunt closed, and the Pott's shunt partly reopened.

The doctors decided to do a bi-directional Glenn instead of the Fontan procedure in February of 1991. I was determined before the surgery that I would be in the ICU no more then four days and in the hospital no more then seven days total. Well, I was in the ICU for three days and out of the hospital in five or six! I was told that if I ever need more surgery it would probably not be for another ten to fifteen years.

After this last surgery, I went on vacation with friends and lived a fairly normal life. I dated a lot, and in October 1991 met a very nice man named Max. We were together for seven months and discussed marriage.

It was then that I found out I was pregnant. Although Max was aware of the risks involved, we felt the same about the pregnancy. When I first told my PC about the pregnancy, he suggested an abortion. For me (and Max) that was not an option. I always said that I did not want to risk a pregnancy, but if it ever happened I would have no choice but to take the risk. Max understood and was agreeable. We also agreed not to marry until after the baby was born, which was more of a personal decision. I always felt if I did become pregnant while single, I would not marry for that reason alone.

The pregnancy went better then expected. I was told by the high-risk OB/GYN that if I went through with the pregnancy, I would need a C-section and close monitoring. I was watched closely but walked at least one mile a day and continued my weekly bowling league until I was hospitalized for observation at five months. I was released after a month because both the baby and I were doing very well. Later, I was put back in the hospital for observation. This time it was found that the baby was not doing well. The baby had in utero growth retardation, so I was not released and had oxygen at night for his sake.

Max had a hard time dealing with the strain of the hospitalizations which put more stress on me. We decided to separate, making me very thankful we had not married beforehand.

I went into labor one month early, so my OB/GYN and PC decided to let me deliver naturally with an epidural. With the help of Pitocin, James Christopher was born nineteen hours after my first pain. Max was there for James' birth, and it was the happiest day of both of our lives. James' birth was a turning point in our relationship, as I suspected it would be. The baby and I went home three days after his birth; although Max and I were working things out, I went to stay with my parents for some time and received a lot of help from them and my grandmother.

Now James is five years old, and Max and I have been married for four years and are very happy. I love being a mother. I also enjoy working part-time as a reservation sales agent.

I am thankful that everything turned out so well for me and that I was given the chance not only to be a mother, but also to experience pregnancy and childbirth. Although I want more children, I do not want to take the risk of another pregnancy. If things did not go well, my parents and my husband and son would suffer. I could never do that to them. Max and I are looking into adoption and will hopefully be able to add to our family in the future.

At this time I am healthy and doing well. I am not taking any medications. I have not taken anything for my heart since I took digoxin when was seven years old. As far as the future goes, it is still uncertain. Of course, nobody's future is certain whether healthy or not. Currently I have annual exams, and if my activity level declines and my heart weakens, we will try medications to strengthen my heart. As far as future surgeries (other then replacing the Pott's shunt), if and when it gets to that point, the only option would be a heart transplant. I hope if that time comes to pass, medical technology will have advanced, and I will have more options.

*Editor's Note: Allison and her family's names have been changed to protect their privacy.

A Healthy Baby

By: Becky Blauvelt

The day after I learned I was pregnant, I called my cardiologist. I was born with a congenital heart defect called transposition of the great arteries (TGA), and when I was sixteen months old, I underwent the Mustard procedure. The surgery was successful, and though I have experienced cardiac symptoms (such as occasional arrhythmias, fatigue and shortness of breath), I have never had any problems.

Still, because of my condition, I knew I should be monitored, so I called my pediatric cardiologist and asked for a referral to a new cardiologist. I felt embarrassed being twenty-three years old, pregnant and still going to the local Children's Hospital for treatment. He gave me the names of a few cardiologists who specialize in the treatment of adults with congenital heart defects (ACHDers). We then chatted for a few minutes about my health, and he asked me what else was going on.

I hesitated because I still had not told anyone about my pregnancy except for my husband, but then I just blurted out, "I'm pregnant!" I will never forget the silence or the words that followed, "You are not planning on keeping the pregnancy, are you?"

I felt as if I were going to be sick. Somehow I managed to express that I wanted to have the baby I was carrying. My doctor immediately apologized for having been so abrupt. He explained to me that because of my condition, pregnancy might be very dangerous for me, possibly life-threatening. He urged me to see one of the specialists as soon as possible to determine whether or not I would be able to keep the pregnancy. When I hung up the phone, I began to wonder why no doctor had ever mentioned the possible dangers to me before.

I began to think of "it" as a condition rather than a baby growing inside me. My husband and I held off telling family and friends. We had to wait about two weeks before my new cardiologist could see me and the waiting was horrible. The excitement over my pregnancy had transformed into silence between my husband and me; there were many heavy sighs and cautious stares in our household.

Finally it was time to meet with my new cardiologist. I had grown accustomed to a very personal one-on-one relationship with my pediatric cardiologist. I was shocked when my husband and I were waiting in the examining room, and three doctors and a nurse came in. One of the doctors began by telling me that they would not discuss my pregnancy until they had examined me. They also warned me that it was possible that they might recommend termination of the pregnancy, dependent on my condition. They emphasized that to protect my own health, I needed to follow their recommendations regarding the pregnancy, whatever they may be. My husband and I looked at each other, and then agreed.

After an examination and an echocardiogram, they led me back into the examining room. I could hear the muffled voices of the doctors discussing my case in the hallway. When they came back into the room, it seemed as though the tension had lifted somewhat; although the doctors' demeanor was still very serious. They informed me that based upon their examination, they believed that I could continue the pregnancy.

Then they began to discuss how my pregnancy would be treated. I would be monitored regularly by my cardiologist who would be in constant communication with a high risk obstetrician. I was very disappointed to learn this because it meant that I would not be able to use my regular OB/GYN, nor would I be able to deliver at the hospital near my home. The doctors also informed me that although my pregnancy was expected to be normal, delivery would not. They planned to induce my labor two weeks prior to my due date (March 19th) to assure that I would labor in a controlled environment where I could be monitored and have doctors available if I needed them.

I was told that when I was admitted to the hospital, I would immediately be attached to an IV with antibiotics to help prevent the risk of infection. I would also be given an epidural. I would not be allowed to push because it would put too much strain on my heart; therefore, the doctors would use other methods to help the baby be born. They told me about vacuum suction, which basically vacuums the baby out and requires the possibility of using forceps. All of this seemed overwhelming to me, but I shook my head and agreed to everything the doctors told me. I realized that this was not going to just be *my* pregnancy or birth experience. If this baby were to be born, there would be a lot of people there who would have more control than me.

Then the doctors told me about something I had not even considered: the possibility that my child might have a congenital heart defect. Although CHD is generally not believed to be hereditary, there seems to be a slightly higher incidence of it among the offspring of people who had a CHD themselves, which warrants fetal testing. A fetal echocardiogram would be done between the fourth and fifth months of pregnancy to determine the health of my child's heart.

Again, the doctors told me that if they suggested an abortion at that point in the pregnancy, I should highly consider following their recommendations. With all of these things racing through my mind, I set up my next appointment, thanked them and said good-bye. As we walked out of the elevator toward the car, Chris said to me, "If there is anything wrong with the baby's heart, I want you to abort."

I can't even express how stunned and hurt I was when I heard him say this. Did this mean he would not love a child of ours if it was not perfect? He tried to tell me that he did not want to have a baby that had a heart like mine. Of course I became defensive. My quality of life was fine, I countered, and besides, they have even greater ability to repair defects today than they did twenty years ago when I was born. He responded by reminding me of my physical restrictions, like not being able to run without getting short of breath and lightheaded.

Chris also reminded me that it would be foolish to risk my health for a pregnancy that already had problems. I know that he was just scared, but it hurt me so badly to think about aborting my child, especially if there was a problem which could be fixed. I also began to wonder if my parents had known of my defect before I was born, would they have chosen to abort me?

The next few months were torturous, as I anxiously waited to see if my child's heart had formed perfectly, or if he or she had inherited something from me which would lead to a defective heart. I kept thinking about the possibility of abortion. It really scared me, and I considered whether or not I could truly bring myself to terminate if that should become necessary.

I reached out to family members and was so surprised by the conflicting attitudes. One person told me that even if my life were at risk and the baby were deformed, I should keep the pregnancy. Though a stubborn part of me kept believing that I would not abort regardless of the cost, my practical side really made me question whether or not I should risk my life. Others told me that they loved me and would support me no matter what I needed to do. I was really comforted by this, and it greatly helped me to lean on these people during the months of moral questioning I faced.

I kept hoping I would not have to make these decisions. I would sit on my bed and imagine the developing parts of the heart and pray that everything was normal. I was careful to eat well and get enough rest, but most importantly I tried to think positively.

I will never forget one of my obstetrical appointments in particular— the day the doctor searched for the baby's heartbeat. I laid on the table, and he got out the Doppler stethoscope, applied some gel and pressed it against my belly. He moved it around, and there was no sound. I just watched the doctor's face. He looked a bit worried but kept pushing the probe, and then, "chug-chug-chug-chug." I could not help but think it sounded fast, but then I had never heard a fetal heartbeat before.

The doctor told me it sounded wonderful, and from that point my fears for the baby began to diminish. His heartbeat sounded strong and definite. Several events followed that reassured me. I went in for an ultrasound and did not know what I was looking at, until I saw the heart. I could see it pumping.

I think that helped me, and then the OB/GYN came in and took the transducer from the technician and did part of the scan himself. He told me that the baby's heart looked normal at this early stage of development, and then reminded me that I would soon have the fetal echocardiogram done. Although I had not felt anything yet, the doctor commented on how active the baby was. I felt him move for the first time the very next day.

Within the month it was time to have the fetal echocardiogram. I do not know why, but I ended up going alone. I realize now that it probably would have been wiser to have had someone there with me. The technicians described how they could rule out around 90% of all congenital heart defects through this testing. They reassured me that if there were a major defect like TGA, they would almost definitely be able to see it.

I was so relieved when they told me that the baby's heart looked completely normal. I went out and bought a few little things for the baby. I was so excited that I went home and showed them to Chris. He asked me not to buy anything more. He later confided that he was sickened by the idea of something happening to me or the baby and then coming home to find a room full of baby things.

During the first week of March, my obstetrician decided that although I was not dilated and the baby had not dropped that we should plan my hospital admission and schedule the induction. We set the date for March 12th, and they told me to expect the birth to take place about twelve hours from the time of admission.

Chris helped a friend plan a baby shower for me. In the days that followed, I went on frenzied shopping sprees in an effort to get the baby's room ready in time. On the appointed day we drove to the hospital, stopping first to have one final romantic lunch.

When I was admitted to the hospital they began the intravenous antibiotic drip. I was then moved into a beautiful labor/delivery/recovery room. It was spacious and had beautiful murals on the wall. It looked more like a hotel room than a hospital room except for the nurses' station in the corner and the tiny isolette.

I was attached to an EKG, a contraction monitor, a fetal monitor and a pulse oximeter. I was examined by a resident who found that I was still not dilated. They applied a topical gel, prostaglandin, which triggers hormones causing contractions and labor to begin. I did have a few minor contractions which were picked up by the monitor, but they were so slight I really did not even feel them. More gel was applied and eventually my membranes were stripped, but nothing happened. I was very sore from the seemingly constant pelvic exams.

I really wanted to get up and walk around but, because of all of the wires and monitors, that was only permitted once or twice very grudgingly. Finally, by the next morning, when I was still not having contractions and had not progressed at all, the doctors decided to send me home. I had been so excited. although I tried to remain calm, but now they were sending me home without a baby. When they told me, I could not help crying.

I went home and waited. I began to focus on all of the pain I had during the twenty plus exams and scraped membranes and wondered how I would do during the actual pain of childbirth. I was so nervous I could not sleep. I would go into the baby's room in the middle of the night and fold and refold his little nightshirts, change the sheets in the bassinet and listen to lullabies. My anxiety was calmed by eating, so I ate a lot. I had gained a significant amount of weight up until that point, but in the last month I just could not stop eating. I ate an ice cream sundae every night for a month. During this time I went to the obstetrician's office twice a week. I was now a week past my due date.

After one of my visits, I had a fetal diagnostic test during which time a resident came in and thought I was dilated to one. I was admitted, so my husband went up to the maternity floor to the beautiful room where my child would be born. Again the prostaglandin was administered, I was left to wait.

By the next day the doctors decided to try something more

aggressive. I was given Pitocin which is supposed to cause very strong contractions. After a while I began to have some contractions, but they were not very regular, so by evening the doctors decided to send me home again. They did another ultrasound to check on the status of the baby, and although the amniotic fluid was greatly diminished, they felt he was not in any immediate danger.

They scheduled another appointment with my OB/GYN and a fetal diagnostic in forty-eight hours. By this time I was very upset. I was convinced that this baby would never be born. I began to think that it was an omen that I was being sent home without my baby again. They had me wait there until the contractions subsided, but when it came time to release me, it felt like they were stronger. Tired of being in the hospital, I just wanted to go home and cry.

My husband and I stopped on the way home to get something to eat, and I told him the contractions were not subsiding. We went home, and I was restless. I tossed and turned all night. By morning I was still having contractions but refused to believe that I was in labor. By noon Chris called the doctor, and he told us to drive to the hospital. I was admitted and hooked up to the IV and monitors. Within a few hours the contractions were very strong and regular, so I was given an epidural.

Finally at 10:15 p.m., I was pushed into an operating room—the beautiful labor/delivery room was unavailable this time. I was overwhelmed by the number of medical personnel in the room— fourteen in all, not counting my own personal cheering squad.

The doctors explained that they would be using vacuum suction to help deliver the baby and that I was not to try to push. The device looked like a drill or a gun, with a cord on one end, a place to grip with a trigger and what looked like a gauge to measure amount of suction and a plunger on the end. The plunger was inserted and then each time I had a contraction it would be accompanied by the suction.

The sensation was uncomfortable, and I was still having very strong contractions. I never once had the urge to push. At one point the suction broke which was both frightening and painful. I was becoming very upset and frustrated, and the baby began to go into fetal distress. At this point the doctors decided to use forceps to help deliver the baby. Within fifteen minutes I felt a rush of relief as his shoulders passed through and his body slid out of mine.

The room was very quiet. Too quiet. The doctors rushed him over to the examining table, and all I heard was the sound of my baby's feet being slapped frantically. Nothing. Finally there was a weak, gurgling sound, but nothing like the lusty cry of the newborn that I had dreamt about for forty-two long weeks.

I was so set apart from all of the activity because I was trapped on the bed, restrained by wires and tubes and legs too heavy to feel. I struggled to see what was happening to my son but could not see anything beyond all of the doctors and nurses.

I heard the pediatrician say to the others that they had to take him to NICU "stat." I was overwhelmed, and cried, "But I haven't held him yet, I haven't even seen him!" As the doctor raced out the door, he lifted my son up so I could get one quick glance. I could not believe how blue he was. A rush of dread swept over me, and I began to wonder how my mother must have felt when I was born blue.

What sort of horrible thing had I done? But just as soon as the fear struck, I also had a wonderful sense of relief. I grew content with the knowledge that, if the baby did have problems, at least he was in one of the best possible hospitals, receiving the best possible care. I knew that I could not control the situation, and so I left it in the hands of the doctors.

I was still very anxious. My family made quick trips between the NICU and the delivery room to assure me that he was fine, but I could not believe them. They told me that my son was going to be all right, but the tension in their voices and their quick returns to the baby's side left me doubting. Finally my dad, knowing of my desperate longing to see my son, asked a nurse to take a Polaroid of him. He brought it to me, and though my son did not look great, he was alive.

Once I was in the recovery room, the pediatricians came to talk to me. They explained that my son had gone into fetal distress. The delivery was very hard on him and that was why he had such a hard time breathing. They told me that he had acidosis, which I later learned is high levels of acid in the blood caused by lack of oxygen.

Then they reassured me that he was indeed very healthy. He remained in NICU for several hours until he was stabilized. Finally, in the early hours of the next morning, I was allowed to hold my son for the first time.

I now realize how fortunate I was to have had a successful pregnancy. I have since had the opportunity to speak to several other ACHD patients who were not properly advised about their pregnancies and who suffered tragic outcomes. I feel very fortunate to have had a cardiologist specializing in the treatment of adults with congenital heart defects and a high-risk obstetrician.

Rites of Passage

The moment I found out my baby had a congenital heart defect, the question, "What kind of life will my child lead?" flashed through my mind. I wondered if I would have a sickly child. Would my child be able to run and play with his older brother? Would he spend a lot of time in the hospital?

I had much more to worry about, though, than quality of life. The first hurdle Alexander had to overcome was the first surgery. He was given such a slim chance of survival that I was scared for my baby. Perhaps more frightening than that, though, were the chances of his surviving from one surgery to the next and ultimately to kindergarten. The one ray of hope the doctors shared was that it seemed that children who survived to the age of five seemed to do fine after that.

My mother and I immediately began planning a huge birthday party for Alexander's fifth birthday. We knew Alexander would make it. He had to. In seven months Alexander will be five years old. We are well on our way to hiring those ponies and clowns.

What I wanted more than anything was to know that a child with Alex's heart defect did make it to five. I wanted to see him or her with my own eyes. I wanted to talk to the parents and ask them a million questions. Better yet, I wished to see and talk to a teenager. What stories parents of teens with HLHS could tell! Why, their children were pioneers in the movement begun by Dr. William Norwood way back in the early 1980s.

What about other children with congenital heart defects? What kind of lives did these children lead? Did they go to college? Get a job? Have first loves? Get married? Have children? What was the "normal" course for a child born with a congenital heart defect? I wanted these answers, but the oldest child I knew of after Alexander was first diagnosed was only a two year old. Joshua Hower was my beacon of hope, born with the same heart defect, operated on by the same surgeon. I knew that if Joshua could make it, so could Alexander! Amy (Joshua's mother) and I became good friends and kept each other apprised of our children's progress.

I remember sitting in the hospital and looking at Alexander. He looked so tiny in that big bed with so many IVs and monitors attached to him. When he was in the hospital, it was hard to think of anything beyond taking him home. How I longed to hold him and love him as I had before the surgery, before I knew about his heart defect.

Before, I had envisioned what Alexander would be like as he got older. I dreamed about Joey and Alex being altar boys, joining Boy Scouts together and being best friends. I wondered what jobs they would aspire towards. Who would they be? What would they do? How would they make a difference in this world?

After I found out about Alex's condition, I was afraid all of those lovely dreams would be shattered. What I would have given for some of the wonderful, true stories that follow. These stories of "everyday" life activities become major milestones to parents of children with congenital heart defects. What some consider an ordinary accomplishment becomes something of wonder to us. What is a very special event to most parents, to us is a miracle.

Summer Camp

By: Beth Hutchinson

It was the summer of 1972, and I was eleven years old. I was about to embark on my first summer camp experience. Buried in the Green Mountains of Vermont, the heavenly place was filled with ninety other children, all hugging parents good-bye, claiming their bunks and throwing belongings into their cubbies. All around was fresh air, the smell of pine, the bubbling brooks, the serenity of the lake. Green, everything was green.

My stomach turned, from terror and excitement at the same time. This was my first time away from home for more than an over-nighter. I was both thrilled and panicked about being away from home for the next eight weeks! Would I survive? Would I make any friends? Would I be homesick?

That summer of '72 turned out to be the first of three summers I would spend in Vermont at that wonderful camp, the best three summers of my life! Yes, I survived! Yes, I made friends, lifelong friends with whom I still keep in touch. Yes, I was homesick, but that passed. I was having too much fun to stay homesick.

Beth Perera Hutchinson (sitting atop the archery target)

Fast forward to Christmas 1986. I am eight months pregnant with my first child. As I sift through the mail, I come across a card from a dear, old friend; someone I have not seen in years. I tear open the envelope to read the words from my old camp buddy and find that she lives just a short drive away! We talk, catch up and promise to meet again and visit our old stomping grounds. We look forward to the day when our own children will be sitting around the campfire creating their own friendships and memories. I could not wait for the birth of my baby and to begin the process of watching her grow up.

Watching my child grow up, this was something I took for granted. We planned this pregnancy; we prepared for the arrival of our new baby; we even began planning for our child's future. Savings bonds, savings accounts, the beginnings of a college fund . . . these were all in place before the big day. Who would our child look like? Dark or fair? Blue eyes or brown? A boy or a girl? Will she love to read? Will she be an artist, a pilot, a computer whiz, a doctor, a singer? Where will she attend college? A million of these questions raced through our minds as we awaited the birth of our baby.

Then the event we had been waiting for finally happened, but Kaitlin's birth was nothing like I had imagined. I had prepared for labor and delivery, of course, but I also saw myself holding my newborn, nursing, cuddling, kissing. My husband and I would no longer be just a couple; the three of us would form a family! I had prepared for the joyous event that every new mother dreams of. What I got was a nightmare.

It was February 2, 1987. Kaitlin came into the world at eight pounds, two ounces in Plattsburgh, New York. She never cried. She never made a sound.

Instead of joy, I felt fear. Instead of excitement, I felt fear. Instead of exhilaration, I felt fear. Fear of the unknown, fear of the blueness of Kaitlin's skin and lips, fear of the tubes and wires the nurses stuck all over her, fear of her silence. It did not take long before I heard the words "heart murmur" for the first time. Heart murmur? What does a heart murmur have to do with my daughter being so blue? I would soon learn more than I ever cared to know about heart defects.

I felt so betrayed, robbed of this once-in-a-lifetime experience! Doctors were preparing to transfer Kaitlin to another hospital that had a better cardiac unit, and I had not even seen her! Realizing this, they wheeled her isolette into my recovery room briefly. The nurse encouraged me to talk to her and touch her. All I could say through my tears was, "Hi, Kaitlin, Mommy loves you . . ." I touched the one arm that did not have tape or tubes or needles in it, only for Kaitlin to pull away from me immediately. She was wheeled away to an ambulance which took her to another hospital, in another city, in a different state. After she left I realized I could not even picture her face.

"This can't be happening!" was all I could think. How could two healthy parents produce a child so ill? All of our plans, all of our hopes and dreams for our child seemed to fly out the window. In an instant it no longer mattered whom she looked like, or what color her eyes were. In an instant our hearts were filled with the fear that our child may not even live, that we may not even see her grow up. It was quite an experience to be discharged from the maternity ward empty-handed.

It is now June of 1997, and ten and a half years have passed. Kaitlin just finished fourth grade as an honor roll student and is preparing to attend summer camp. She is bright, beautiful, funny, mischievous, and a wonderful big sister to our six year old, Rachel. She does not seem like the same Kaitlin as the baby in 1987. She's come so far! Our lives are no longer ruled by her heart defect. I never thought this day would come, but it is here, and it is glorious!

Kaitlin's diagnosis was pulmonary atresia with an atrial septal defect and hypoplastic right ventricle. She was flown to Boston Children's Hospital where she underwent open-heart surgery at two and a half days of age. We drove there immediately after my discharge so we could see her before surgery. For all we knew, this might be our only chance to see her.

Kaitlin's surgery went well, and she came through it beautifully! At five days I got to hold her; at two weeks she came home. At four weeks she was hospitalized again with pleural effusion, then she was home again for good at six weeks. She had in-home visits from a nurse twice weekly plus two doctor appointments weekly at first. Her oxygen saturations and weight were closely monitored. The checkups became less frequent, but we returned to the hospital each year for a cardiac catheterization.

We went through living from feeding to feeding, wondering how many ounces of formula Kaitlin would drink and keep down this day, charting each ounce in and each ounce out. We prayed she would show some weight gain at her next appointment and hoped not to have "Failure to Thrive" recorded in her medical records yet again. Above all else we hoped that her doctors would be able to manage her deformed heart enough to keep her stable, keep her improving so that we would have the privilege of watching her grow up.

We fondly nicknamed Kaitlin the "Ethiopia Poster Child," as she resembled a malnourished third-world child. Eating was not Kaitlin's thing. It was a constant struggle to get and keep food in her. The first nine months were incredibly difficult. Kaitlin weighed just fifteen pounds at age one. At nine months, she began keeping food down more regularly, enough to put on some pounds and muscle that would make walking a possibility.

Kaitlin army-crawled at ten months, walked at fifteen months (exactly the same age her little sister would later walk! A sister who was bigger, rounder and heart healthy!) and talked at eighteen months. What she lacked in physical ability, she more than made up for mentally. Her fine motor skills were excellent and advanced, while she was several months behind in her gross motor skills. But we knew she would eventually catch up. (She weighed twenty pounds at age two, twenty-four pounds at age three—which is what she should have weighed at age one in the "normal" scheme of things!)

We had been told that Kaitlin would need a second operation around age four, possibly a Fontan. We returned to Boston at age four and a half, with six-month old Rachel in tow, prepared for surgery number two. Kaitlin was first scheduled for a cath.

She left for the cath lab her normal dusky blue, pale self. She returned several hours later with pink skin and red lips . . . more color than we had ever seen on her before! We also received the wonderful news that surgery would not be necessary! Music to our ears!

The "miracle" was a tiny device called a "clamshell" that was placed over the hole in Kaitlin's septum via the cath tube. The tube was carefully placed; the clamshell was released, springing open like an umbrella to patch the hole. Kaitlin's own heart tissue would grow over the device to permanently hold it in place. For the first time in her life, Kaitlin's blood was pumping through her heart and going where it was supposed to go!

Kaitlin was just one of five hundred patients to receive this device. Although it has not yet been FDA approved (to my knowledge), it holds great promise in saving lots of others, adults and children alike, from open-heart procedures to repair holes! That was six years ago; we have never had to return to Boston. Kaitlin's only scheduled visits now are to our local pediatric cardiologist for a chest X-ray, EKG, and every other year an echocardiogram. All of the data from her visits are sent to her Boston cardiologists so they can monitor her status. It is one day at a time for Kaitlin. Her heart is far from normal, but it has been skillfully modified and repaired to allow her the life she so deserves.

It seems like a lifetime ago that we had a critically ill baby. What once ruled every minute of everyday has been reduced to an annual checkup. We can never forget those earlier days, and we would not want to. I am so very proud of Kaitlin for all she has endured and for the young lady she has become. Ten years have faded her chest scar, but it will always be there, a constant reminder of her violent entry into this world. She wants to hide it, seemingly ashamed and embarrassed, but I tell her to be proud of that scar! She is a walking tribute to the wonders of medical science. Kaitlin probably would not be here today had she been born ten years earlier.

I am in awe of the advances of pediatric cardiology. I am eternally grateful to the professionals whose dedication and expertise saved my daughter's life. They are out there still, constantly researching ways to improve and advance their techniques so even more lives can be saved.

What does the future hold for Kaitlin? Well, at least four more summers at camp! She cannot wait to reunite with her camp friends and I cannot wait to read the excited postcards and letters she will send home to us. She is looking forward to riding the horses, to brook-slopping, to bike hikes, and I am looking forward to hearing all about it!

I cannot describe how it felt last summer to step out of the car and see this beautiful young lady walking toward me. She had long tan legs, a pony tail, rolled up denim shorts, unlaced hiking boots and a grin from ear to ear! My Kaitlin! The stories poured from her, stories of new best friends, silly pranks, summer crushes, campfires and dances. The smiles turned to tears as one-by-one all the campers had to say good-bye to counselors and each other. We were surrounded by people hugging each other, hating to let go of this wonderful summer experience. I never had to ask, "Do you want to come back next summer?" I had my answer right there among the smiles, hugs and tears.

Summer camp was a big step for Kaitlin. She was away from home for seven weeks and next summer will be for eight weeks! I remember the day when I could not leave her for an hour, let alone a whole summer! We missed her terribly, but she had the time of her life. She learned new skills, made new friends and became more independent.

What lies ahead? School, college, moving out to be on her own (with lots of dogs, she says), maybe having a family of her own if that is possible. Kaitlin is remarkably healthy, but we are blazing new territory here. No doctor can tell us what her situation will be in another ten years. I have faith that as her medical needs change, medical science will already be one step ahead and ready to deliver whatever Kaitlin and her heart need.

Kaitlin has put me to the test! People have always said, " How did you do it? I don't think I could've handled a child like that." I know they could. I know I did because I had no choice. Kaitlin is my daughter, and I love her. I brought her into this world, and I have loved every trying minute of watching her grow up in it. I would not have missed this for the world!

Kaitlin Hutchinson (bottom row, third from left)

Moving Day

By: Arlyn Kerr

My husband Les and I recently helped our daughter Julie move from Ann Arbor, Michigan to Baltimore. We were thrilled that she asked us to assist her because it was a momentous time in her life, and we were happy to be a part of it. The move marked the end of her formal education, and the start of her career and a new life.

Julie had recently finished her doctoral thesis in combinatorics at the University of Michigan, passed the intimidating oral defense of the thesis and obtained her Ph.D. degree in mathematics. She was now leaving the furnished apartment that had been home for four years and moving to Baltimore, where she would start her first permanent job doing math research. This was August, and because she did not plan to go back in December for her graduation ceremony, the move was the closest we would get to attending graduation, where she would wear the special gown reserved for doctoral students. I was especially sorry that she would not get to again wear the special gold medal she had been awarded at her undergraduate ceremony for being the "Outstanding Student in the Sciences" at Washington State University. She graduated Phi Beta Kappa and Summa Cum Laude, but watching her sitting on the podium during the ceremony for the honor of receiving that prize was the moment that brought tears to my eyes.

During some of Julie's early years, we did not know if she would graduate high school, never mind college and graduate school. She was born with several congenital heart defects, necessitating surgery at eighteen months and two open-heart surgeries at age thirteen. At one of those early appointments, I asked the cardiologist what kind of life expectancy she might have, and he wisely refused to name a time. "I might say six years, and then she might live to sixty!" he protested. Although he meant well, I pessimistically took it to mean that he really thought she would only live to six and felt quite relieved when she reached that age and did not seem to be in imminent danger. Other than always having less energy than her peers, she was fairly healthy throughout childhood.

Because of her easy tiring, it was perhaps harder for me than for most mothers to gradually "let her go." In grade school, I often volunteered to chauffeur class trips so that I could watch from afar how she was doing. Although she had very good judgment about pacing herself, I always feared that pressure from other kids or from adults who did not know her condition might force her to overdo it ("Walk faster, Julie, keep up with the rest of the class!"). It was difficult to watch her go off to summer camp and later to four-week training sessions at West Point and Annapolis, when she was chosen to train with the national high school mathematics Olympiad team.

Worst was when she left for college, even though it was only five hours away by car from our home near Seattle. Our son David is a year older than Julie, and the four of us had always been a close-knit family doing many activities together. David was already away at college but only a half-hour away so we could still often spend whole evenings together playing cards and board games. I had a bad case of empty nest syndrome for the first few months. Nobody else except Les and Julie shared my sense of silliness, and I felt as if I was losing my best friend. But I adapted and learned to settle for eagerly-awaited letters and the occasional visit. We did not see her much even in the summers because she participated in math research programs in California and Indiana.

A couple of years later, she ventured even farther, studying math one semester in Budapest. I knew that she would choose a graduate school far away, so I was not surprised when she settled on Michigan, but I always hoped that afterwards she would return to the Northwest. For the past five summers, she had worked as a math researcher near San Diego, which was already far from Seattle, but the ideal job turned out to be even farther, 3,000 miles from home in Baltimore.

So here we were participating in the big move. We flew to the Detroit airport and rented the biggest car we could since we would be driving in-tandem with her small car, attempting to carry all her belongings. Although Julie had no furniture, she had clothes, dishes, dozens of stuffed animals. Amidst the many file folders was a collection of her poetry; for many years in childhood she wrote, illustrated, and self-published an annual book of stories, but even after she ceased those, she kept journals and wrote poetry, especially during times of depression. Among her many math books and favorite novels were some of her Esperanto books; she had started studying this international language as a teenager and got Les and me interested also so that now we all use it very much with pen pals, foreign visitors, and traveling. Julie even lived with an Esperanto-speaking family during her five months in Hungary.

One of Julie's many hobbies is miniatures for which she makes teeny room arrangements, but fortunately those fragile items were being shipped from our house. Another item being shipped from our house was her foosball table. Foosball was almost like an answer to my prayers. I had always felt badly that Julie was not able to participate in sports because she had such good physical coordination. She learned to ride a bicycle at a very early age, later learned to juggle—fun stuff but not really participative sports. Julie herself did not seem to mind, but being a sports buff myself, I felt she was missing out on the fun of pitting skill, as well as intelligence, against other players. So I was very happy when Julie, as a teenager, discovered foosball and found that she excelled at it. In her college apartment she serendipitously found a foosball table in the storage locker, apparently abandoned by a long-gone tenant. What fun it has been over the years to see her playing with her brother and friends, her infectious laughter ringing through the house! She said she did not have room for the table in Baltimore, but I sent it in hope that she would soon have a group of friends there; I wanted to picture her in that far-off place again laughing and shrieking with glee with the fast-paced action.

We did have to pack into the cars her bulky cello. She had been playing since age eight, when her cardiologist, a violinist himself, recommended the cello as being a good orchestral instrument, given her condition—it doesn't require the lung power that a wind or brass instrument does and is not as tiring to hold as the violin or viola. I hoped she would find an orchestra in which to play in Baltimore. In addition to the thrill of seeing her win state math contests over the years, we enjoyed watching her play in orchestras, right from the third grade school string group to the Seattle Youth Symphony and college orchestra.

Also taking a lot of space were her two pet ferrets and all their paraphernalia. Julie had always loved animals, but Les and I resisted a larger animal for many years, trying to keep her content with chameleons and white mice. But, when we found out after her two heart surgeries that she would need to wear a body brace for a year because of scoliosis, I decided, "This kid needs to have something good in her life right now," and we got a ferret. That ferret was a real sweetie, a joy to Julie and the rest of us for her eight years, and, shortly after her death, Julie bought two new fellows, boys from the same litter.

After stuffing the two cars with all the items, we headed out for dinner at a favorite restaurant joined by Julie's boyfriend, Joel, another math grad student who fortuitously lived in the apartment just below, and Joel's roommate, Jeremy. I was so glad for Julie that she had had good friends in Ann Arbor; through high school and college, she had been somewhat of a loner, but somehow after that she had made very good friends wherever she went and been much more sociable. It made Les and me feel especially good because from the start in Ann Arbor she had problems with arrhythmias, necessitating frequent trips to the emergency room for cardioversion, and it was such a load off our minds to know that Julie had friends to take her there, stay with her, and keep us informed by phone of her progress. When she had a catheter ablation to try to cure the arrhythmia, Les and I flew out to be with her, but we saw that Joel had really taken over our role; he was the one now holding her hand as she was wheeled off, whereas in past surgeries I had been the one. Even when Les joined Julie for another ablation in San Francisco (this one successful at stopping the arrhythmia), Joel also flew there and was Julie's main support. It was Joel who stayed overnight in the hospital room with Julie, whereas in the past it would have been Les. It was a strange sensation for us but just another step in the "letting go" process, whereby parents become less and less necessary in their children's lives. Joel was joining us on this trip also and planning to take other transportation back after spending a few days.

Back at the apartment, we helped Julie give it a thorough cleaning so that she would get her damage deposit back. I asked whether she had gone to the math department to say good-bye to her professors, but she said she had not; apparently she was just thinking in terms of her new life ahead, not the one behind her. She had, though, paid a good-bye visit to the woman she had been visiting for many months through a hospice program. While a teenager she started volunteering at a nursing home and has since worked with many elderly women. They all love her for her sweet nature; she seems to have always been mature beyond her years and had a compassion for others with problems. I have always felt that her heart condition contributed to this empathy toward others with physical limitations and health problems. Before her Fontan procedure, while I was almost numb with fear at the risks, she was the one keeping up my morale. Through her kindness, cheerfulness, sense of humor and shy modesty she has made many friends. Even acquaintances of mine who have met her only one time ask about her whenever I see them.

The next day we woke early, packed all the final items; only one last item could not be crammed in and was left behind— the humidifier I forced on a reluctant Julie when it seemed as though she was always catching a cold in the harsh Michigan winters. Probably another case of my being an overprotective mother. The four of us went to my favorite deli for breakfast and take-out items for later meals. Since all four of us are vegetarians, I suspected (correctly, it turned out) that it might be difficult to find food to our liking at the restaurants along the highway. I was somewhat fearful of driving 540 miles in one day, but the other three thought it would be no problem. Part of the reason I was anxious to participate in this move was to share the driving burden, even though Julie assured me that she felt fine about driving the entire distance. She takes after Les in that, certainly not after me. Joel was not able to drive Julie's Honda Civic because it has manual transmission, and he was not signed up to drive the rental car, so his role was to keep Julie alert in her car.

We knew it would be almost impossible to keep in sight of each other for the entire trip, so Les had brought along two ham radios. Julie passed her novice license at age twelve, but after a year or so of talking with other hams around the world in Morse Code, she had gone on to other hobbies. But in cases like this, it was useful having the license. Les and I (in the rental car) kept in contact throughout the day with Julie and Joel in her car; we could say, "Do you see all the deer over on the right?" or "Do you want to stop at that rest area coming up?"

And we did stop often, both to keep the humans from falling asleep and to let the ferrets run around. Since they usually have free reign in Julie's apartment, they were not used to being caged up for so long. So, since you do not walk ferrets as much as they walk you, we explored the back alleys of restaurants in many rest areas along the turnpikes of Ohio and Pennsylvania. Les had already discovered on the Internet the frequencies of all the National Public Radio (NPR) stations along the route, so as one would fade out we would tune to another, telling Julie and Joel over the ham radio the new frequency. As it turned out, I only drove an hour that day; Les and Julie did all the rest of the driving. Sitting in the car for so long had been the part of the trip I dreaded beforehand, and Julie had suggested that I could fly directly to Baltimore and skip that part. But I felt that the packing and long drive were a major part of the entire experience, that I wanted to be a part of it, and I was glad that I had not skipped that aspect of the move.

The next day we continued on to Julie's new apartment, which she had selected the previous month. Unloading was a lot faster than loading without the "jigsaw puzzle" aspect of fitting it all in. Over the next few days, we helped Julie register her car (which involved a car inspection and getting new insurance), buy a bed and tools and some of the other items you need when you are on your own for the first time. We even had time to go to the monthly meeting of the local ferret club, where Delta and Epsilon (the ferrets) made some new friends and swam in a small pool. By chance that was Julie's twenty-sixty birthday, so it was a pleasant way to spend the day, in between ferret-proofing the apartment, shopping and unpacking boxes. Joel fortunately likes games as much as our family does, so we spent the evenings sitting on the floor playing May I, a version of Rummy, while listening to CDs of classical music.

It was very reassuring to get through the move and this initial time in the new place without any problems for Julie with arrhythmias. We had other family trips in the past few years either canceled or cut short because of needing to get to a hospital. If not for the successful ablation, an essential item of business—even before leaving Michigan—would have been to line up a cardiologist and hospital in Baltimore, but this time we had not even done that.

I did not know it at the time, but Julie herself was feeling very grateful all the time that she felt so well, that she did not have to think about every action ("Is it OK to carry that box? How long can I afford to spend wandering around this store looking at furniture?"). In previous years a simple thing like running down a long flight of stairs or playing broomball for a few minutes with friends at the university ice skating rink had resulted in hospital stays, so she had become quite aware of what might trigger an episode. But now it was a huge load off her mind to do the normal things most of us take for granted.

On the fourth day there, Julie started her new job, while Joel, Les and I continued to explore the area and help her stock up. It felt really good to meet the neighbors and apartment managers, get to know the local stores, the library and Julie's workplace so that now back in Seattle I can really picture things. When she says she just bought a vacuum cleaner at K-mart, I can even envision which aisle it was. I know she is in a safe and friendly environment, doing the work she is trained for and loves. (And, after years of difficulty in obtaining health insurance, she even has a group policy now!)

So it was not quite like going to graduation but a very fulfilling rite-of-passage experience nevertheless. The trip made this new turning point in Julie's life more concrete for me and easier for me to accept that she is all grown up, not dependent on her parents and doing a fine job with her life. As Les first recognized when we were discussing important events in Julie's life, no one occasion takes on extra-special importance; rather, every single time we see Julie, or get a letter, an email, or phone call, feels like a "special moment" because of the wonderful person she is.

Julie and Arlyn Kerr

Karen's New Car

By: Mary Kay Klein

As Karen drove away from the house in her brand new strawberry red Neon, I could not help but remember all the moments in the past twenty-four years when we all wondered whether or not she could have the life she has today. Though she is still cyanotic at times and her truncus arteriosus is uncorrected, Karen has a very full and engaging life. She drives her new car to her full-time job at the Boston College Library, where she is rapidly advancing in skills, and then on Monday nights to her graduate class in library science at Simmons College. She is actively in communication with other ACHDers in other parts of the country and is working to help start an organization for adults with CHD. She traveled to Texas last fall to visit with some ACHD friends and will be going to Florida in January.

In preparing for Karen's birth, I had done all the things the typical early 1970's mother would have thought appropriate—taken Lamaze classes, arranged for rooming in at the hospital, read all the books I could find on breast-feeding, and made sure I did not even take an aspirin while I was pregnant so as not to jeopardize my baby. After trying for three years to conceive, my pregnancy with my firstborn was probably the happiest time of my life. The pregnancy was so easy—not even a touch of morning sickness—that I found it hard to believe that there could possibly be anything wrong with the baby.

When I was told a few hours after her birth that Karen was blue, and the doctors did not know why, I was devastated. It would be almost two years before doctors correctly and fully diagnosed the problem, but in those early hours I was very frightened and sad every time I looked at the empty crib in my hospital room. They would not let Karen out of the nursery, and I can remember dragging myself out of bed and to the other side of the hospital floor several times a night to breast-feed her.

Finally she was released from the hospital with assurances that there were no major medical problems, and we settled down to what we thought would be a quiet family life. However, she did not gain weight—only one pound in two months—and the pediatrician blamed the small gain on the fact that I was breast-feeding her. I was sure this was not the real reason (I later had two sons who were nursed into little butterballs in the early months) but did not know what was. At the age of two months, she was hospitalized with pneumonia and congestive heart failure and was diagnosed with double outlet right ventricle.

At the time, there were suggestions by medical personnel that I should think about having another baby. Karen was struggling for every breath at that point, and I sensed that she had to make a decision as to whether she wanted to keep trying to breathe or whether she wanted to let go. I realized that it was up to her, and all I could do was to hold her tiny hand and wait. She reached a point where I felt she had made a decision to fight for her life and that turned me into "Mama Bear"—fiercely protective of her in every way.

I watched the hospital personnel very carefully and made sure she had all her medications and treatments on schedule. When she came home, I kept everyone with even the slightest sniffle away from her. She made it through the first two years with no more major infections but was still very small. During that time, there was a group of people who prayed for her regularly; I am convinced that their prayers and support are helpful even now. Just before her second birthday, Karen received another cath in preparation for surgery. It was discovered that she actually had a truncus with a single pulmonary artery, and her cardiologist reported with great sadness that no surgery could be done.

This allegedly sad news made me very happy because I had had a very bad intuition about the surgery and felt that she could survive with the strength she had. I had—and still have—a feeling that she will never have surgery and that she will live a long and productive life.

It was questioned whether or not she would ever walk or be able to go to school. I was convinced at that point that the dire predictions were wrong and that if we provided an environment which nurtured her strengths, she would do all right

Gradually she did do well. By first grade, she was catching up in height and weight. She took ballet for awhile, since she was somewhat uncoordinated from walking so late; the ballet lessons really seemed to help. She also seemed to live on a river of antibiotics for awhile for ear infections and other assorted ailments. Her digoxin helped, and then later she outgrew the need for it.

When Karen was almost twelve, we moved from rural Ohio to Boston. The first two years were difficult, but things got better as she moved into high school. She went to a very small school, where there were no great distances to walk. She received a lot of support. Her graduation from high school—at which she received a number of awards—was one of the happiest and proudest moments of my life.

Karen moved on to Boston College. There were times when things were difficult, but BC did provide the most convenient housing it could, a class schedule arranged so that she did not have to rush from here to there and other items like elevator keys for a number of the buildings. Karen majored in art. Her senior art show exhibit contained a number of paintings of hearts, lungs, blood cells and other body organs. I saw this as part of her way of coming to terms with her physical challenges. During the four years she lived away from home, Karen had two boyfriends and established a number of lasting friendships. It was clear she had reached the point where she could handle her life well and independently. Again, the academic recognition she received at the BC awards ceremony and graduation was immensely satisfying.

As I see her driving her car, making plans for her future and reaching out to others, I realize what wonderful things she has done, even without having the normal amount of strength. The sparkle she brings to everything amazes me, and her determination is still very strong. I am so proud of her!

Karen Klein and the "Karenmobile"

The Heart of a Mother

One of the things that we parents of children with Fontans have been told is that our children must not go into areas of extremely high elevation or go deep sea diving. These changes in air pressure are very hard on the human body, but for a person with a modified heart, the effects can be life-threatening. So what do you do when your teenager insists on going on the class ski trip? If you are Rita Scoggins you sign up as a chaperone, ask your Internet friends for their prayers and off you go! Here is Rita's report.

Victoria's Ski Trip

By: Rita Scoggins

In general the trip was good and Victoria did fairly well. After thirty and a half hours on the bus, we finally arrived in Breckenridge. Since we were late, we had to go directly to the high school to perform. The band did fantastic and brought home several trophies. Victoria was doing fine and even managed to play her clarinet for one of the songs.

Victoria Scoggins

By the time we got to the hotel, it was after midnight. It was almost 2:00 a.m. when we finally got into our rooms. At this point, Victoria was not feeling well,and I gave her oxygen. She slept well and planned to get up at 7:00 a.m. to be fitted for skis. Well, we got up a bit later than that but did go down to be fitted.

I waited in the line as she sat on the sidelines. She was bound and determined to ski and was saving her energy by not standing in the line with me.

After I had been in line for about an hour and was almost at the end, she came up, and I asked her if she thought she could walk in those ski boots.

She looked at me and said, "I don't want to do this." Boy, was I glad! By this time she was feeling very bad, and I gave her oxygen again.

We went on to lunch, but she would not eat. Later that afternoon we went walking around the town (oxygen tank in tow and used as needed). It is a beautiful town! Later in the afternoon I let Victoria go into town with her friends. I was feeling sorry for her because she had been spending most of her time with me! She did fine in town but did have to use the oxygen a few times. I met them at Pizza Hut, and by then she was not feeling well, could not eat and threw up. UGH.

The worst part, though, was that she was almost out of oxygen. We went back to the resort, and I tried to find a place to refill her tank. What a pain! No one could refill it. Meanwhile, one of the boys was really getting sick (had not been out of bed all day), and so we decided to take him, Victoria and a girl who had bronchitis to the emergency room in the next town.

Victoria was seen so that they could prescribe oxygen for her. She was feeling fine while we were there. As a matter of fact her SATs were 99! I was surprised at that. The doctor there sent us home with oxygen for the night and next morning and prescribed the same for the girl with bronchitis. The boy was admitted to the hospital overnight with high altitude sickness. He had the worst form and had fluid in his lungs. We were at the ER from about 7:00 p.m. until 1:00 a.m.

While we were there it started to snow! It was so pretty. We were all impressed. Victoria woke up the next morning with her appetite much improved. I think it was because she was on the oxygen all night. We left Breckenridge at noon (after picking up the boy that was in the hospital), and twenty-nine and a half hours later, we were back home in Harlingen, Texas! It was such a long trip—a total of sixty hours on the bus and only thirty-six hours in Breckenridge!

I asked Victoria what she had learned from the trip, and she said "I can't live there!" She also said that even knowing what she did (not being able to ski, feeling bad, having to spend time with mom, etc.) that she would not have wanted to miss the trip because she had fun and really enjoyed the town. I am glad that she was able to make this trip and that things went as well as they did.

I am so glad that this trip is behind us. I was really dreading it. The bus ride was the worst . . . too many hours. The kids were all great. I couldn't believe how well-behaved they all were. They each deserve a medal! I am glad that Victoria was able to make the trip. I think it did her good to see that she was not the only one affected by the altitude. She did not get to ski, but I do not think she was crushed by that . . . disappointed but not crushed.

The Heart of a Mother

Camp Del Corazon

By: Jill Sorensen

Camp Del Corazon in Spanish means "Camp of the Heart." It is a camp about children, for children and about teaching children with heart disease that they are not alone. Some of the counselors at this camp are adults with congenital heart defects (ACHDers), and their presence alone teaches more than words can say. They are living examples of how one can be strong enough to overcome any obstacle. They are role models for the children who may have never seen a grown-up with a congenital heart defect and who wonder what life will be like for them when they are older.

Dr. Kevin Shannon, cardiologist, and Lisa Knight, electrophysiologist RN, are the co-founders of the camp which started three years ago on Labor Day weekend in 1995. The camp is located on Catalina Island and is equipped to provide medical assistance if needed.

This camp allows children, who are not normally eligible for the average summer camp, to participate in a summer camp. Regardless of medical histories or complex medication schedules, these children are permitted to have the same experience as any other child going to summer camp.

Some of these "heart" kids might be at a higher risk for a disastrous event to occur, but that is why this camp is so unique. They are prepared for any emergency. About forty adult volunteers, including doctors and nurses, are right there with the kids.

For the adult volunteers with congenital heart defects, it is a rare opportunity to be with children and adults like themselves who understand and have similar problems. For the children, it is an opportunity to see that as they grow older they can be successful, even though their lives may be somewhat limited. But at least they see that children with heart defects can grow up! Best of all kids, like my Jeni, have had the opportunity to meet other kids with similar disabilities and do not have to feel ashamed or inadequate because they cannot do certain activities.

Any child with heart disease is eligible to attend the camp. They simply need to be between seven and fifteen years of age. These kids are allowed to do all the things that normal campers do such as kayaking, swimming, hiking, archery, dancing, attending barbecues, acting in a skit, climbing "The Wall" called Mt. Everest or singing around a campfire. These children can experience all these wonderful things, perhaps with some limitations, but because they are protected in this environment, they can feel comfortable and know they are safe. They know they will not be laughed at or cruelly ridiculed because of their disabilities or their scars. They can just be themselves, unashamed of their bodies;

they can fit in.

Jeni was a little apprehensive her first time going to camp, but now she cannot wait for the next summer camp! She absolutely loves her heart camp. She even reassures me now by saying, "Don't worry about me, Mom. I am safer at camp than at home, and I'm in great hands."

Jeni Sorensen

When I found out Cheryl's son had celebrated his Bar Mitzvah, I begged her to share her story with me. This last heart story symbolizes the journey through discovery, support, and hope of all heart children and their parents. I knew Ryan's coming-of-age ceremony stood for all of the heart children in this book and everywhere whose milestones in life are truly miraculous truimphs. Many of us can only dream of the day when our children will enter into adulthood.

Cheryl's story—and Ryan's—shows how parents and their children unite in the profound hope of survival regardless of religion, race, gender or type of heart defect. May God grant you all "a lifetime of peace, love of family, companionship of special friends, courage to face life's obstacles and bless you with good health."

The Heart of a Mother

When Milestones Become Miracles

By: *Cheryl Goldstein*

Ryan was delivered by emergency C-section on August 23, 1982. He was critical at birth, affected by a B Strep infection contracted in utero. He received two blood transfusions and platelets, but these efforts did not seem to be working. At around 3:00 a.m., my doctor told us that Ryan was dying and that there was nothing else they could do.

My first glimpse of this precious baby was horrifying. He was very blue, in a coma and intubated. There were tubes and wires everywhere, and my husband and I were surrounded by doctors and nurses who could not bring themselves to look us in the eye. I can vividly recall touching every inch of his tiny body, and I remember talking quietly to him. I did not want him dying without me telling him how much I loved him.

About one hour later, my doctor returned and said that Ryan had begun to respond to the antibiotics; however, he was concerned about possible heart problems. We gave permission to perform additional tests and were later informed that he had multiple heart defects. The plan was to try and stabilize him for transfer to the Children's Hospital for further diagnostic studies.

Early that morning, joined by our family, friends and our Rabbi, we said our tearful good-byes and prayed for a miracle.

That afternoon, Ryan had several seizures. Other complications arose, and the situation seemed to become more serious by the moment. On his third day of life, a catheterization was performed. After the procedure, we were confronted by several specialists, each taking their turn explaining their diagnoses. Ryan had tetralogy of Fallot and critical pulmonary stenosis. He would require surgery as soon as he was stable enough to go into the OR. The neurologist explained that there was a very good chance he had suffered significant brain damage as a result of the infection and seizures. The geneticist wanted to run studies to determine if he had Down syndrome. And the prognosis, even if he were to survive the surgery, was not encouraging.

At the age of four days, Ryan had his first operation. Twenty-four hours later, he was awake and alert and had almost been weaned off of life support. On his sixth day of life, I was finally able to hold him—not an easy task considering all of the tubes and wires still attached to his tiny body. I had worked hard all that week to develop a milk supply so that he could have breast milk. We were told that most heart babies were not strong enough to nurse, but I was determined to try.

When he was seven days old, I was finally able to breast-feed him for the first time. It was difficult to get comfortable, because he was still on a heart monitor and had several IV lines. But our first try went very well, and he was able to nurse without difficulty.

Ryan had his Bris (circumcision ceremony typically done on the child's eighth day of life) in a waiting room at the hospital when he was two and half weeks old. The nurses had decorated the room as a surprise for us, and several of them were there to witness this important event. Our minds were filled with questions as we wondered what the quality of his life would be and how long he would live. And we wondered, would he survive to celebrate his Bar Mitzvah?

When he was finally able to come home for the first time, he was on numerous medications, had a chronic cough and was quite cyanotic. Too weak to crawl or sit up, he started occupational therapy at the age of seven months. He was very small but quite bright and alert. He had a remarkable interest in music and books, and his language skill continually amazed us.

Ryan was hospitalized several times throughout his first two years of life—for caths, tests and complications from colds and viruses. At around two and a half years of age, he began to show signs of congestive heart failure. He was getting frequent bouts of bronchitis and pneumonia, his appetite had diminished, and he was sleeping most of the day. When he was awake, Ryan continued to wow us with his extraordinary intelligence, determination and zest for life. As the months passed, we scheduled his next operation, the second stage repair for tetralogy of Fallot.

We were getting to be old hands at preparing him for medical procedures and saying good-bye as he would be wheeled away into the care of strangers; however, watching him enter the operating room a second time was devastating to us.

I will never forget seeing him for the first time after the surgery. Although he was still on life support, he was actually pink for the first time in his life! Gone were the purple lips and blue cheeks!

Within less than twenty-four hours, he was sitting up in bed wearing his favorite baseball cap and asked for pancakes! He came home six days later, a little weak, but very happy and looking great. The next morning, he rode his big wheel around the block for the first time ever without having to stop and catch his breath.

Ryan did very well for the next two years. He was able to read the newspaper by the age of five, was extremely active and embraced life with even more enthusiasm and joy than ever before. He had boundless energy, and we were continuously reminded of the miracle of his survival.

At the age of five and a half, he began getting sick again. He was tiring more easily and had pneumonia from which he could not recover. After many tests and consultations, a balloon angioplasty was performed to try to enlarge his pulmonary artery.

The period of time between that procedure and his next operation can only be characterized as extraordinary. Ryan enjoyed a perfectly normal quality of life. He was able to take gym at school, play Little League baseball and go to summer camp like any other child his age. He had expressed an interest in dance, and we enrolled him in a tap class. Over the next several years, we witnessed astounding things! He performed in regional, state, and national competitions in groups (tap and jazz) and as a soloist. He won many gold medals and special awards for outstanding performances and quickly became a favorite of judges and audiences alike.

Each time we watched him perform, we were always a little nervous, and we often cried, knowing that we were witnessing something very special. He had come so far and had achieved so many great things . . . and he continued to beat the odds.

At the age of ten and a half, Ryan was to perform at a regional competition with his tap group. He had not been feeling well, and we urged him not to dance that day. But he insisted, saying that the girls depended on him, and he did not want to let them down. Reluctantly, we allowed him to dance. He had some kind of event that day—we are still not sure exactly what happened. He appeared to get dizzy and looked as though he would pass out. It was terrifying for me, and I can recall running at top speed down the corridor to the backstage area.

During the diagnostic and decision-making process that was to follow, my niece was celebrating her Bat Mitzvah. As we sat in the Temple at her service, again, we wondered if Ryan would make it to his coming-of-age ceremony.

A few months later, we had to tell him that he would need another operation to fix his heart. He began to cry and asked me if he was going to die. Imagine being eleven years old and having to face this possibility! Death was very real to him having just lost both of his beloved grandfathers. We have handled many difficult situations and tough questions with him before, but this was the most difficult and most painful conversation of them all.

The night before he was admitted for surgery, he handed me a piece of paper. He had written a will, and wanted me to know that if he died, he wanted to be buried with his good luck stuffed animal, his tap shoes autographed by Savion Glover and his baseball glove.

Ryan came through the operation beautifully. He was extubated in less than an hour and was sitting up in bed, breathing comfortably before the other kids who had been operated on that day had even stirred! Things went downhill from there, however, and he had a rocky post-operative course. He had severe pain and getting him to cough and walk around was very difficult.

After his discharge, his incision became infected, and despite repeated visits to the surgical staff, our pleas to do something to help clear this infection went unheard. We were well aware of how dangerous these infections can be because my father had died as a result of a post-op wound infection only a year before this. We sought another opinion, and the decision was made to debride the wound, to culture it, and to possibly perform a biopsy to make sure that the infection had not invaded his heart.

Ryan did not handle this very well, and neither did we. He cried bitterly when we told him the news, and he begged us not to put him through this. Unfortunately, we felt that it was extremely important to proceed with the plan because we wanted to do everything possible to prevent a potentially serious situation. This brave young man somehow got it together; he summoned up admirable courage and cheerfully waved good-bye to us, once again, as he was wheeled back into the OR.

His incision tested positive for staph aureus, and we would have to wait for five days to find out if it was MRSA (a life-threatening infection). We were told that if he tested positive for MRSA, that he would require eight weeks of IV antibiotics with "no guarantees" of survival.

The waiting was intolerable—sleepless nights and restless days. It was Yom Kippur, and while my family was at the Temple, I was home with Ryan waiting for the phone to ring. Late that day the call came—the test was negative for MRSA!

Ryan suffered from depression following these events. Having two operations within two weeks had taken its toll on his body and his spirit. He should have been spending his first days at middle school, but instead, he needed four weeks of recuperation at home. With great difficulty, he managed to keep up with his school work, and at our urging and insistence, he took walks each day to try to rebuild his stamina and strength.

Six months later, Ryan performed a tap solo in competition. He had worked hard to get back into shape and was determined to compete. The entire competition team (over a hundred members) and all of the parents came to watch him that day. I think we all cried through the entire routine, since once again, we knew that we were witnessing something quite extraordinary.

We began to make plans for a very special event in our lives, Ryan's Bar Mitzvah. Many Jewish children celebrate their transition from childhood into adulthood during this special ceremony. This event represents the culmination of the child's religious education and is the first time that he is welcomed into the community as an adult member. During this ceremony, the child leads the congregation and his guests in prayer and is called to read from the Torah (the five books of Moses) for the first time.

This coming of age ritual is enthusiastically anticipated by family and friends who witness the service and often celebrate the child's accomplishment with a party. For us, this event had tremendous importance . . . for there were many times when we wondered if our son would ever reach this day.

At a typical service, immediate relatives are given special honors called Aliyot. These honors, usually reserved for grandparents, aunts and uncles, and siblings, include the reading of special prayers before and after the reading of each portion of the Torah and opening and closing the Ark (the place where the Torah scrolls are kept). We knew that this day was important to so many people and wanted to make it special for those who stood by our side, paced the hallways, gave blood for Ryan, and offered their love and friendship to us throughout the years. So we added additional readings, music and poetry in order to allow twenty-seven relatives and friends to participate. These special honors enabled us to publicly express our gratitude to some very special people, and it meant a great deal to us to have so many involved in this rite of passage.

It was an emotional day not only for us as parents but also for everyone who attended the service. I think we underestimated the emotion and the joy that all would feel . . . for we all knew that we were indeed witnessing a miracle. There were many tears on that morning—tears of relief, of joy, and some trepidation and fear.

Near the end of the ceremony, the Bar Mitzvah is called to stand in front of the open Ark, with parents at his side, and is blessed by the Rabbi and Cantor with a special prayer. Although I managed to maintain control of the tears, for the most part, that moment is one I will never forget. Overcome by emotion, my husband and I embraced our child, read a special prayer we had written for him, and listened to the beautiful music of the Cantor's voice, and the prayers recited by the Rabbi. When we turned around to face the congregation, we realized that we were not the only ones who had been overcome by the importance of this event. Looking into the faces of those we love and whose friendship we cherish, we saw the same emotion we were feeling—the tears and smiles, and the relief for having reached this day. His prayer read:

> For all parents, the occasion of their son's Bar Mitzvah is a time of great pride and happiness. Most moms and dads find themselves thinking about their child's life, the happy moments and special times in their family's history—sort of a "mental rerun" of images and sounds. But for those of us who have been blessed with a special child, life's experiences take on a different meaning. Because for kids like you, every accomplishment is a milestone, and every milestone a miracle.
>
> We remember the day of your Bris. You were about two weeks old and still in the hospital. We recall the moment when the moel held you up for the picture we all have of our sons; you know, the one with the tiny Kipah. When we looked at your beautiful face, we knew that we were really witnessing a miracle, for you had beaten overwhelming odds.
>
> We have celebrated many milestones since then and have witnessed many miracles. But there is no single moment that could compare with the joy we feel on this very special day. To be here, by your side, as you are called to the Torah as a Bar Mitzvah, is a moment we have looked forward to, and prayed for. What

makes this momentous occasion even more wonderful, is the ability to share this event with all of these special people. Their prayers, support, and love have helped us to reach this day.

From your earliest days, you have embraced life with passion and energy, often making your behavior a little difficult to manage, but nonetheless, a joy to behold. You have been blessed with many skills and special talents, and have achieved great things. And you have faced difficult challenges with courage and determination that have been an inspiration to all who know you.

So, on the occasion of your Bar Mitzvah, as we see before us the confident, capable young man you have become, we want you to know how very proud of you we are. We are grateful for the milestones of the past and look forward to the miracles yet to come.

May God grant you a lifetime of peace, the love of your family, the companionship of special friends, the courage to face whatever obstacles may come your way, and may you be blessed with good health.

Later that evening, we celebrated life with a party in our son's honor. There is a Bar Mitzvah tradition, typically at the very beginning of the party, during which the Bar Mitzvah child is placed on a chair and lifted high in the air by the men who are closest to him. The guests encircle him and dance around him in celebration. It is that moment which will remain in my memory forever. As our son was joyously raised into the air, the room seemed to explode with shouts and cheers! We had survived the long journey and were overjoyed to share this important moment with our family and friends.

Editor's Note: *Names were changed to protect the family's privacy.

Live,
Love,
Laugh . . .
and be happy.

Appendix A: Native Language Essays

Lebens und Leidensweq eines herzkranken Kindes

Beate Lemmer

Am 29.04.89 kam unsere zweite Tochter mit Namen Mareike zur Welt. Nach der schweren Geburt waren mein Mann und ich sehr glücklich, dass wir ein gesundes Kind bekommen hatten. Doch drei Tage nach der Geburt diagnostizierten Kinderärzte ein Nebengeräusch am Herzen. Eine schreckliche Angst nahm Besitz von mir. Mein Mann wurde verständigt und man besprach mit uns die Verlegung des Kindes in eine kardiologische Klinik. Am nächsten Tag wurde Mareike in eine Kölner Kinderklinik verlegt. Nach eingehenden Untersuchungen wurde uns mitgeteilt, dass unsere Tochter an einem schweren komplexen vierfachen Herzfehler leide (Fallotsche Tetralogie) und dass sie in der Klinik stationär aufgenommen wurde. Mit der Diagnose konnte ich damals nichts anfangen. Es war mir unheimlich. Ich wußte nur eines: „Man wollte mir mein Kind wegnehmen. Ich sollte es fremden Menschen überlassen." Nachdem der Kardiologe uns dann erklärte wie schwer krank unser Kind sei, brach ich zusammen. Es folgte der Schock, aber es folgte auch das Erwachen, die Erkenntnis mit dieser schrecklichen Wahrheit zu leben. Ich wußte nicht wie ich das unserer erst siebzehn Monate alten Tochter erklären sollte, die zu Hause auf ihr Schwesterchen wartete. Sechs Wochen mußte sie warten, bis Mareike endlich entlassen wurde. In diesen Wochen wurde Mareike auf Medikamente eingestellt, denn sie litt an zunehmender Blausucht. Zu Hause fing für uns alle ein ganz anderes Leben an. Alles drehte sich um Mareike. Sie durfte nicht weinen, weil sie sonst blau wurde. Kein Besuch durfte ins Haus, der erkältet war. Freunde, die sonst regelmäßig kamen, zogen sich zurück. Mein Vater gab mir sogar die Schuld an Mareikes Krankheit. Mein Bruder, der zwei Jahre später Vater eines Jungen wurde, gab mir die Schuld, dass sein Sohn ein winziges Loch im Herzen habe, der aber nie operiert werden muß. Für uns war es hart festzustellen, dass wir auf einmal ganz alleine waren. Doch der Kampf um Mareikes Leben fing erst an.

Alle sechs bis acht Wochen wurde Mareike untersucht. Bei Gewichtszunahme wurde der Dosis der Medikamente erhöht. Anhand von Größe und Gewicht entwickelt Mareike sich gut. Im Juli 1990 entschied der Kardiologe, dass Mareike in ein Herzzentrum eingewiesen wurde, zwecks Herzkatheter. Am 01.08.90 wurde der Katheter durchgeführt und man teilte uns mit, dass man eine Notoperation machen mußte, da die Lungengefäße bei Mareike unterentwickelt seien.

Zu diesem Zeitpunkt war Mareike sechzehn Monate alt. Sie konnte weder sprechen, krabbeln oder laufen. Am 05.08.90 wurde sie operiert. Sie hat bestimmt gespurt, dass etwas mit ihr geschieht, denn auf dem Weg zum Operationssaal schrie sie ganz laut: ,,Mama." Dieses ,,Mama" höre ich manchmal heute noch. Der Eingriff war gut verlaufen. Es gab keine Komplikationen. Als ich Mareike dann auf der Intensivstation wiedersah, hatte ich keine Angst vor der ganzen Technik, vor Infusionen usw. Ich sah nur mein Kind. Ich habe in dem Moment noch nie ein schöneres Kind gesehen. Mareike sah wunderschön aus. Nichts Blaues war mehr zu sehen. Rote Wangen, rote Lippen und blaue Augen. Und es ging ihr gut. Ich war sehr glücklich. Am 21.08.90 wurde Mareike entlassen. Zwei Tage vorher lernte sie laufen. Ich war zu diesem Zeitpunkt schwanger und habe zwei Tage, nachdem wir wieder zu Hause waren das Kind verloren. Es war nervlich doch alles zuviel gewesen.

Mareike machte große Fortschritte und wir alle konnten erst einmal aufatmen. Am 07.08.91 wurde Mareike wieder in ein Herzzentrum eingewiesen zwecks Herzkatheter. Man wollte nun feststellen ob die korrigierende Operation durchgeführt werden könnte. Es verlief alles komplikationslos und man setzte die Operation auf den 28.03.92. So hatten wir dann noch eine kleine Ruhepause, denn im Oktober 91 kam unser drittes Mädchen zur Welt. Die anfänglichen Schwierigkeiten nach der Geburt wie Sauerstoffmangel, Blausucht, (Verdacht auf Herzfehler) konnten nach einigen Tagen behoben werden. Unsere Madeleine hatte drei Tage nach der Geburt einen Temperatursturz, weil sie zu früh auf die Welt kam. Was ich in diesen Tagen durchgemacht habe, kann ich nicht beschreiben. Doch ohne meinen Mann hätte ich these Zeit nicht durchstehen können. Er konnte zwar nicht immer bei mir sein, da er sich ja um die anderen Kindern kümmerte. Aber er war immer da, wenn ich abends aus der Klinik kam, wenn ich vor Angst nicht mehr ein noch aus wußte. Durch meine Angst und Sorge war ich sehr pessimistisch. Mein Mann dagegen war immer optimistisch. Er hat immer gesagt: ,,Mareike wird es schaffen."

Die Operation am 28.03.92 verlief ebenfalls ohne Komplikationen. Sie erholte sich sehr schnell und wurde am 12.04.92 entlassen. Jetzt hatten wir es geschafft. Mareike war laut Aussage der Ärzte fast gesund. Aber weit gefehlt. Im August 93 kam Mareike in den Kindergarten. Ende August entdeckt der Kardiologe ein Nebengeräusch am Herzen. Am 30.09.93 wird Mareike wieder ins Herzzentrum zur Herzkatheteruntersuchung eingewiesen. Man entdeckt Pulmonalstenosen (Verengungen in der Lungenarterie). Es scheint aber geringfügig zu sein. Wir sollen Mareike gut beobachten, ob sie eventuell wieder blau wird. Die kardiologische Untersuchungen werden wieder engmaschiger. Bei jeder Untersuchung kommt wieder die Angst, was werden wir jetzt wieder erfahren? Mareike darf sich nicht anstrengen, sie darf sich beim Spielen nicht verausgaben. Sie muß ständig beobachtet werden. Wenn Mareike im Kindergarten ist, traue ich mich nicht ans Telefon zu gehen, aus Angst, es könnte etwas passiert sein.

Am 05.10.94 wird Mareike wieder im Herzzentrum aufgenommen. Ihr Zustand ist kritisch geworden. Sie wird nun bei den kleinsten Anstrengungen blau, der Sauerstoffgehalt im Blut nimmt ab, sie ist nicht mehr belastbar. Mittels eines Katheters wird eine Ballondilatation vorgenommen, um die Verengungen zu erweitern. Der Eingriff verläuft ohne Komplikationen. Doch er war umsonst. Schon viereinhalb Monate später haben sich die erweiterten Pulmonalstenosen wieder geschlossen. Mareike muß wieder operiert werden. Ihr rechter Herzmuskel wird immer größer. Durch die Verengungen muß das Herz so stark arbeiten. Die Gefahr, dass das Herz versagt wird immer größer.

Am 03.04.95 wird Mareike wieder operiert. Die Chirurgen wollen durch eine Patcherweiterung (Kunststoffflicken) die linke Pulmonalarterie weiten. Auch diese Operation verläuft wieder ohne Komplikationen. Auf der Intensivstation muß Mareike zweieinhalb Tage beatmet werden, weil Ärzte bei der vorangegangenen Untersuchung einen Lungeninfekt nicht erkannt haben. Aber sie hat sich auch davon erholt. Bei der Entlassung am 17.04.95 wird eine abschließende Untersuchung gemacht. Auf meine Frage, ob die Operation den gewünschten Erfolg gebracht hat, bekomme ich keine Antwort. Den Entlassungsbericht will man mir nachsenden. Ich habe ihn sonst immer selber bekommen. Auch die guten Wünsche für die Zukunft bleiben aus. Es ist alles sehr sonderbar. Vier Wochen später erfahren wir einen Teil der Wahrheit. Die Operation war umsonst. Es hat alles nichts gebracht.

Diesmal bekommen wir einen neuen Termin in einem anderen Herzzentrum. Dort soll mit einem Katheter eine Stentimplantation vorgenommen werden. Am 20.09.95 ist es soweit. Wir haben die größte Hoffnung, aber auch Angst. Der Wechsel in eine neue Klinik ist für Mareike sehr schwer. Sie bekommt Panik, schreit und weigert sich bei Blutabnahmen. Sie ist jetzt in einem Alter, wo sie sehr viel begreift. Sie spricht mit niemandem vom Klinikpersonal, weint aber in sich hinein. Und man läßt sie einfach weinen. Ich bleibe immer, solange bis sie eingeschlafen ist. Wenn ich dann leise gehen will, wird sie wach und weint. Um nach hause zu kommen brauche ich eine Stunde mit dem Auto. In den drei Tagen habe ich mich immer wieder verfahren, weil ich mich einfach nicht konzentrieren konnte. Nach dem Eingriff habe ich ein Gespräch mit dem Kardiologen. Die geplante Stentimplantation konnte nicht durchgeführt werden, weil nach der letzten Operation die Pulmonalarterie abgeknickt ist. Ich begreife den Sinn nicht. Es wird noch eine andere Klinik vorgeschlagen, in der man Mareike vorstelien könnte. Vielleicht wissen die noch eine Mö glichkeit. Mareike wird entlassen.

Bei der nächsten kardiologischen Untersuchung bei unserem

Kardiologen erfahren wir dann die volle Wahrheit: Mareike ist inoperabel. Alle haben es gewußt aber keiner hat es uns gesagt. Keiner hatte den Mut, uns die Wahrheit zu sagen. Ich fange an, Ärzte zu hassen. Unser Kind ist zum Sterben verurteilt. Kliniken haben die Krankenakte geschlossen. Man erkundigt sich noch in einer anderen Klinik, ob eine Behandlung möglich sei, aber es wird abgelehnt. Es ist schrecklich, ein Kind vor sich zu sehen und zu wissen, dass es sehr krank ist. Aber es ist ein vernichtendes Gefühl zu wissen, dass das eigene Kind sterben muß, weil kein Arzt in der Lage ist zu helfen.

Ich glaubte nicht mehr an Wunder. Und doch geschah eins. Unser Kardiologe flog im Januar zu einem Ärztekongress nach Genf in die Schweiz. Nach Absprache mit uns wollte er dort weltbekannten Kinderherzchirurgen die Krankenunterlagen von Mareike vorlegen.

Und es geschah ein Wunder.

Wir bekamen schriftlich und auch telefonisch Bescheid, dass man eine Möglichkeit hätte, Mareike zu helfen. Zwar könnte man Mareike nicht mehr operieren, was die eine Seite betrifft, aber durch einen speziellen Katheter könnten sie doch eine Stentimplantation durchfuhren. Das war der schönste Brief den ich je bekommen habe. Es gab jemanden auf der Welt, der unserem Kind helfen konnte. Wir bekamen auch sofort einen Termin und konnten Dank der schnellen Kostenzusage der Krankenkasse am 31.03.96 in die Schweiz fliegen. Ich mußte mit Mareike alleine fliegen, da mein Mann auf die anderen drei Kinder aufpassen mußte. Mittlerweile hatten wir nach drei Mädchen nun auch endlich einen Jungen bekommen. Hinzu kam, ich war noch nie geflogen. Aber ich mußte dadurch.

Der Eingriff in der Schweiz war ein voller Erfolg. Nach dem geglückten Eingriff (ich wartete vor dem Operationssaal) brachten Ärzte und Schwestern in einem Jubel aus. Musik spielte und sie fielen sich gegenseitig in die Arme. Ich hatte so etwas noch nicht erlebt. Der Chirurg kam zu mir und sagte nur immer wieder: „It's fine, all's O.K." Es war unbeschreiblich. Und was Mareike sehr genoß, ich war Tag und Nacht bei ihr. Man hatte unsere Betten zusammengestellt, so dass wir uns ganz nah sein konnten. Mareike hatte keine Angst. Sie weinte nicht und was ich sehr schnell festgestellt habe, sie hatte wieder Vertrauen zu Ärzten und Schwestern.

Drei Monate später flogen wir wieder in die Schweiz, wo Mareike dann auf der anderen Seite operiert werden konnte. Und diesmal war ebenfalls ein voller Erfolg. Mareike wurde am 25.07.96 operiert und, was für alle Beteiligten unbegreiflich war, am 29.07.96 entlassen! Zu Hause angekommen, wollte keine glauben, was geschehen war. Für uns wird es immer ein Wunder bleiben. Dass unser Kind lebt, verdanken wir unserem Kardiologen, weil er Mareike auch nicht aufgeben wollte und die Suche nach einem Spezialisten auch ins Ausland weiter gefuhrt hat. Und wir verdanken es einem Kardiologen und einem Chirurg, aus

USA, die ihr ganzes Wissen und können bei unserem Kind in der Schweiz eingesetzt haben.

Der Herzfehler wird immer bleiben, aber Mareike kann jetzt mit kleinen Einschränkungen genauso leben wie ein gesundes Kind. Nur drei Wochen nach der Operation konnte Mareike eingeschult werden.

Am Beispiel von Mareike möchte ich allen betroffenen Eltern herzkranker Kinder Mut machen. Die Diagnose "inoperabel" muß noch lange nicht "aufgeben" bedeuten.

Es ist zwar manchmal mit einem Kampf verbunden, aber zum größten Teil bekommen unsere Kinder doch noch die berühmte letzte Chance gesund zu werden. Der Weg für uns war ins Ausland to gehen. Für alle beteiligten war das die letzte Hoffnung. Wenn ein Kind trotzdem sterben muß, ist es aber auch ein Bißchen innerer Frieden wenn man sagen kann: "Wir haben alles in unserer Macht getan und auch um diese letzte Chance für unser Kind gekämpft."

Tjasijeva Zgodba

Jasmina Henderson-Reuter

Jaz sm Slovenka in moje ime je Jasmina. Porocena sem z Darrenom, ki je Novozelandcan. Imava dva sinova. Starejsemu je ime Mikey, mlajsemu pa Tjas. Mikey je bil rojen v Sloveniji 26. Februarja 1992, Tjas pa v Novi Zelandiji 18. Septembra 1994.

Tjas je bil rojen s srcno napako, transpozicijo velikih arterij (TGA). Skoraj vso nosecnost z drugim sinom sem se pocutila slabo. Tolazila sem se z mislijo, da je temu kriv malcek Mikey in premalo pocitka, vendar me je kljub temu skrbelo, da ni kaj narobe z otrokom, ki sem ga nosila. V 18. Tednu nosecnosti, sem imela ultrazvok in ker je bilo vse v najlepsem redu, bi morala biti vsaj malo razbremenjena skrbi, vendar nisem bila. Cutila sem, da je nekaj narobe, vendar sem se tolazila, da si le namisljam. Kljubsemu sem prosila babico za drugio ultrazvok ob koncu nosecnosti. Na zalost babica mojih obcutkov ni jemala resno in se je odlocila proti drugem ultrazvoku.

Rojevanje Tjasa je bilo zelo dolgo in bolece. Ob koncu mu je padel srcni utrip pod 60 utripov na minuto, tako so ga morali resevati iz mene. Ker je bil uklescen, je bilo prepozno za cesarski rez. Tjas je bil rojen s klescnim porodom, jaz pa sem dobila novo epizotomijo. Rojen je bil brez iskre zivljenja. Vendar pa so na njegovo in naso sreco bili okoi nas zdravniki, ki so vedeli, kaj pocnejo in so ga oziveli. Z Darrenomnama ni bilo jasno, kaj se dogaja. Tjasa so odpeljali se predno sem si ga lahko ogledala. Odvihrali so z njim na Oddelek za Intenzivno nego novorojenckov (NICU). Pol ure kasneje so mi prinesli sliko z mojim majhnim fantom. Oci je imel odprte okoli njega pa je bilo polno cevk in zic. Kar verjeti nism mogla, da je moj. Takrat se nihce ni vedel, kaj je bilo narobe z njim: mislili smo, da je v stresu zaradi tezkega poroda. Tjasijevi prve ocene ob rojstvu dojenckov (APGAR) so bile 2, 4 in zadnje 6 deset minut kasneje. Kljub temu, da je njegovo dihanje, zivljenje podpiral mehanicni ventilator in da je bil FiO2 na ventilatorju 100%, je bil moder in cinoticen, s saturacijo nizjo kot 50%. Z Darrenom sva bila koncno obvescena, da je nakaj hudo narobe z najinim drugorojenim. Rendgendska slika je pokazala, da Tjas nujno potrebuje ecogram, ker so sumili, da ima srcno napaka Transpozicijo velikih arterij.

Nama z Darrenom spet ni bilo nic jasno. Pediater nama je narisl sliko Tjasijevega srca in sliko normalnega srca ter naju obvestil, da bomo morali na prvo letalo, ki leti v Auckland (okoli 1700 km stran od Christchurca, na drugem otoku), ker imajo tam pediatricno-srcno bolnico, kjer bo Tjas moral biti cimprej, v roku enega dneva operiran. Bila sva cisto iz sebe. Zdi se mi, da sva jokala, ali pa sem samo jaz, ne vem tocno. Darren je sel domov povedati starsem, pripraviti nekaj pritljage in seveda po Mikeya, ker brez njega ne bi mogla nikamor.

Kmalu za tem sem bila obvescena, da imajo ze karte in da bo Tjas moral na letalo v inkubatorju. Tjas je bil kar velik dojencek (3790 g in 54 cm), zato je bil na pogled v inkubatorju zelo stisnjen.

Predno smo se odpravili na pot sem sla k Tjasu v NICU da ga vidim in mogoce fotografiram. Zelo me je bilo strah, da je to zadnjic, ko ga vidim zivega. Ko sem se vrnila v svojo sobo, kjer sem bila sama, nisem mogla spati (Tjas je bil rojen ob 00.41). Lezala sem v postelji in cakala na soncen vzhod. Sprasevala sem se kaj nas caka in si nisem mogla niti predstavljati, kaj nas je v resnici cakalo. Poklicala sem medicinsko sestro in jo prosila, da je sla in fotografirala Tjasa (sama nisem imela moci in ne srca).

Zgodaj zjutraj so prispeli Darren, njegovi starsi in Mikey, veliki bratec, ki ni mogel drzati svojega malega bratca. Vso nosecnost sem mu namrec razlagala, da bo lahko drzal svojega dojencka in da ga bo nesel domov iz bolnice. Nasmesto tega smo sli na letalisce. Bila sem cisto iz sebe, brez kakrsnih koli obcutkov.

Resilni avto je odpeljal Tjasa z medicinsko sestro in zdravnico. Tudi mi smo bili pripravljeni. Darrenovi starsi niso rekli skorajda besede. Mene je bilo strah klicati mojo mami. Strah me je bilo, da bo zacela se ona jokati in me bo s tem se bolj spravila v obup. Ko sem klicala, se je oglasil oci, bil je zelo umirjen in me poskusal ohrabriti ter mi zagotoviti, da bo vse v redu. Tudi sama sem upala v to.

Ko smo prispeli v Auckland v bolnico, je bil Tjas ze tam. Dodelili so mi enoposteljno sobo v porodnisnici v pritlicju, Tjas pa je bil v tretjem nadstropju. Darrenu in Mikeyu so obljubili postelje v domu za medicinske sestre nedalec od bolnice.

Pediatricni kardiologinja nam je prisla razloziti, da bo Tjas moral biti operiran zelo kmalu (v prvih dveh tednih zivljenja). Narisala nam je sliko Tjasvega srca in nam povedala, da morajo narediti prvi poseg kar takoj. Ta poseg naj bi ustvaril umetno luknjo med atrijama, ker se kisik v telesu se ni povecal, kljub temu, da je Tjas prejemal najvecjo mozno infuzijo Prostaglandina (kateri je drzal odprto naravno luknjo, ki jo imajo novorojencki pred porodom). Povedala nam je tudi, da je Tjas na listi za operacijo naslednji teden. Meni ni bilo nic jasno, oz. mi ni hotelo biti nic jasno. Zelela sem si le drzati svojega dojencka in ga deliti z njegovim starejsim bratcem in ockom.

K Tjasu smo smeli po opravljenem prvem posegu, Balonsko septosomijo. Ko smo prisli v NICU, smo se slikali z njim in slikali Mikeya z bratcem. Darren je ostal s Tjasem, midva z Mikeyem pa sva sla v mojo sobo. Z Darrenom sva si tako delila cas katerega sva prezivljala s Tjasem in Mikeyem (eden je bil z Mikeyem drugi pa s Tjasem skoraj ves cas). Prvo noc sem prespala (bolj prebila) v svoji sobi. Bila je strasna noc. Vse naokoli mene so jokali novorojencki, Sama pa sem imela le sliko in upanje.

Tjas je cakal na operacijo mesec dni. Postajal je vedno bolj bolan in nalezel se je vseh mogocih bolezni, ki so bile okoli v intenzivni negi. Po septosomiji, ki so jo opravili brez kakrsne koli narkoze, je dobil epilepticen napad (doktorji si niso bili sigurni, ce je bil pravi napad). Da se ne bi ponovilo je zacel dobivati zdravilo proti napadom, phenobarbital. Nekaj dni kasenej je dobil pljucnico, ki je bila razlog za nizke saturacije (prve dva tedne niso bile nikdar visje od 50%, temvec veckrat zelo nizje). Ko je pljucnica presla, so zapazili, da ima znake nekretitisa v crevesju. Na sreco so bili znaki odkrtit v zgodnjem zacetku, da so lahko vse naenkrat pozdravili.

Tjas je potreboval veliko inekcijskih posegov, veliko intravenskih linij. Ker se je na zacetku boril in poskusal jokati in mu ni nic pomagalo (to je moja razlaga), je po dveh tednih obupal. Ko so ga vbadali, da bi nasli linijo (preko katere bi lahko dobil nesteto zdravil), se ni nic vec upiral. Se vec niti premaknil se ni vec. Se huje pa je bilo to, da se mu kolicina kisika v telesu ni zvecala in da ni poskusal dihati sam za sebe. Pediater in kardiolog sta mi povedala, da je moznost, da so Tjasijevi mozgani prizadeti, ker je imal tako malo kisika po telesu tako dolgo in ker je bil rojen brez znakov zivljenja. Medicinsko osebje, zdravniki in kardiologi so se odlocili, da ga ne bodo operirali, ce so njegovi mozgani prevec prizadeti, ker ne bi prezivel.

Morali smo se potruditi, da ga spravimo z ventilatorja, tako da smo ga lahkoo peljali na CT scan. Seveda nam je uspelo. Ko smo se vrnili iz bolnice, kjer so je imel CT scan, je Tjas spet resno zbolel, dobill je zastrupitev krvi. To noc bi ga skoraj tri krat izgubili, ce ne bi bilo moderne tehnologije. Kljub vsemu, CT scan je pokazal, da so mozgani neprizadeti. (HURA!)

Koncno je Tjasu in nam vsem borba uspela in bili smo na poti v kardiolosko bolnico. Bolnisnica za srcno kirurgijo je bila oddaljena 200 metrov. Zelo me je bilo strah operacije, vendar sem vedela, da brez nje, Tjas ne more ziveti. Na poti v bolnico za srcne operacije, sem upala, da Tjasa ne morejo vec premakniti iz liste za operacijo, kot so ga velikokrat pred tem. Zal sem se motila.

Zadnjo noc predno so nas premestili v novo bolnico se je Tjas pocutil zelo dobro in njegove saturacije so bile okoli 80 do 90 procentov. Ko sem videla na monitorju 94, sem skoraj verjela, da se je l zgodil cudez in, da se je Bog odlocil, da Tjas ne bo potreboval operacije. Seveda sem se spet motila.

Ko smo prispeli v Green Lane bolnico, je bil Tjas na prosteglandinu in je imel kisik prikljucen skozi nosne cevcice. Na nesrecu se je tudi ta zila skozi katero je dobival prostaglandin zamasila in so se kardiologi na podolagi umetno narejene luknje v srcu in odprtih dukt, odlocili, da bodo opustili prostaglandin do operacije. Na zalost je Tjas preko nocil pomodrel in saturacije so mu padle pod 50%. Tjas je potreboval novi "vhod" v telo tako da so lahko nadaljevali s terapiijo s prostaglandinom. Bila je sobota in Tjas je bil na listi za operacijo v ponedeljek. Zelo me je bilo strah, da bi v teh dveh dneh spet zbolel ali kaj podobnega, kar bi prestavilo operacijo.

Darren in sincek Mikey (ki sta se vrnila nazaj v Christchurc po tednu dni v Auckalndu, in naju prisla obiskat en konec tedna) sta priletela iz Christchurcha, da bi bila blizu Tjasa za cas operacije. Ko sta prispela, sem jima morala povedala slabo novico, da je operacija prestavljena na torek popoldan. Nihce se ni potrudil, da bi mi to sporocil osebno, slisala sem mimogrede, ko sta se o Tjasu pogovarjala dva kardiologa. Ko sem zacel ob tej novici jokati, kardiologa nista razumeal, kaj je narobe z mano. Nista vedela, da je bil dan Tjaseve operacije prestavljen iz tedna v teden in da je bil vedno bolj bolan zaradi tega.

Koncno smo docakali dan operacije. Skupaj smo se fotografirali, vsa druzina in Tjas brez brazgotine. Darren je prvic drzal v rokah svojega drugega sina, do zdaj ga je bilo prevec strah. Sicer smo vsi verjeli, da je Tjas prezivel najhujse in da bo prezivel tudi operecijo, vendar je bilo zelo hudo mu dati zadnji poljub in ga oddati medicinskim sestram. Nesla sem ga do operacijske sobe. Tam smo cakali na medicinsko sestro, da ga je odnesla naprej. Zelala sem da bi se cas ustavil (samo za nekaj trenutkov). Darren in Mikey sta poljubila Tjasa in zapustila predoperacijsko, ker je bil Mikey preglasen. Ne vem tocno, kako sem sama prisla iz predoperaciske, roke so bile prazne in srce se mi je skoraj zlomilo. Mikey je sel za par ur v otrosko varstvo, ki so ga imeli v bolnici, da naju ne bi gledal v solzah (uboscek je bil komaj 2 in pol leti star). Midva z Darrenom pa sva sla v park pri bolnici na sprehod. Ko sva se vrnila sva sla takoj vprasati, ce je kaj novic (vedela sva, da bo Tjas prazivel, tezko je bilo le, ker je en dan prej, v ponedeljek, umrl na operacijski mizi par dni star fantek s TGA—isto diagnozo kot Tjas).

Po pribljizno 4-ih urah sva dobila dobre novice, Tjas je bil iz "bypass." Se malo pa bo v intenzivni negi in ga bomo sli lahko obiskati.

Z Darrenom sva bila tako presrecna! Sla sva po Mikeya v otrosko sobo in cakali smo na klic, da lahko gremo na intenzivno nego. Medicinska sestra nas je koncno poklicala in nam rekla, da gremo lahko pogledati nasega heroja. Povedali so nama da je se vedno zelo bolan in da se bo vse pokazalo v 24-ih urah.

Tako sem bila vesela, ko sem ga videla. Uboscek je bil drogiran, ampak je kljub temu odprl oci zame, za ocka in bratca.

Prikljucen je bil na cevke in cevi, skozi nogo je imel speljano centralno linijo za vsa zdravila, ki jih je dobival. AMPAK BIL JE ZIV! Z Darrenom sva spet zacela z izmenskim sihtom. Enkrat sem bila jaz s Tajsem, enkrat Darren. Preko noci pa so nama svetovali, da greva spat, ker bova potrebovala veliko moci. Jaz sem spala dve nadastropji vise, tako, da bi bila lahko pri Tjasu takoj, ko bi me potreboval.

Prvo jutro po operaciji, ko sem videla Tjasa nisem mogla verjeti svojim ocem. Tjas je bil ROZA, tako roza. Morala sem ga sllikati. Tekla sem v dom medicinskih sesster, kjer sta spala Darren in Mikey, da sem jima povedala. Zaradi Tjasejevega prvotnega zdravja, so doktorji napovedali, da bo moral ostati na intenzivni negi vsaj 10 dni. Narobe. Tri dni po operaciji je sam dihal, ostali pa smo se stiri dni na intenzivni negi za vsak slucaj. Na dan, ko smo prestavili Tjasa nazaj na oddelek, sem vedela, da se mu nic ne more vec zgoditi. Imela sva svojo sobo in Tjas je koncno postal moj otrok. Cisto sama sem skrbela zanj. Se vedno je imel pacemaker in cevcice za odvod tekocin iz telesa in cez dan je imel cez glavo poveznjeno skatlo s kisikom. Deset dni po operaciji sem mu prvic ponudila prso in zacel je sesati. Nikoli prej ni bil dovolj mocan za to. Mleko sem iztiskala ves cas ko je bil bolan in zdaj sem dobila placilo za to. Dojila sem svojega sincka. Na zacetku nisem imela dovolj mleka, zato je moral dobivati dodatke skozi cevko v nosu, kar pa je bilo odmrznjeno moje mleko.

Darren in Mikey sta morala domov. Darren se je ucil za novo sluzbo in ni imel vecdopusta inne neplacanega dopusta. Tokrat se ni bilo tako hudo posalovit, ker smo vedeli, da bomo kmalu spet vsi skupaj. Tjasu je slo vedno bolje in po nekaj dneh je medicinska sestra odstranila monitor, ki je meril njegove saturacije in srcni utrip. Na zacetku sem protestirala, vendar mi je rekla, da se bom morala nauciti ziveti brez monitorja. Prva dva dneva sem bila zivcna in sem komaj cakala da pride medicinska sestra, da izmeri srcni urtip in saturacije z monitorjem, potem pa sem se unesla. Zivljenje na oddelku je bilo lepo in hudo. Spoznala sem ogromno bolnih dojenckov in njihovih starsev. Imeli smo posebni bond, ki nas je povezoval. Bili pa so tudi tezki trenutki, ko je dojencek umrl, ali pa ni bilo upanja za ozdravitev.

Pocasime je zacelo dajati domotozje. Hotela sem odnesti Tjasa domov, vendar naju doktorji niso hoteli odpustiti, vsaj dokler je Tjas se imel cevko za hranjenje.

Moje telo je pocasi delalo vec in vec mleka, toda se vedno ne dovolj, da bi Tjas lahko imel dovolj. Tjas je popil vso mojo zalogo zmrznjenega mleka, tako smo mu zaceli dajati formulo mleko. Na zalost ni hotel sprejeti steklenicke. Po tednu dni na pediatricnem kardioloskem oddelku, sva s Tjasem sama letela v Christchurch bolnico (domov), kjer naj bi Tjas ali zacel jesti s steklenicke, ali pa bi morala pocakati tam dokler jaz ne bi imela dovlolj mleka.

Bila sem srecna toda zivcna. Dali so nama karto za letalo, prvi razred, ampak sla pa naj bi, cisto sama, brez medicinske sestre ali zdravnika. V Christchurcu naj bi na naju cakal resilni avto.

Oblekal sem svojega dojencka, spakirala pritljago in odpeljala sva se s taksijem na letalisce. Seveda sva se prvo poslovila od vseh in se slikala z vsemi na oddelku in na intenzivni negi (v bolnisnici za novorojencke). Na letaliscu se mi je razletel kovcek. Tako sem morala prositi zensko, ki je bila v vrsti pred mano, da je prijela Tjasa. Nikoli ne bi verjela, da go bom dala z rok za minuto, se posebno ne tujki. Na letalu sem dojila Tjasa, da ga ne bi bolela usesa in jokala od veselja.

Darren in Mikey sta cakala na naju v Christchurcu in resnicno smo bili vsi veseli. V Christchurcu v bolnici sva s Tajsem ostala samo en dan in noc, potem pa sva smela oba domov.

Ves ta cas sem bila v stiku z mojo mami preko telefonskih vez. Prvi klic v Slovnijo je bil najtezji. Bala sem se , da bo mami zacela jokati in potem se bom tudi sama zlomila. Ampak ne, moja mami je bila zelo mocna zame. Zagotovila mi je, da bo vse v redu s Tjasem in da bodo vsi molili zanj. Bilo ji je zelo tezko, da je bila tako dalec od nas, se posebno, ker ne zna prevec anglescine. Kljub temu me je klicala velikokrat v bolnico in je bila zelo mocna tudi, ko sem imela slabe novice zanjo.

Darrenovi starsi so bili tudi dalec (na drugem otoku—1 uro z latalom), zato je bilo tudi zanje hudo. Darrenova mama je pazila na Mikeya, ko je bil v Christchurchu. Mikey je bil tako pogumen. Nekako je razumel, da je njegov bratec bolan in da moram ostati z njim. Nikoli ni jokal, ko je moral stran od mene, ceprav pred tem nisva bila nikoli eden brez drugega. Po vrnitvi domov, je Tjasa obiskovala medicinska sestra dvakrat na teden. Tjasu so predpisali dve zdravili Phenobarbal in Frusemide, po treh mesecih pa nic vec. Medicinska sestra je tudi nehala hoditi na obisk, ker ni bila vec potrebna. Vendar sva s Tjasem zelo pogsto obiskovala Druzinskega zdravnika, ker sem bila vedno v skrbeh.

Mikey je bil zelo pridn cez dan, ponoci pa je imel grozne more in se je drl ure. Tjas je bil po operaciji cisto spremenjen—na bolje. Na zacetku smo ga vodili k pediatru vsake tri mesece, potem vsakih sest mesecev in zdaj enkrat na leto. Pet mesecev po operaciji, ga je pregledal pediatricni kardiolog in bil zelo vesel s Tjasevim razvojem, vendar je se vedno bilo slisati sum na srcu. Zadnji pregled maja 1997 pa je bil tako uspesen, da se tudi suma ni vec slisalo. Zdaj gremo h kardiologu cez dve leti.

Zdravniki kardiologi napovedujejo Tjasu veselo in zdravo prihodnost brez kakrsnih koli omejitev. Tjas je kar zdarv otrok, razen prehladov, vnetij uses (kot kateri koli zdrav otrok), ima astmo, kar pa je v Novi Zelandiji zelo pogosto med otroci. Je zelo aktiven otrok. Njegova rast in teza sta v skladu s popolnoma zdravimi otroki, se celo v visokih procentih. Je zelo prijazen fant, vendar tudi zelo trmast (kdo bi ga lahko krivil zaradi tega). Zaradi mocnih antibiotikov ima malce deformiran sprednji zob in je zlo hripav zaradi mnogih inkubacij (ko je bil na napravi za dihanje v NICU pred operacijo) in mozno zaradi poskodbe zivca med operacijo. Tjasev razvoj je na nivoju in je poleg tega zelo bister fant. Do nedavnega je zelo rad gledal slike na katerih je bil v bolnici, zelo bolan. Hotel je tudi videti video, toda ko je videl solze v mojih oceh, se je strinjal, da bova gledala to kdaj drugic. Tjas je prinesel luc v moje zivljenje, naucil me je vere v zivljenje in ljubezni. Zelo sem srecna, da je moj sin. Pokazal mi je kaj je pomembno v zivljenju in za kaj je vredno ziveti.

Friendship is the only cement that can hold the world together.

Appendix B: Summer Camps (in the United States)

California

Camp Del Corazon
5655 Halbrent Ave #10
Van Nuys, CA 91411
(818) 901-0323
(818) 901-0323 (faz)
e-mail: info@campdelcorazon.org

This free camp is held on Catalina Island over Labor Day weekend.

Florida

The Boggy Creek Gang Camp
30500 Brantley Branch Rd.
Eustis, FL 32736
352-483-4200
352-483-0358
email: info@boggycreek.org
URL: http://www.boggycreek.org

This free camp is for Florida residents 7-17 years of age with heart or kidney problems. The Boggy Creek Gang Camp also has a special session for the whole family.

Georgia

Camp Braveheart
3495 Brittany Way
Kennesaw, GA 30152
(888) 988-9979 or
(770) 919-2775
e-mail: campbraveheart@geocities.com

This free camp is for children 7-18 years of age.

Louisiana

Camp Bon Coeur, Inc.
A Rehabilitative Cardiac Camp
P.O. Box 53765
Lafayette, LA 70505
318-233-8437

Camp Bon Coeur is a free camp for children 8-16 years of age who
have severe, congenital heart defects. Only 50 campers per session
are accepted.

Massachusetts

Madden Open Hearts Camp
250 Monument Valley Rd.
Great Barrington, MA 01230
413-528-2229

This free camp for children 7-12 years of age runs for two weeks.
There are four summer sessions offered accomodating approximately
13 boys and 10 girls per session.

New York/New Jersey

Hope with Heart
P.O. Box 2736
Fair Lawn, N.J. 07410
973-728-3854

This camp is also free and is located in Orange County, New York.

Texas

Camp Moss
P.O. Route 329
Meridian, TX 76665
817-635-8811
817-635-4441 (fax)

Appendix C: Cardiac Anatomy

Basic Heart Anatomy

Below is a diagram of a normal heart with labels for the basic structures.

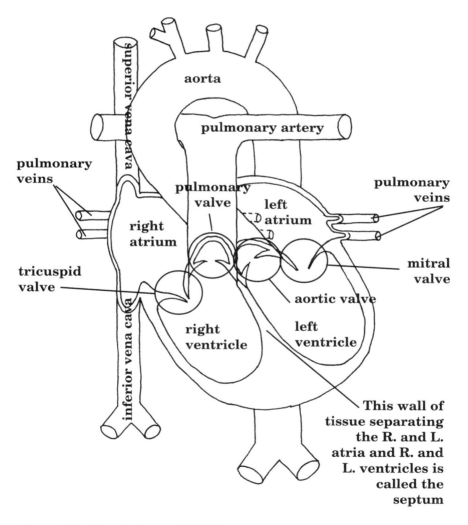

Artwork by Frank Jaworski, RN

Pediatric Heart Anatomy

Below is a diagram of a pediatric heart
with labels for the basic structures.

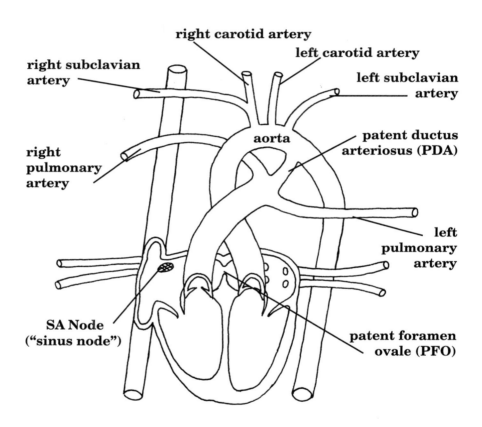

right carotid artery

left carotid artery

right subclavian
artery

left subclavian
artery

aorta

patent ductus
arteriosus (PDA)

right
pulmonary
artery

left
pulmonary
artery

SA Node
("sinus node")

patent foramen
ovale (PFO)

Artwork by Frank Jaworski, RN

Glossary of Terms

A

A-V canal defect (atrioventricular septal defect)—a congenital defect where there is such a large ASD and VSD that they combine to form one very large hole with mixed blood flowing into both the atria and ventricles

acidotic—a condition where the body's fluids become more acid than usual (low pH)

afterload—the pressure in the vessels the heart has to pump against

Aldactone (spironolactone)—a potassium sparing diuretic

alpha fetoprotein test—a test given to a pregnant woman for congenital birth defects, specifically spina bifida

amniocentesis—a test done on a pregnant woman to look for birth defects, specifically Down syndrome

anemic—a condition where the body lacks sufficient red cells

angioplasty—a catheterization where a vessel is opened or widened usually with the use of a balloon at the end of the catheter

antibiotic—a drug used in the treatment of infections

anticoagulation—a therapeutic condition induced to reduce blood clotting (usually with aspirin, heparin, coumadin)

anti-rejection drugs/medications—medications given to a transplant recipient to prevent the body from rejecting the donor organ

aorta—see diagram of the heart at the end of the Glossary; the artery which directs oxygenated blood from the heart to the body

APGAR—a test administered immediately after birth (babies are given a number from 0-10 with 10 being a perfect score)

apnea—a condition where a person stops breathing for a certain time (often occurring at night and referred to as sleep apnea)

aspiration pneumonia—fluid congestion and inflammation of the lungs usually caused by stomach contents being drawn into the lungs (reflux)

atrial septal defect (ASD)—a hole in the heart, specifically a hole in the septum between the atria

atrial septostomy—an operation where part of the septum between the atria is cut away

atrial switch—Mustard or Senning procedures used to treat TGA (vs. arterial switch commonly done today); this is an open-heart procedure utilizing the heart/lung machine. The right atrium is opened and the wall between the atria is fully removed. Using pericardium (Mustard) or flaps created from the atrial septal wall (Senning) a baffle is made to direct blood from the veins in the right atrium to the left ventricle. The baffle also directs blood from the pulmonary veins to the right ventricle.

B

B strep infection—Group B streptococcus (GBS) is a common type of bacteria which is potentially life-threatening, especially for newborns or babies with other birth defects as it is the most common cause of sepsis (blood infection) and meningitis (infection of the fluid and lining surrounding the brain) in newborns. GBS is also a frequent cause of newborn pnemonia which is particularly problematic for a baby with a congenital heart defect.

bacterial endocarditis (BE)—a bacterial infection inside the heart (the lining or the valves), causing it to be inflamed

balloon catheterization (balloon cath)—a catheterization where a balloon is inserted into the vessel (i.e. aorta, pulmonary arteries, a valve) to widen an area

bi-directional Glenn—the second stage of the Norwood procedure; an operation where the superior vena cava is sewn to the pulmonary artery (the Blalock-Taussig shunt is usually removed at this time, too)

Blalock-Taussig shunt—part of the Norwood procedure; an aortopulmonary shunt connecting the right/left subclavian artery to the right/left pulmonary artery

bloodpatch—the repair of a hole in the dura of the spine by using the patient's own blood (usually needed after an epidural or spinal tap.

C

Capoten (captopril)—a drug used to control blood pressure

cardiologist—a doctor who specializes in the care of the heart

cardiopulmonary resusitation (CPR)—the act of doing chest compressions and breathing for a patient whose heart has stopped

cardio-thoracic surgeon—a surgeon who operates on the heart and lungs

cardioversion—an electrical method of restarting the heart or getting the heart back into a normal sinus rhythm

CAT scan—computerized axial tomography—a non-invasive diagnostic X-ray which examines body parts in detail

catheterization—a procedure where a catheter (tube) is inserted into the body to measure pressures inside the heart and to look for certain congenital heart defects

central line—an IV inserted into the neck or under the collarbone (and sometimes in the groin)

chest tubes—tubes inserted into the chest after open-heart surgery to allow for drainage and air

chlylothorax—a leak from the thoracic lymphatic duct into the chest cavity causing fluid build-up

chromosomal defect—a genetic birth defect

clamshell device—an umbrella-like device introduced into the heart via a catheter which is used to close off openings in the septum or a baffle; these devices are still experimental and cannot be used to close off large openings

coarctation—a narrowing of a vessel (such as the aorta)

C (cont.)

compassionate care (compassionate route)—an option offered to HLHS parents where a pregnancy is terminated or no surgical intervention is initiated after birth

completion Fontan—the third stage of the Norwood procedure; an operation where the inferior vena cave is sewn to the pulmonary artery

congenital heart defect (CHD)—a heart defect present at birth

congestive heart failure (CHF)—a condition where fluid has backed up on the heart causing it to fail to pump efficiently

cord prolapse—a condition where the umbilical cord descends into the vagina

Coumadin (warfarin)—a powerful anticoagulant (blood thinner)

Creustzfeld-Jacob disease—an infectious, rapidly progressive fatal brain-deteriorating disease which has no treatment or cure; commonly misdiagnosed as Alzheimer's disease; in most cases the cause of this disease is unknown although in a small percentage of cases there appears to be a familial link; sometimes referred to as "mad cow disease"

CT scan—computed tomography—multiple X-rays interpreted by computers to show detailed structure inside the body

cyanosis—a condition where a person appears blue due to lack of sufficient oxygen in the blood

cyclosporine (Sandimmune)—a drug used by transplant patients to prevent rejection

D

Dacron—an artificial material used to repair some heart defects

defibrillator—a machine which introduces an electrical shock into the body to start the heart beating or help it resume a normal sinus rhythm

diaphragm—the breathing muscle in the body

DiGeorge syndrome—a condition where a child is born without a thymus gland resulting in the absense of T cells necessary for development of the autoimmune system; this syndrome often has heart defects associated with it

digoxin (Lanoxin)—medication which helps the heart pump more efficiently

diuretic—a drug used to increase urine output and decrease the fluid load on the heart

duodenal feeding tube—a feeding tube inserted into the small intestines just past the stomach

Duoderm—an adhesive dressing

E

echocardiogram (echo)—an ultrasound of the heart, often done with Doppler to determine the flow of oxygenated and unoxygenated (or mixed) blood

ECMO (extracorporeal membrane oxygen)—a special machine used to oxygenate the blood when the lungs are not working properly

edema—swelling due to fluid in the tissue

E (cont.)

Eisenmenger's syndrome—characterized by a large VSD and pulmonary vascular resistance (PVR) which increases with age resulting in high pulmonary artery pressure causing difficulty breathing (dyspnea), insufficient levels of oxygen in the lungs and edema (swelling) of lung tissue. This is an extreme form of pulmonary vascular obstructive disease (PVOD) resulting in irreversible pulmonary hypertension.
electroencephlagram (EEG)—a test used to measure electrical activity in the brain
electrocardiogram (EKG/ECG)—a test used to measure electrical activity in the heart
endocarditis—an inflammation of the inside of the heart
enteral feeding—feeding which goes through the normal digestive tract (either by mouth or via a feeding tube—but NOT an IV feeding)
extubate—removal of a breathing tube

F

fenestrated Fontan—a completion Fontan including an opening in the baffle which acts a pressure release valve
fetal scan/echo—an ultrasound conducted on a pregnant woman to determine whether or not the baby has a congenital heart defect (and the severity of that defect)
Fontan—an operation where the superior and inferior vena cava are connected to the pulmonary arteries thereby creating a heart which only pumps blood to the body (blood travels to the lungs for oxygen due to passive pressure in the body)

G

gamma globulin—a drug administered IV for a variety of reasons including platelet transfusion rejection and as a prophylaxis of infections in immunocompromised patients.
gastroenterologist—a doctor who specializes in gastrointestinal problems
Gavage method—tube-feeding where the tube is placed directly into the stomach (forced feeding)
gentomycin—an antibiotic
g-tube feeding (gastrostomy-tube feeding)—a feeding tube surgically implanted in the stomach by a surgeon

H

hemi-Fontan—the second part of the Norwood procedure (see bi- directional Glenn)
heparin—an anticoagulant (thins the blood to prevent it from clotting)
Holter monitor—a devise worn for 24 hours to track the electrical activity of the heart

H (cont.)

Horner's syndrome—a congenital or acquired neurological defect which usually affects only one side of the face and is characterized by a droopy eyelid, sunken eyes, a smaller-than-normal pupil and a lack of facial sweating
hypoplastic—smaller than usual
hypoplastic left heart syndrome (HLHS)—a severe, congenital heart defect characterized by a combination of heart defects which may include any or all of these primary and secondary criteria: a hypoplastic left ventricle, problems with the aortic and/or mitral valves, requirement of PDA for survival and/or narrowing of the aorta. The HLHS diagnosis often includes a variety of other heart defects not covered in the primary and secondary criteria listed.
hypoxia—lack of oxygen

I, J

ICU/CCU/NICU/PICU/ICN—intensive care units
Imuran (azathioprine)—a drug used to prevent rejection of a transplanted organ
innocent murmur—a heart murmur which is not life-threatening
intravascular hemolysis—the breakdown of red blood cells and release of their contents (i.e. hemoglobin) into the bloodstream which can result in kidney failure
intravenous pyelogram (IVP)—a test for blockage in the kidneys
intubate—insert a breathing tube
IV—intravenous; a needle inserted into a vein or artery to administer drugs as needed

K, L

Konna—an open-heart surgery where the aortic valve is replaced with either an artificial valve, a pgi's valve or the pulmonary valve (Ross procedure); the aortic valve ring (annulus) is also replaced with a bigger ring , the aorta is enlarged and the left ventricular out-flow tract is enlarged with a patch in the septum
Lasix (furosemide)—a diuretic
lifeday—the day a heart transplant recipient receives the donor heart
level II ultrasound—an ultrasound which examines the heart in detail
LVN—licensed vocational nurse

M

maternal-fetal specialist—also known as a perinatologist; an OB/GYN with a subspeciality in the field of obstetrics involving the care of complicated or high-risk pregnancies
mediastinum—the space between the lungs and above the diaphragm containing the heart, the great vessels, the esophagus and the trachea

M (cont.)

microlipids—fats

mitral valve—the valve in the heart between the left atria and the left ventricle

MRI—magnetic resonance imagine—a non-invasive diagnostic study which utilizes strong magnetic fields instead of X-rays to examine parts of the body

MRSA—methicillin resistant Staphylococcus aureus—a life-threatening infection due to resistance to antibiotics

murmur—an additional heart sound that is heard with a stethescope

Mustard procedure—see atrial switch

N

nasal cannula tube—the clear, plastic tubing connected to a nasal cannula (pronged tube taped to the face under the nose to introduce oxygen into the body) and the oxygen tank

nasogastric tube feedings (NG tube feedings)—liquid nutrition placed directly in the stomach through a tube that goes into one of the nostrils

necrotising entercolitis—an inflammation in the bowel where the tissue dies

neonatologist—a doctor specializing in care of the critically ill newborn

neural tube defects—congenital defects concerning closure of the bony casement of the spinal cord or the skull

neurologist—a doctor specializing in treatment of diseases and injuries of the central nervous system (the brain and spinal cord)

NICU—Neonatal Intensive Care Unit

nippling—the process of using a small tube filled with breastmilk held near the mother's nipple to stimulate the sucking reflex

nitrogen—a gas that composes 79% of the air

Noonan's syndrome—a genetic series of defects similar to Turner's syndrome and characterized by a group of defects in a variety of areas including craniofacial malformations (especially in the ears and eyes); organ malformations (especially heart defects, central nervous system dysfunction, and endocrine problems—resulting in short stature as well as other problems); muscloskeletal manifestations, as well as other deformities

Norwood procedure—the first stage of a surgical treatment used for HLHS babies; the pulmonary artery and the aorta are sewn together, the atrial septum is removed and a Blalock-Taussig shunt is placed in the heart

O

OB/GYN—obstetrical/gynecological; a doctor specializing in the treatment of women for pregnancy and medical problems with the female reproductive system

OR—Operating Room

P

pacemaker—the part of the heart which sends electrical stimululation to the heart muscle causing it to beat; an artificial device implanted into the chest to take over the function of the heart's natural pacemaker

P (cont.)

palliative repair—a temporary fix used to allow the child to grow stronger before a more definitive plan of action can be taken

patent ductus arteriosus (PDA)—a natural connection between the aorta and the pulmonary arteries which normally shuts down within the first 10 days after birth

patentforament ovale (PFO)—a natural connection (hole) between the right and left atria which normally closes within the first days of life; a type of ASD

pediatric cardiologist (PC)—a doctor specializing in the care of children's hearts

pediatrician—a doctor specializing in the care of children

penicillin—an antiobiotic

perinatologist—an OB/GYN specializing in the care of critically ill babies (see *maternal-fetus specialist*)

peritoneal dialysis—a form of dialysis (the function of helping or replacing the kidney) where a catheter is placed into the peritoneal space and dialysis fluid is put into the body in order to filter the body's impurities which are removed after a period of time with the fluid

phenobarbital—anti-seizure medication

PICU—Pediatric Intensive Care Unit

Pitocin (oxytocin)—an IV drug used to stimulate contractions in the uterus (to help a woman go into labor)

pleural effusion—fluid accumulating in the space around the lungs

pneumonia—an infection or inflammation of the lungs

pneumothorax—air in the space around the lungs (preventing the lungs from expanding properly)

post-op—postoperative; the period following surgery

Pott's shunt—an aortopulmonary shunt created for the relief of cyanotic heart disease

pre-eclampsia—a toxic condition occuring late in pregnancy characterized by a sudden rise in blood pressure, excessive weight gain, generalized edema, proteirn in the urine, severe headache, and visual problems

Pregestimil—the brand name of a formula with pre-digested proteins for easier digestion

propanol—a beta-blocker used to lower blood pressure

prostaglandin E1 (PGE1)—a hormone which occurs naturally in the body and helps to keep the PDA open

pulmonary artery—the artery which carries oxygen-poor blood to the lungs from the heart (see diagram)

pulmonary artery band (PA Band)—a band put on the pulmonary artery to decrease the flow of the blood to lungs in order to decrease blood pressure in the lungs

pulmonary atresia—usually refers to the pulmonary valve which is absent or poorly formed

pulmonary embolism—a blood clot or obstruction in the pulmonary vessels

pulse rate (normal child/adult)—the number of times your heart beats per minute which changes with age; normal for an adult is 60-100 beats per minute (bpm); the rate is higher in children and babies

Q, R

radio frequency ablation (RFA)—a procedure performed in a special cath lab (called an EP lab or electrophysiology lab) which utilizes radio frequency energy to kill tissue in order to change conduction pathways in the heart thus alleviating arrhythmias

rejection—the body's normal response to a foreign tissue specifically transplants; this is normally repressed by anti- rejection medications

renal failure—kidney failure

respirator/ventilator—a machine which breathes for patients during surgery or in the ICU when they cannot breathe effectively for themselves

RN—registered nurse

Ronald McDonald House—a facility supported by McDonald's Corporation which provides lodging for families of critically ill children in major cities where children's hospitals are located

S

SAT—oxygen saturation level

septicaemia—an infection in the blood

septum—the tissue separating the left and right side of the heart

shunt— 1) an artificial channel (tube) to divert blood (i.e. B- T shunt or Glenn shunt)

2) a natural opening or channel that causes a change in blood flow (i.e. PDA or PFO)

3) any change in physiology that causes decreased oxygenation of the blood (i.e. pulmonary edema)

SIDS—Sudden Infant Death Syndrome; the sudden and unexplained death of an otherwise apparently healthy newborn; the death of a baby which cannot be explained by an autopsy, investigation of the circumstances surrounding the death or through the baby and family's medical history

sodium chloride—common table salt; a common component of IV solutions, normally present in the body

sonogram—see ultrasound

spina bifida—a neural tube defect involving the spinal cord

staph infection—an infection with staphylococcus bacteria; these bacteria normally occur on the body's surface

stenosis—narrowing of a vessel or valve opening

stent implantation—the placement of a device to hold open a vessel or passageway, placed during a catheterization

stress test—a test to determine the response of the heart to increased workload (conducted when there is a suspicion of a problem with bloodflow to the heart muscle)

subacute bacterial endocarditis (SBE)—a chronic case of bacterial endocarditis (infection) with periods of dormancy and occasional flair-ups causing severe infection of the heart (see BE)

subaortic stenosis—narrowing of bloodflow below the aortic valve in the heart

sub-clavian artery—artery which supplies bloodflow to the arm

surgical emphysema—air trapped under the skin following surgery

T

tachycardia—rapid heart rate (a type of arrhythmia)
"taps"—a process where fluid is removed from a body space (usually around the lungs or the heart)
Tegaderm—a brand name for a sterile, transparent dressing
tetracycline—an antibiotic
Tetralogy of Fallot (Fallot's tetralogy; TOF)—a cyanotic, congenital heart defect where there are four things wrong with the heart: pulmonary stenosis, VSD, an overriding aorta (the VSD is beneath the aorta so blue blood is introduced into the body) and right ventricular hypertrophy (the right ventricle is stronger than normal contributing to the appearance of blueness)
thrombophlebitis—inflammation of a vein due to a blood clot
tobramycin—a powerful antibiotic
toxins—poisons in the blood
TPN—total parenteral nutrition (IV feedings)
transposition of the great arteries/vessels (TGA/TGV)—a cyanotic, congenital heart defect where the aorta and the pulmonary are "switched" so that blue blood is introduced into the body and red blood is carried to the lungs
tubal ligation—surgical sterilization by tying off a woman's Fallopian tubes
tube feedings—nutrition placed into the stomach or the duodenum (the intestines just after the stomach) through a tube which enters either through the nose or directly through the abdomen
twin-to-twin transfusion syndrome—a condition where identical twins (who share a placenta and blood supply) can have unequal supply of blood and nutrition

U

ultrasound—a non-invasive procedure used to examine the structure and function of the the area of the body being examined through the use of sound waves
umbilical line—an IV line placed into the umbilical vein immediately after the birth of a child

V

VCFS—velocardiofacial syndrome—is a rare, genetic defect which affects the body in various ways. Velo- means there could be problems with the velum (roof of the mouth) resulting in a partial or total cleft palate; cardio- stands for congenital heart defects (most commonly VSDs) and facial means problems with the head or face possibly including microencephaly (unusually small head), and/or distortions of facial features. Other problems associated with VCFS include small stature, mental retardation, and absence of the thymus gland resulting in autoimmune deficiency.
ventilator—see respirator
ventricle—the large pumping chambers of the heart (see diagram of heart)
ventricular septal defect (VSD)—a hole in the septum between the ventricles; also commonly referred to as "a hole in the heart"

V

vitals—vital signs usually taken by a nurse including heart rate, blood pressure, respiratory rate, temperature and other measurements depending on the level of care the patient demands

W, X, Y, Z

Waterston shunt—an aortopulmonary shunt created for the relief of cyanotic heart disease; a shunt connecting the right pulmonary artery to the ascending aorta

Available from **Baby Hearts Press**:

Hypoplastic Hearts: A Handbook for Parents

(formerly *Hypoplastic Left Heart Syndrome: A Handbook for Parents*)
by: Anna Marie Jaworski   illustrated by: Frank Jaworski, RN
ISBN: 0-9652508-7-3
Available December 1999

Hypoplastic Hearts: A Handbook for Parents is a revised edition of Anna Marie Jaworski's first book, *Hypoplastic Left Heart Syndrome: A Handbook for Parents*. This newly revised book includes stories by parents of children with hypoplastic left heart syndrome, as well as, hypoplastic right heart syndrome and single ventricle. There are chapters on normal anatomy and anatomical defects, testing and diagnostic equipment, surgical procedures, medications and drugs, nutrition and feeding, social services and more.

My Brother Needs an Operation

by: Anna Marie Jaworski   illustrated by: Linda Ball
ISBN: 0-9652508-2-2
Available May 1999

My Brother Needs an Operation is Joey's story when his brother was hospitalized. This interactive book discusses feelings and the transitions and events which occur when a child is in the hospital and there is an unhospitalized sibling in the family. This full-color book has tips for parents on how to reduce the trauma of having a loved one in the hospital. The last section of the book is an activity section for the parent and child to fill out, making the book part of your family's legacy.

The Heart of a Mother

ISBN: 0-9652508-1-4
Available June 1999

The Heart of a Mother is a compilation of essays and poems by women around the world who have been affected by congenital heart defects. Written by mothers, grandmothers and adults with congenital heart defects, this book takes the reader from discovery of the heart defect, through the trials and tribulations surrounding such a crisis, and ends with essays of hope for the future.

Baby Hearts Press Pin

Available June 1999 (while supplies last)

This is a special lapel pin sporting the Baby Hearts Press logo. It has a small white heart embedded in a larger red heart and is outlined in gold.

Check out the Baby Hearts Press website for up-to-date information and products!

http://www.babyheartspress.com

Order Form

Qty	Title	Price	
_____	Hypoplastic Hearts: A Handbook for Parents	$20.00	_____
_____	My Brother Needs an Operation	$20.00	_____
_____	The Heart of a Mother	$25.00	_____
_____	Baby Hearts Press Pin	$ 3.00	_____
	(while supplies last)		

Shipping & Handling ($4 in the U.S./$5 outside U.S.) _____

Grand Total: _____

Name: _____

Address: _____

_____

Phone/Fax _____

Email address _____

Gift Ship To Address:

Name: _____

Address: _____

_____

Phone/Fax: _____

Email address: _____

(If shipping books to more than one address, please add appropriate shipping costs and specify which books go to which address.)

Credit Card Information:

Name as it appears on credit card: _____

(please circle appropriate card): MasterCard Visa AmEx Discover

Credit Card Number/Expiration Date: _____ _____

Baby Hearts Press
6618 Sunrise Drive
Panama City Beach, FL 32407
http://www.babyheartspress.com
Aj@babyheartspress.com
(850) 236-9732
(850) 235-6365 (fax)
(888) 222-4649 (toll-free)

Please make checks or money orders out to: Baby Hearts Press